2013 SCIENCE YEAR

The World Book Annual Science Supplement

A review of science
and technology
during the
2012 school year

World Book, Inc.

a Scott Fetzer company
Chicago

www.worldbook.com

© 2013 World Book, Inc. All rights reserved. This volume may not
be reproduced in whole or in part in any form without prior written
permission from the publisher. Portions of the material contained in
this volume are excerpted from *The World Book Encyclopedia* © 2012
World Book, Inc. SCIENCE YEAR, WORLD BOOK, and the GLOBE DEVICE
are registered trademarks or trademarks of World Book, Inc.

World Book, Inc.
233 N. Michigan Ave.
Chicago, IL 60601

ISBN: 978-0-7166-0566-9
ISSN: 0080-7621
Library of Congress Control Number: 65-21776
Printed in the United States of America
by RR Donnelley, Willard, Ohio
1st printing August 2012

STAFF

EXECUTIVE COMMITTEE

President
Donald D. Keller

Vice President and Editor in Chief
Paul A. Kobasa

Vice President Marketing/ Digital Products
Sean Klunder

Vice President, International
Richard Flower

Director, Human Resources
Bev Ecker

EDITORIAL

Associate Director, Supplementary Publications
Scott Thomas

Managing Editor, Supplementary Publications
Barbara A. Mayes

Contributing Editors
Robert N. Knight
Alfred J. Smuskiewicz

Senior Editor, Supplementary Publications
Kristina A. Vaicikonis

Researcher, Supplementary Publications
Annie Brodsky

Editors
Michael DuRoss
Brian Johnson
Daniel Kenis
Jon Wills

Editorial Assistant
Ethel Matthews

Manager, Contracts & Compliance (Rights & Permissions)
Loranne Shields

EDITORIAL ADMINISTRATION

Director, Systems and Projects
Tony Tills

Senior Manager, Publishing Operations
Timothy Falk

Associate Manager, Publishing Operations
Audrey Casey

Manager, Indexing Services
David Pofelski

GRAPHICS AND DESIGN

Senior Manager
Tom Evans

Coordinator, Design Development and Production
Brenda B. Tropinski

Contributing Designer
Lucy Lesiak

Senior Designers
Don DiSante
Isaiah Sheppard

Photographs Editor
Kathy Creech

Contributing Photographs Editor
Carol Parden

Manager, Cartography
Wayne K. Pichler

Senior Cartographer
John M. Rejba

Media Designer/Animator
Matt Carrington

MANUFACTURING/ PRODUCTION

Director
Carma Fazio

Manufacturing Manager
Barbara Podczerwinski

Production/Technology Manager
Anne Fritzinger

Proofreader
Emilie Schrage

MARKETING

Director, Direct Marketing
Mark R. Willy

Marketing Analyst
Zofia Kulik

CONTRIBUTORS AND ADVISERS

Brett, Carlton E., M.S., Ph.D.
Professor, Department of Geology,
University of Cincinnati. *[Fossil studies]*

Bruce, Timothy J., B.S., Ph.D.
Professor and Associate Chair, Department of
Psychiatry and Behavioral Medicine, University of
Illinois College of Medicine at Peoria. *[Psychology]*

Dine, Michael, Ph.D.
Professor, Department of Physics, University of
California at Santa Cruz. *[Physics]*

Dodelson, Scott, Ph.D.
Scientist, Fermi National Accelerator Laboratory,
and Professor, Department of Astronomy and
Astrophysics, University of Chicago. *[Astronomy]*

Dreier, David L., B.S.
Free-Lance Science Writer and Editor.
[Energy; Medical research]

Fiala, Rebecca J., M.A.
Free-Lance Science Writer. **[Consumer Science,**
The "Skinny" on Gluten; Drugs]

Graff, Gordon, B.S., M.S., Ph.D.
Free-Lance Science Writer. *[Chemistry]*

Hay, William W., B.S., M.S., Ph.D.
Professor Emeritus, Geological Sciences,
University of Colorado at Boulder. *[Geology]*

Haymer, David S., M.S., Ph.D.
Professor, Department of Cell and Molecular
Biology, John A. Burns School of Medicine,
University of Hawaii at Manoa. *[Genetics]*

Hester, Thomas R., B.A., Ph.D.
Professor Emeritus of Anthropology,
University of Texas at Austin. *[Archaeology]*

Klein, Catherine J., Ph.D., R.D.
Director, Bionutrition Research, Children's
National Medical Center. *[Nutrition]*

Kowal, Deborah, M.A., P.A.
President, CT Communications and Adjunct
Assistant Professor, Rollins School of Public Health,
Emory University. *[Public health]*

Lunine, Jonathan I., B.S., M.S., Ph.D.
Professor, Department of Physics, University of
Rome Tor Vergata. *[Astronomy]*

Milo, Richard G., B.A., M.A., Ph.D.
Professor of Anthropology,
Chicago State University. *[Anthropology]*

Morring, Frank, Jr., A.B.
Senior Space Technology Editor,
Aviation Week & Space Technology.
[Space technology]

Ricciuti, Edward, B.A.
Free-Lance Writer. **[Special Report,** *Meltdown:
Climate Change in the Arctic; Biology]*

Rubenstone, Jeffrey, B.A.
Editor, *Engineering News-Record* magazine.
[Special Report, *Sky-High Tech]*

Schafer, Sara, B.S.
Business & Crops Online Editor,
Farm Journal Media. *[Agriculture]*

Schweitzer, Amy, B.S., M.S.
Bionutritionist, Children's National
Medical Center. *[Nutrition]*

Snow, John T., B.S.E.E., M.S.E.E., Ph.D.
Dean, College of Atmospheric and Geographic
Sciences, University of Oklahoma.
[Atmospheric science]

Teich, Albert H., B.S., Ph.D.
Director, Science and Policy Programs,
American Association for the
Advancement of Science. *[Science and society]*

Tsai, Irene, B.S., M.S., Ph.D.
Free-Lance Writer. *[Engineering]*

Witmer, Scott, B.A.
Free-Lance Writer. **[Special Report,** *Knocking
Heads: The Dangers of Concussions;* **Close-Ups,**
*A Big Stink on the Farm; Escape from the
Digital Dark Ages; Rare Earths: The Essential
Modern Metals]*

4

ADVISERS

Ali Banuazizi, B.S., M.A., Ph.D.
Professor of Political Science and
Director of the Program in Islamic
Civilization and Societies, Boston
College, Chestnut Hill,
Massachusetts, United States

David J. Bercuson, O.C., B.A.,
M.A., Ph.D. Professor of History
and Director, Centre for Military
and Strategic Studies, University
of Calgary, Calgary, Alberta,
Canada

Marianna Anderson Busch, B.A.,
Ph.D. Professor of Chemistry and
Co-Director Center for Analytical
Spectroscopy, Department of
Chemistry and Biochemistry,
Baylor University, Waco, Texas,
United States

Jesus Garcia, M.A., Ed.D. Professor
of Social Studies Education,
Department of Curriculum and
Instruction, University of Nevada,
Las Vegas, Las Vegas, Nevada,
United States

Marc B. Garnick, M.D. Clinical
Professor of Medicine, Harvard
Medical School, Harvard
University; Physician, Beth Israel
Deaconess Medical Center,
Boston, Massachusetts,
United States

John T. Greene, B.A., M.A., Ph.D.
Professor Emeritus of Religious
Studies, Michigan State
University, East Lansing,
Michigan, United States

Robert Hodierne, B.A.
Associate Professor of Journalism
University of Richmond,
Richmond, Virginia, United States

Alan E. Mann, B.A., M.A., Ph.D.
Professor of Anthropology,
Princeton University, Princeton,
New Jersey, United States

William McKeen, B.A., M.A.,
Ph.D. Professor of Journalism and
Chair, Department of Journalism,
Boston University, Boston,
Massachusetts, United States

Jay M. Pasachoff, A.B., A.M.,
Ph.D. Field Memorial Professor of
Astronomy and Director, Hopkins
Observatory of Williams College,
Williamstown, Massachusetts,
United States

Michael Plante, B.A., M.A., Ph.D.
Jessie J. Poesch Professor in Art,
Newcomb Art Department,
Tulane University, New Orleans,
Louisiana, United States

Robert B. Prigo, B.S., M.S., Ph.D.
Professor Emeritus of Physics,
Middlebury College, Middlebury,
Vermont, United States

Ken Rebeck, B.A., M.A., Ph.D.
Associate Professor of Economics,
St. Cloud State University, St.
Cloud, Minnesota, United States

Michael Seidel, B.A., M.A.,
M.Phil., Ph.D. Professor Emeritus
English and Comparative
Literature, Columbia University,
New York City, New York, United
States

Scott L. Waugh, B.A., Ph.D.
Executive Vice Chancellor and
Provost, University of California,
Los Angeles, California,
United States

CONTENTS

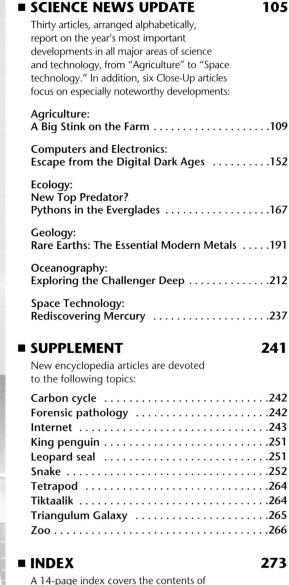

■ SCIENCE NEWS UPDATE 105

Thirty articles, arranged alphabetically, report on the year's most important developments in all major areas of science and technology, from "Agriculture" to "Space technology." In addition, six Close-Up articles focus on especially noteworthy developments:

■ SUPPLEMENT 241

New encyclopedia articles are devoted to the following topics:

■ INDEX 273

A 14-page index covers the contents of the 2011, 2012, and 2013 editions.

MAJOR SCIENCE STORIES

The discovery of a huge feathered dinosaur in China, new findings about the dangers of concussions and abuse of prescription drugs, the end of the space shuttle era, and an inside look at tornadoes were among the many developments that made the year eventful in science and technology. These two pages present highlights of stories chosen by the editors of *Science Year* as among the most memorable or important of the year, along with page references for articles about them.

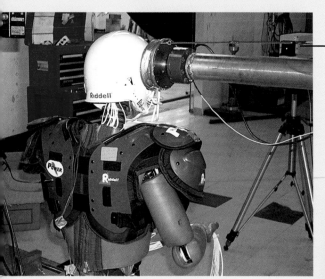

CONCERNS ABOUT CONCUSSIONS

The suicide of former National Football League player Dave Duerson in February 2011, as well as news stories about other high-profile athletes in 2011 and 2012, focused public attention on the dangers of sports-related concussions and the psychological and physical effects of multiple concussions. In the Special Reports section, see **KNOCKING HEADS: THE DANGERS OF CONCUSSIONS**, page 70.

ARCTIC THAW

Throughout the Arctic, it's getting warmer—fast. Changes due to global warming are becoming obvious, and many of these changes may be irreversible. The implications for the Arctic region—and the rest of the world—are profound. In the Special Report section, see **MELTDOWN: CLIMATE CHANGE IN THE ARCTIC**, page 42.

TORNADO ONSLAUGHT

Throughout the early 2000's, an unusual number of major tornado outbreaks have struck parts of the Southeast and Midwest. Each of the first three months of 2012 surpassed long-term averages for numbers of tornadoes reported in the United States. In the Special Reports section, see **TWISTED— MORE TERRIBLE TORNADOES?** page 28; in the Science News Update section, see **ATMOSPHERIC SCIENCE**, page 127.

NEW ERA IN SPACE FLIGHT

The final flight of NASA's space shuttle in July 2011 and the launch of the Dragon cargo capsule atop a Falcon 9 rocket in May 2012 together marked a new era in space flight. Dragon and Falcon, both developed by Space Exploration Technologies Corp. of Hawthorne, California, constituted the first private, commercial launch to the International Space Station. In the Science News Update section, see **SPACE TECHNOLOGY,** page 231.

MERCURY'S SECRETS REVEALED

Messenger, NASA'S small robotic spacecraft that began orbiting Mercury in March 2011, has revealed surprising findings about the planet closest to the sun—including its unusual core and mysterious pits in the surface. In the Science News Update section, see the Space Technology Close-Up, **REDISCOVERING MERCURY,** page 237.

A PLAGUE OF PYTHONS

Researchers tracking invasive species in the United States have raised the alarm over the great number of Burmese pythons that are now living—and breeding—in the Florida Everglades. In the Science News Update section, see the Ecology Close-Up, **NEW TOP PREDATOR? PYTHONS IN THE EVERGLADES,** page 167.

"BEAUTIFUL FEATHERED TYRANT"

Archaeologists have discovered a new feathered dinosaur in China that is larger than any other feathered dinosaur ever found. They named the new species *Yutyrannus huali,* which means "beautiful feathered tyrant." In the Science News Update section, see **FOSSIL STUDIES,** page 179.

PRESCRIPTION DRUG ABUSE

In January 2012, the Centers for Disease Control and Prevention (CDC) in Atlanta reported that prescription drug abuse was the fastest growing drug problem in the United States. The abuse is a multi-level problem, involving pharmaceuticals obtained from both legal and illegal sources. Demand for prescription drugs has also created a black market that fuels abuse, especially among younger people. In the Science News Update section, see **PUBLIC HEALTH,** page 224.

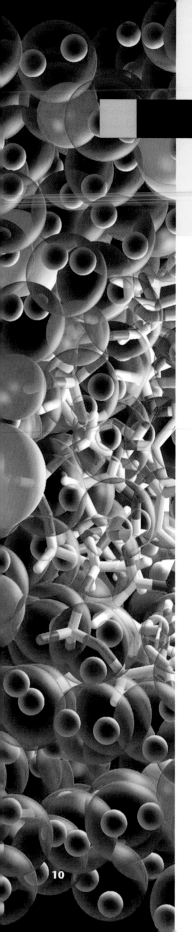

SPECIAL REPORTS

These feature articles take an in-depth look at significant and timely subjects in science and technology.

When Galaxies Collide

by A. J. Smuskiewicz

Mergers, cannibalism,
and other cosmic collisions
occur frequently among
galaxies, once thought of
as isolated islands in space.

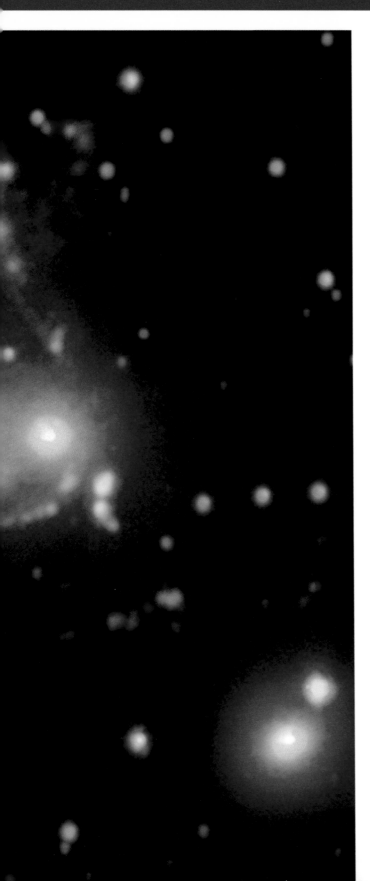

ackyard astronomers interested in witnessing a cosmic clash of giants should train their telescopes on Stephan's Quintet, a visual group of galaxies in the constellation Pegasus. Decades of scientific observations have revealed that the spiraling star clusters and twisted clouds of luminous gases in this beautiful grouping are actually the wreckage from violent galactic encounters powered by gravitational forces. In one such encounter, hundreds of millions of years ago, an outside galaxy tore through much of the group, leaving a streamer of trailing stars and dust 100,000 light-years long. (A light-year is the distance that light travels in one year—approximately 9.5 trillion kilometers [6 trillion miles]). Today, one member of the quintet can be observed ripping through the core of the group at a speed of 1.6 million kilometers (1 million miles) per hour. Powerful shock waves generated by the galactic collisions in Stephan's Quintet have triggered the formation of untold numbers of stars, mainly in clouds of hot gases between the galaxies.

The galaxies of Stephan's Quintet are not unique. The universe is continually changing, evolving, developing. Nothing

A monstrous shock wave (shown as a green arc in a false-color image) is evidence of the violent history of a visual grouping of galaxies known as Stephan's Quintet. The shock wave, which is larger than our Milky Way Galaxy, is being created as one of the galaxies (left pink spot at center) rams through the core of the group at a speed of more than 1.6 million kilometers (1 million miles) per hour. Clusters of new stars (bright yellow) are being born in clouds of the hydrogen gas heated and expelled from the galaxies by the movement of the shock wave.

TERMS AND CONCEPTS

Black hole: A region of space with such strong gravitational force that nothing—not even light—can escape.

Cannibalism: A type of galactic merger in which a large galaxy strips gas and other material from a small companion galaxy.

Cluster: A grouping of thousands of galaxies.

Collision: General term for interactions in which two or more galaxies come together.

Computer model: Simulation performed on a computer to learn about "real-world" events.

Electromagnetic spectrum: Refers to the six forms of electromagnetic radiation—gamma rays, X rays, ultraviolet rays, visible light, infrared rays, and radio waves.

Elliptical galaxy: A galaxy shaped like a round or flattened sphere.

Intergalactic: Between galaxies.

Irregular galaxy: A galaxy with a patchy, disordered appearance.

Light-year: The distance that light travels in one year—approximately 9.5 trillion kilometers (6 trillion miles).

Nucleus: The bright center of a spiral galaxy, containing a dense concentration of stars.

Tidal forces: Physical strains caused by the uneven pull of gravity on different parts of an object.

The author:

A. J. Smuskiewicz is a freelance writer, editor, and artist.

stays the same, especially galaxies. For many years, astronomers thought galaxies were isolated islands in the cosmos. Now we know that galactic collisions, mergers, and even cannibalism are common. By studying these interactions with both space- and ground-based telescopes, scientists are gaining a better understanding of the nature of the universe, including how it developed, how it has changed over time, and how it may change in the future.

What are galaxies?

A galaxy is a system of billions or even trillions of stars—as well as planets, gas, dust, and other matter—held together by mutual gravitational attraction. For hundreds of years, astronomers thought that the Milky Way, the galaxy in which the sun and Earth are located, was the only galaxy in the universe. Since the early 1900's, astronomers have learned that the visible universe contains billions of

A typical spiral galaxy, such as our Milky Way, has a disc-like shape consisting of long arms of stars wrapped around a bright center called a nucleus. The arms also contain vast clouds of gas and dust between the widely spaced stars. The nucleus contains a crowded concentration of stars and a supermassive black hole, a dense region of space with enormously strong gravitational pull. The approximate location of the sun in the Milky Way is shown in yellow.

Massive clusters of bright new stars light up vast clouds of dust and gas (shown in red in a false-color image) in the irregular galaxy NGC 1569. Unlike spiral or *elliptical* (sphere-shaped) galaxies, irregular galaxies have asymmetrical, chaotic-looking shapes.

galaxies—500 billion, according to one estimate. Galaxies range in size from a few thousand to millions of light-years in diameter.

Galaxies exist in a variety of shapes, but the three main types are spiral, elliptical, and irregular. A spiral galaxy, such as the Milky Way, has a rotating disc-like structure with long sweeping arms of stars wrapped around the galactic center. The arms also contain clouds of gas (mostly hydrogen and helium) and dust called nebulae, where new stars form. The *nucleus* (center) of the galaxy consists of a crowded concentration of stars in a bright bulge that extends above and below the disc. Typically at the center of this bulge, according to astronomers, is a supermassive black hole, an extremely dense region of space where the gravitational pull is so strong that nothing—not even light—can escape. Astronomers also believe that a huge sphere of dark matter surrounds the visible part of a typical spiral galaxy. Dark matter is the invisible substance or substances thought to make up the majority of the matter in the universe. Unlike ordinary matter, dark matter does not give off, reflect, or absorb light rays.

An elliptical galaxy is shaped like a sphere—though the sphere may be round or flattened—with most of its stars concentrated in the bright central region. Stars in elliptical galaxies are generally many billions of years old. Because these galaxies contain little gas and dust, few new stars form within them. Elliptical galaxies sometimes result from the merger of spiral galaxies.

An irregular galaxy has a patchy, disordered appearance. These galaxies generally contain large amounts of gas and dust, with enough nebulae to generate new stars for many billions of years. Like spiral galaxies, irregular galaxies appear to be surrounded by large halos of dark matter. The strange shapes of irregular galaxies often result from the gravitational tugs of nearby galaxies.

How do scientists study galaxies?

Astronomers use a variety of telescopes to study galaxies and their interactions. Space-based telescopes offer a view of space that is not obscured by Earth's atmosphere. Some of the most spectacular images of galaxies have been made by the space-based Hubble Space Telescope (HST), launched in 1990. In 2009, the HST was refurbished with the Wide Field Camera 3, which can detect the *infrared* (heat) radiation emitted by extremely distant galaxies dating from when the universe was only about 600 million years old. (The farther away a galaxy is, the longer its light must travel to reach us. Thus, galaxies that are farther away in distance are also farther away in time. Scientists believe that galaxies began developing soon after the formation of the universe roughly 14 billion years ago.)

The Spitzer Space Telescope, which was launched in 2003, can also be used to analyze some of the most distant galaxies known. The Chandra X-ray Observatory is another space-based telescope that has been used to observe many colliding galaxies since its launch in 1999.

One of the more ambitious ground-based observation projects, the

An astronaut installs the Wide Field Camera 3 on the Hubble Space Telescope (HST) high above Earth's surface in 2009. This camera has enabled the HST to capture images of some of the most distant (and earliest) galaxies ever seen.

Sloan Digital Sky Survey (SDSS), relies on the Apache Point Observatory near Sunspot, New Mexico, to conduct detailed surveys of the sky. Astronomers have used the SDSS to map the locations of more than 900,000 galaxies, produce high-quality images of many of these galaxies, discover previously unknown "companion" galaxies to the Milky Way, map the distribution of dark matter around galaxies, and analyze clustering and interactions among galaxies.

Other major ground-based telescopes used in galaxy observations include the Keck I, Keck II, and Subaru telescopes on Mauna Kea volcano in Hawaii; the Very Large Telescope array on Cerro Paranal, a mountain in northern Chile; and the Very Large Array, a group of 27 radio telescopes near Socorro, New Mexico. A radio telescope detects radio waves coming from objects in space.

Astronomers use different telescopes to analyze galaxies based on the different forms of electromagnetic radiation that galaxies emit. The six

Collisions and other interactions among galaxies occur most commonly in such relatively crowded clusters as Abell 2218, shown in an image made by the Hubble Space Telescope. Abell 2218 (yellow lights in foreground) is so massive and compact that its tremendous gravitational force can bend and magnify light from more distant galaxies (faint arc-like shapes).

forms of electromagnetic radiation—gamma rays, X rays, ultraviolet rays, visible light, infrared rays, and radio waves—make up the electromagnetic spectrum. The gas, dust, stars, and other material in galaxies reflect, absorb, or emit all forms of electromagnetic radiation. Analyses of all these forms is important for a thorough understanding of the chemical composition, large-scale structure, internal behavior, and external interactions of galaxies. Images and other data obtained through telescope observations of galaxies are often analyzed with the aid of sophisticated computer programs.

How do galaxies interact?

Most galaxies are located within groups of 20 to 100 galaxies or within clusters of thousands of galaxies. The Milky Way, for example, belongs to the so-called "Local Group," which consists of some 40 galaxies, including the Andromeda Galaxy (which is similar in size and shape to our own galaxy) and the irregular Large and Small Magellanic clouds (which orbit our galaxy at distances of more than 150,000 light-years). Groups and clusters of galaxies reside in enormous superclusters, which may contain tens of thousands of galaxies. Interactions among galaxies occur most commonly in the relatively crowded regions of groups and clusters.

Galaxies interact in four main ways—through collisions, mergers, cannibalism, and distortion. Many galactic interactions fall into more

Long ribbons of new stars trail from NGC 2623, a pair of galaxies in the late stages of merging. The centers of the galaxies have combined into a single nucleus. Many new stars are forming in the gas clouds surrounding the combined galaxy because of the tidal forces generated by the merger.

Streams of cast-off stars, dust clouds, and bright clusters of new stars swirl around spiral galaxies NGC 2207 (left) and IC 2163 as they collide. Tidal forces and other violent gravitational effects are pulling IC 2163, which is about the size of the Milky Way, around the larger galaxy in a counterclockwise direction. The merger will take billions of years.

than one of these categories. The term *collision* is often used as a general term for interactions in which two or more galaxies come together. In some cases, the colliding galaxies eventually merge into a single, larger galaxy. When galaxies collide, it is usually the nebulae and other gaseous and dusty components that make contact with one another. The vast amount of space between the stars in a galaxy means that the stars themselves are most likely spared direct collisions.

As two galaxies approach each other, they may exert strong tidal forces on each other. Tidal forces are physical strains caused by the uneven pull of gravity on different parts of an object. The tidal forces spread through the interacting galaxies and stretch and twist them into new shapes.

The tidal forces and other gravitational effects within the colliding galaxies also produce *supersonic* (faster-than-sound) shock waves that cause nebulae to collapse. If the gas collapses upon itself with enough pressure, nuclear fusion reactions are triggered. These reactions, in which *atomic nuclei* (cores of atoms) chemically combine and release the energy of heat and light, mark the violent "birth" of new stars. The gravitational and tidal forces may also cause long "tails" of hot gas and

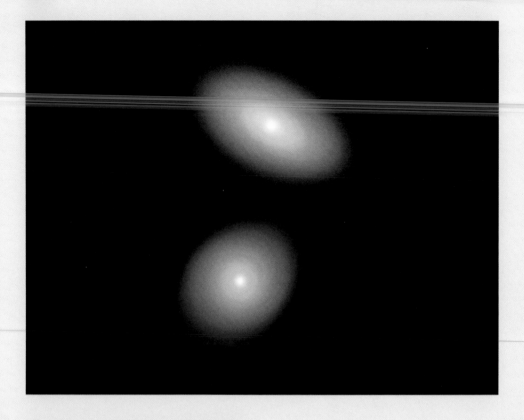

The Milky Way Galaxy (bottom) and the Andromeda Galaxy, the nearest spiral galaxy, approach each other in a still image from a computer simulation of their merger, projected to occur in about 3 billion years.

Our Milky Way is expected to collide and merge with the Andromeda Galaxy in approximately 3 billion years. These two spiral galaxies, currently 2.2 million light-years apart, are speeding toward each other at a rate of 500,000 kilometers (311,000 miles) per hour. Hundreds of millions of years after the collision, according to computer simulations, tidal forces will cause long tails of stars to stream from each galaxy, as well as a bridge of stars to form between the galaxies. The sun may be among the stars ejected into intergalactic space by gravitational forces in the wake of the collision.

The galaxies will then move apart briefly before falling back together for a second collision. Next, physical convulsions will throw off more stars in ripple patterns. The merged star systems will eventually settle into a single enormous elliptical galaxy. The new galaxy will have many new stars—the formation of which will be prompted by merger-caused tidal effects on galactic nebulae. A computer simulation of this process can be seen at: http://www.galaxydynamics.org/tflops.html. Three images from the simulation, produced at the San Diego Supercomputing Center in California, are shown on these pages.

Within the next few hundred million years—well before the merger with Andromeda—the Milky Way will merge with the Large and Small Magellanic clouds, two small irregular galaxies that currently orbit our galaxy between 160,000 to 180,000 lights-years away. This "cannibalism" will increase the size of the Milky Way and destroy both small star systems.

Streams of stars and gas are flung from each galaxy, while a bridge of stars forms between them about 540 million years after the merger begins. The sun may be among the many stars ejected from the Milky Way into deep space as the galaxies are wracked by tidal convulsions—or it may remain within the combined star system.

The spiral galaxies have merged into a single elliptical galaxy some 1 billion years after the initial collision. Tidal forces prompt gases in the galaxy to collapse, triggering the forma-tion of many new stars. The sun will continue to shine as a yellow star—whether inside or outside the galaxy—until it runs out of hydro-gen fuel about 5 billion years from now.

The enormous, expanding ring of bright stars at the outer edge of the Cartwheel Galaxy (shown in a composite, false-color image) likely formed as a large spiral galaxy and a smaller companion galaxy crashed into each other nearly head-on. The collision sent shock waves through the spiral—some of which remains in the nucleus—setting off a burst of star formation.

The early stage of a collision between spiral galaxies VV 340A (seen edge-on at top) and VV 340B (seen face-on at bottom) is captured in a false-color image by the Chandra Space Telescope. The collision is triggering the formation of huge numbers of massive, brilliant stars in VV 340B.

stars to be ejected from the galaxies and into *intergalactic* (between galaxies) space.

When galaxies ram into each other at relatively high speeds, they sometimes can pass through each other, changing their shapes to various extents in the process. These powerful head-on collisions may result in shock waves that spur the formation of a huge ring of bright star-forming material surrounding a smaller, central part. A beautiful example of such a ring appears in the Cartwheel Galaxy. A faint trail of hydrogen gas extends from this giant ring to a small galaxy off to the side. Astronomers suspect that the small galaxy may be a remnant of a star system that plowed through the original Cartwheel. So-called "Sacred Mushroom" galaxies—consisting of a ring and a companion galaxy resembling a mushroom cap and stalk—are in the early stage of ring development after a collision. An example of a partial, crescent-shaped ring—evidence of an off-center collision—can be seen in a pair of galaxies, NGC 7714 and NGC 7715, in the constellation Pisces.

Other evidence of a galaxy collision can be seen in the Sleeping Beauty Galaxy, in which the center of this spiral galaxy appears to be rotating in the opposite direction from the spiral's outer regions. This strange activity may be the result of a small galaxy colliding with a large galaxy—with the combination not yet fully merged.

Galaxies typically merge over a period of millions of years when they collide at relatively slow speeds. Astronomers believe that such mergers have been happening since the formation of the first galaxies more than 13 billion years ago. Since that time, innumerable small galaxies have merged to produce the large galaxies, groups, and clusters that astronomers observe today. Deep-space observations with the HST suggest that during the past 9 billion years, virtually every galaxy has merged with at least one other galaxy. Computer *models* (simulations) based on HST observations suggest that small "dwarf" galaxies have come together with large galaxies three times more often than large galaxies have come together with other large galaxies. Observations have also revealed cases in which numerous galaxies are merging simultaneously, such as the central group of nine elliptical galaxies within the cluster called V Zw 311.

Computer models indicate that the collision and merger of two or more equally large spiral galaxies can produce a giant elliptical galaxy. Scientists believe, for example, that in about 3 billion years, our spiral

The large spiral galaxy NGC 1532 is cannibalizing its companion dwarf galaxy NGC 1531, which is losing gas and stars to the spiral. Bright blue stars along the leading edge of NGC 1532 have burst into existence as tidal forces have triggered nuclear fusion in surrounding dust clouds.

An object called "the Bird" formed as three galaxies collided. Gravitational forces created during the collision distorted the star systems into a shape resembling a hummingbird with outstretched wings. Two of the galaxies were massive spirals, and the third was an irregular galaxy.

Milky Way Galaxy will merge with its nearest spiral neighbor, the Andromeda Galaxy, to produce a giant elliptical star system.

Astronomers have discovered many elliptical galaxies in the crowded centers of galaxy clusters, where gravity has apparently pulled large numbers of spiral star systems together. As galaxies merge, the pull of gravity tends to draw matter toward the center of the merging mass. This process can cause extremely massive stars—that is, stars consisting of a great amount of matter—to form at the galaxy's center. These giant stars deplete their fuel and "die" quickly—often after less than 1 million years—in violent explosions called supernovae. These explosions may leave behind black holes, several of which may merge to form a single supermassive black hole with a mass of more than 1 billion times that of the sun.

Cannibalism is a type of merger in which a large galaxy interacts with a small companion galaxy that is typically in orbit around the larger galaxy. The gravitational field of the more massive galaxy captures the smaller galaxy and gradually strips gas and other material from it. The stripped material is incorporated into the larger galaxy—heating up the larger system—and the small galaxy is ultimately destroyed. Scientists believe that the gravitational field of the Milky Way will fully cannibalize the Large and Small Magellanic clouds within the next few hundred million years. The Milky Way is already growing by incorporating material from these irregular clouds.

Examples of cannibalism in a more advanced stage include the internaction between large elliptical galaxy NGC 4472 and its dwarf companion UGC 7636. The dwarf galaxy in this system shows signs of extreme tidal disruption, including a large cloud of gas stripped from it by the gravitational field of NGC 4472.

In distortions, the gravitational and tidal forces resulting from galaxy interactions may cause long tails, bridges, ripples, or other forms of galactic material to stretch out for vast distances from the main bodies of galaxies. Such effects can be seen in the two colliding galaxies known as the Antennae Galaxies. Bright clusters of star formation triggered by this collision can also be seen around the two adjacent nuclei of the combining systems.

Distortions resulting from collisions can produce galaxies with bizarre shapes. The nicknames of some of these distorted galaxies reflect their appearance. For example, two large spiral galaxies that collided with an irregular galaxy have formed an object known as "the Bird" (ESO 593-IG 008), which appears to have a central body with wings to either side. In "the Mice" (NGC 4676A and NGC 4676B), two spiral galaxies in the process of merging have apparently passed through each other,

"The Mice" consists of two merging spiral galaxies that have been distorted by gravitational forces. The galaxies have already passed through each other once, causing "tails" of stars to be flung out into space.

GALAXY ZOO PROJECT

Most of the computer analyses of data gathered by telescopes are conducted at observatories and universities. However, in a project known as Galaxy Zoo, members of the public can use their home computers to assist scientists in the study and classification of galaxies. Volunteers in this project look at online photographs of galaxies taken by cameras on the Hubble Space Telescope (HST) and answer a series of questions about the shape and color of each galaxy.

The Galaxy Zoo website (http://www.galaxy-zoo.org/), launched in 2007, is based on a concept developed by astronomers Kevin Schawinski (of Yale University in New Haven, Connecticut) and Chris Lintott (of the University of Oxford in England). Their idea was to recruit tens of thousands of volunteers with home computers to help classify more than 1 million galaxies based on shape and color. Such classification is an important first step in understanding galaxies and galaxy interactions. Because of the immense variety of galaxies, it is difficult to develop a computer software program to accomplish this task.

As of early 2012, more than 250,000 volunteers had participated in the project. After volunteers sign up, they can access Web pages featuring a tutorial, HST photographs of galaxies, and a series of detailed questions about each photo. The volunteers then submit their answers to the questions. The Galaxy Zoo project has resulted in a number of astronomical discoveries about galaxy development and evolution that have been published in scientific journals. Among the areas that Galaxy Zoo scientists continue to investigate is the role that galaxy mergers have played in producing the galaxies we see today.

The home page of the Galaxy Zoo project includes information for potential participants.

forming what appear to be two oval bodies (the galaxies' nuclei) with long tails made of clusters of bright young stars.

Plans to learn more

Astronomers hope that several new, highly advanced telescopes will help them gain an even better understanding of the intricacies of galaxy interactions and the ways in which galaxies have evolved over time. Some of these telescopes, such as the James Webb Space Telescope, scheduled for launch in 2018, may be able to spot the first generation of galaxies that formed in the cosmos. The NuSTAR (Nuclear Spectroscopic Telescope Array) X-ray space observatory, scheduled for launch in 2012, and the Atacama Large Millimeter/submillimeter Array, an international radio telescope project scheduled to be operational in 2013, are both expected to reveal fresh information about star formation and the behavior of gases in galaxies. In addition, increasingly advanced computer models are helping scientists to create more realistic simulations of galaxy interactions. These simulations may help researchers clarify the physical processes involved in such interactions.

Chaotic conditions following the violent collision of at least two massive galaxy clusters characterize Abell 520, nicknamed the "Train Wreck Galaxy," shown in a false-color image created by combining data from three telescopes. Starlight (orange) and gas (green) surround an area (blue) believed to pinpoint the location of dark matter, a mysterious, invisible substance that makes up most of the mass of the universe.

Twisted—More Terrible Tornadoes?

By Kristina Vaicikonis

In the early 2000's, tornadoes seemed to have become more numerous—and more destructive—than ever before.

A tornado that struck Joplin, Missouri, on May 22, 2011, caused 160 deaths, making it the single deadliest tornado since modern record keeping began in 1950.

TERMS AND CONCEPTS

Air mass: A huge volume of air that is relatively uniform in temperature and humidity. Air masses can be cold and dry, cold and humid, warm and dry, or warm and humid.

Cyclone: A violent, swirling windstorm. A cyclone in the Northern Hemisphere blows counterclockwise and inward; a cyclone in the Southern Hemisphere blows clockwise and inward. Hurricanes, typhoons, and tornadoes are all types of cyclones.

Enhanced Fujita scale: A system developed by scientists in the early 2000's to estimate the wind speed of a tornado based on the damage it caused. The system is a revised version of the scale developed by T. Theodore Fujita in 1971.

Eye: The calm central part of a tornado.

Meteorologist: A scientist who studies Earth's atmosphere and the weather that it produces.

Supercell storm: The most destructive type of thunderstorm. Supercell storms produce large hail, strong winds, and violent tornadoes.

Tornado: A rapidly rotating column of air that is the most violent of all storms.

Tornado Alley: A belt in the United States in which most tornadoes form.

Vortex: A swirling mass of air or water.

The author:

Kristina Vaicikonis is the senior editor of Science Year.

The tornado season of 2011 was the second-worst the United States has ever experienced, according to the National Oceanic and Atmospheric Administration. During that time, 1,691 confirmed tornadoes touched down in the United States, which is struck by far more tornadoes each year than any other country in the world. Only the 2004 season surpassed 2011 in the number of tornadoes—1,817. In comparison, the average number of U.S. tornadoes confirmed per year from 1991 to 2010 was 1,253. In 1916, 90 tornadoes were confirmed; in 1949, 249.

Seven outbreaks of tornadoes or other severe weather in 2011 caused more than $1 billion damage each. And based on the number of fatalities—553—2011 tied 1936 as the second-deadliest year for tornadoes in the United States, exceeded only by 1925, when 794 people died in tornado-related deaths. The tornado that struck Joplin, Missouri, on May 22, 2011, caused 160 deaths, making it the single deadliest tornado since modern record-keeping began in 1950.

So what does this mean? Is Earth's weather getting weirder? Is global warming causing an increase in the number of tornadoes that occur annually? Are we doomed to experience more and more of these deadly natural disasters in the future? Most scientists believe that the answer to all of these questions is "probably not." Then what IS going on?

For the most part, scientists believe that it is not that more tornadoes are occurring, but rather that more are being detected and reported. There are several reasons for this. One reason is simply that there are more people in the United States to report tornadoes—and more of them are living in areas that had previously been sparsely settled.

Another reason is that after the Weather Bureau (now called the National Weather Service) began issuing tornado watches in 1953, more people became aware of tornadoes and began reporting sightings. In addition, in the mid-1990's, about 100 Doppler radars were set up in the United States to monitor weather systems. Doppler radar is able to detect tornadoes before they touch down and provide advanced warning to people in the area. Meteorologists have noted that since the 1950's, the number of weak confirmed tornadoes has increased from fewer than 100 per year to more than 800 per year. That figure, they believe, reflects the fact that such tornadoes are being detected and reported more frequently than they were in the past.

Still, greater detection and reporting cannot explain away the above-normal number of tornadoes that struck in 2011. There must be a reason for the increase. Some scientists believe that a weather phenomenon known as a La Niña (the Spanish words for *the girl*) was to blame. A La Niña often occurs after a better-known weather

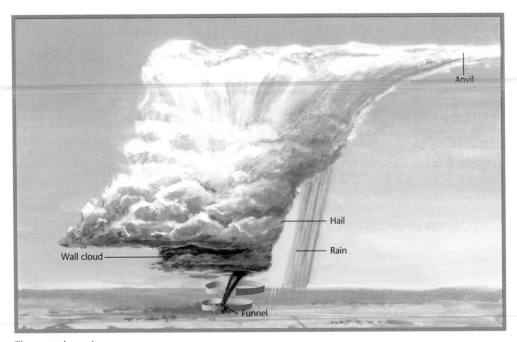

The most damaging tornadoes form in large, powerful thunderstorms called supercells, whose clouds spread sideways to form a characteristic anvil shape at the top. Inside the supercell, a rising column of air starts to rotate. A dark, heavy cloud called a wall cloud forms beneath this rotating column. In most cases, a twisting, funnel-shaped cloud then descends from the wall cloud and touches the ground as a tornado.

pattern called an El Niño (the Spanish words for *the boy)*. During an El Niño (which occurs about every two to seven years), a current of warm water in the eastern Pacific Ocean flows along the coast of Ecuador and Peru. The warm water interacts with the atmosphere, causing the climate in the United States to become wetter than normal in the south and drier than normal in the Pacific Northwest. It also causes the band of winds called the polar jet stream that circulates in the upper atmosphere in the Northern Hemisphere to shift downward. The shift brings the dry, cool air of the north southward and suppresses tornado activity.

During a La Niña, the opposite occurs: The weather in the United States becomes wetter than normal in the north and drier in the south. At the same time, the subtropical jet stream, which circulates in the Southern Hemisphere, shifts northward, bringing with it the warm, moist air of the tropics and setting the stage for violent storms that can produce tornadoes. A very strong La Niña was in effect in 2011, possibly bringing with it more—and more violent—tornadoes.

What is a tornado?

A tornado is an extremely violent windstorm that moves over land. It has stronger winds than any other kind of storm. The winds form under a thundercloud or a developing thundercloud and become a whirling column of air in the shape of a funnel.

Tornadoes are sometimes called whirlwinds or twisters because of the spinning nature of the storm. They are one of several spiral-shaped windstorms that meteorologists call cyclones. Hurricanes and typhoons, which form over warm seas, are cyclones, too. Cyclones spin in a counterclockwise direction in the Northern Hemisphere and a clockwise direction in the Southern Hemisphere.

Where and when tornadoes strike

Although tornadoes can strike in any part of the world, more of them occur in the United States than anywhere else. The United States experiences an average of more than 1,000 tornadoes each year.

Tornadoes may strike at any time of day or night. But they occur most often in the afternoon and evening because they are associated with thunderstorms, which form in the warmest part of the day. Most tornadoes in the United States occur in the spring and summer.

Supercell storms

The most damaging tornadoes come from powerful thunderstorms called supercells. To form, a supercell must have a good supply of moisture. Such a storm also needs a layer of warm, moist air near the ground and a layer of cooler air above.

When two air masses with widely different temperatures meet, the atmosphere becomes unstable. At

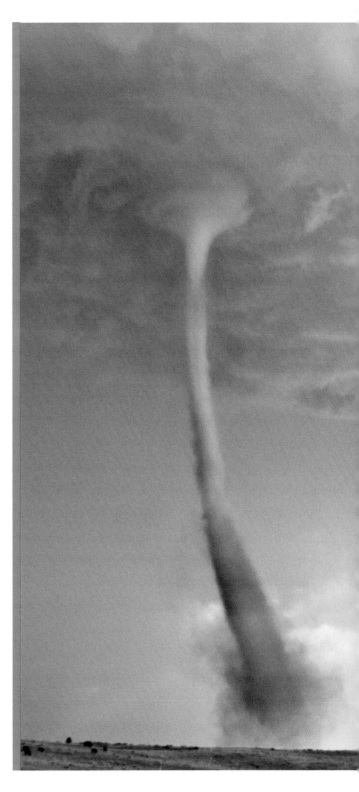

The funnel of a tornado, formed in a thundercloud, reaches toward the ground above Parker, Colorado, in May 2010. The funnel grows darker toward the bottom because of the dust and dirt sucked up from the farmland below.

the border between the two air masses, called a front, warm air begins to flow upward. As it rises, the air cools. The moisture it holds as water vapor condenses and forms clouds. The air stops rising at high levels and spreads sideways to form the characteristic anvil shape at the top of a thundercloud.

Inside a storm cloud, as warm air rises and cool air sinks, these columns create powerful air currents called updrafts and downdrafts. For a tornado to develop, the winds high up in the cloud must differ from those at lower levels in speed, direction, or both. This difference in wind speed or direction is called wind shear. Wind shear makes the column of rising air start to rotate, forming a broad, horizontal tube of swirling air. As the storm continues, this tube starts to tilt upright until eventually it turns on its end, creating a rotating column of air called a mesocyclone.

Meteorologists believe that most supercells that contain mesocyclones eventually produce tornadoes. First, a low, dark, heavy cloud called a wall cloud forms underneath the rotating mesocyclone. Tornado funnels develop out of the wall cloud.

Anatomy of a tornado

A tornado is a vortex, a system of spinning winds similar to a whirlpool formed by swirling water. At the center of the vortex is a calm area called the eye. The eye of a tornado may be only a few feet or yards (meters) across.

Around the eye, moist air creates a pale cloud in the shape of a funnel. Scientists do not completely understand how a whirling vortex forms. However, they believe that the updraft that causes warm air to rise in a supercell plays an important role. As the air rises, it creates a vacuum, sucking in winds blowing along the ground and perhaps setting them into circular motion. Some tornadoes have more than one vortex swirling around a common center.

A rotating wall cloud in a supercell menaces a field in eastern Colorado. Such wall clouds often produce the twisting columns of air that touch the ground as tornadoes.

On the ground

The funnel acts like the hose of a powerful vacuum cleaner. As it sucks up the winds at ground level, it also begins to pull in dust and dirt from the ground. Soon after it touches the ground, the funnel becomes gray or brown from all of the debris it has collected.

At its base, the funnel may be very narrow or as much as 1 to 2 miles (2 to 3 kilometers) across. But the size of a tornado does not help forecasters predict how dangerous the twister will be. Very narrow tornadoes are sometimes more destructive than much wider ones.

Supercell storms usually last for several hours as they are pushed through the sky by prevailing winds high up in the atmosphere. Their tornadoes travel along with them. Most tornadoes are short-lived, lasting only for about 5 to 10 minutes. However, some have been known to last an hour or more.

Tornadoes generally move over the ground at 25 to 35 miles (40 to 56 kilometers) per hour, though some have been clocked at speeds up to

A tornado smashes into a farm in Orchard, Iowa, in June 2008. Iowa is part of a band of states known as Tornado Alley for the high number of tornadoes that occur there each year.

Average Annual Number of Tornadoes from 1991 to 2010

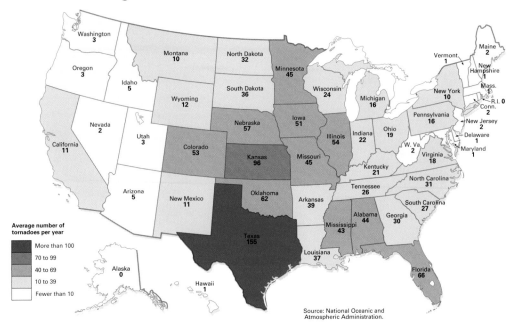

Source: National Oceanic and Atmospheric Administration.

65 miles (105 kilometers) per hour. Few tornadoes travel a distance greater than 25 miles (40 kilometers).

Tornado Alley and Dixie Alley

More than 48,000 tornadoes were reported in the United States from 1950 to 2005—an average of 860 each year. In the mid-1990's, the average began to increase to more than 1,000 tornadoes per year.

The majority of tornadoes in the United States occur in one of two areas—a belt in the Midwestern and Plains states known as Tornado Alley and a less well-known area in the Southeast dubbed Dixie Alley. Meteorologists do not agree on the exact boundaries of either "alley." Tornado Alley is generally described as covering an area north from Texas to Nebraska and from Arkansas to Iowa and east through Illinois and Indiana. Dixie Alley is generally considered to include all or parts of Arkansas, Louisiana, Mississippi, Alabama, Georgia, and South Carolina.

Both areas are the site of so many tornadoes because two great air masses often meet there. Cool, moist air moves eastward from the North Pacific Ocean. As it is forced upward over the Rocky Mountains, this air mass cools down even more and drops much of its moisture as rain. By the time it reaches the other side of the mountains and blows across the Great Plains, the air is cold and dry.

Farther south, warm, moist air moves up from the Gulf of Mexico. It warms up even more as it crosses land before meeting the cold air from the north. The warm air is forced to rise quickly, producing massive thunderclouds and everything associated with them—including tornadoes.

Tornadoes have struck every state of the United States. However, the majority of U.S. tornadoes occur in Tornado Alley and Dixie Alley, two loosely defined areas stretching across the Midwestern, Plains, and Southern states. In these regions, two great air masses meet—cool air from the Pacific Ocean, cooled further as it passes over the Rocky Mountains, and warm, moist air from the Gulf of Mexico. The collision of these air masses produces huge thunderclouds and the tornadoes associated with them.

Collapsed houses, downed trees, and debris mark the path of a tornado that struck Tuscaloosa, Alabama, in April 2011. The tornado was one of a swarm of twisters that killed hundreds of people across the South.

Tornado damage

The winds of a supercell storm have devastating power. Before a tornado strikes, violent wind gusts usually blow through the area. The spiraling winds of a tornado cause great damage because they are constantly changing direction as the tornado moves over the ground. A tornado is often followed by severe hail, torrential rain, and more gale-force winds.

Most deaths and property damage during a tornado are caused by flying debris. When a tornado strikes, it picks up such large, heavy objects

Number of tornado deaths in the United States from 2000 to 2011 by location

Location	Number of deaths	Percentage of total
In a mobile home	426	37
In a permanent home	422	37
At a business	124	11
In a vehicle	79	7
Outdoors	27	2
Other, unknown	27	7
TOTAL	1,155	101*

*Figures do not total 100 percent because of rounding.
Source: National Oceanic and Atmospheric Administration.

as cars, trees, and other pieces in its path, whirls them around, and flings them out at an angle. The debris sprays out from the tornado's funnel, smashing into other objects.

Although many tornadoes are relatively weak, with wind speeds of less than 110 miles (177 kilometers) per hour, the most violent

Calculating Wind Speed

The Enhanced Fujita scale uses the level of damage caused by a tornado to calculate the storm's wind speed. The scale, which ranges from 0 to 5, is based on a system developed in 1971 by Japanese-born scientist Tetsuya Theodore Fujita (1920–1998), who conducted much of his important tornado research at the University of Chicago. Fujita used his scale to describe and record storms during the so-called Super Tornado Outbreak of 1974, during which 148 tornadoes hit more than 12 U.S. states and 1 Canadian province. Fujita's scale for estimating damage worked so well that it has since been used to describe all tornadoes in the United States. Over the years, other researchers found that lower wind speeds can cause more damage than originally thought. The Enhanced Fujita scale was adopted in 2007.

Enhanced Fujita scale

Category	Wind speed per hour		Damage description
	(miles)	(kilometers)	
EF0	65–85	105–137	Light
EF1	86–110	138–177	Moderate
EF2	111–135	178–217	Considerable
EF3	136–165	218–266	Severe
EF4	166–200	267–322	Devastating
EF5	Over 200	Over 322	Incredible

tornadoes have wind speeds of more than 300 miles (480 kilometers) per hour. Yet even "weak" tornadoes can be deadly. There are no "typical" tornadoes. One twister may tear the roof off a house and collapse its walls. Another tornado may pick up a house, turn it around, and set it down again with little damage.

Before a tornado strikes, no one can predict the damage it will cause. Scientists can sometimes measure a tornado's wind speed with instruments, but generally they estimate wind speed after the tornado has passed by the damage it left behind. In the United States, scientists use a system of measurement called the Enhanced Fujita (EF) scale, which ranks tornadoes by the extent of damage.

The EF scale has five categories. The wind speeds of hurricanes are also divided into five categories. But the wind speed of the highest category hurricane starts at 156 miles (251 kilometers) per hour. Such a wind speed for a tornado would make it only a category EF3.

A wind with a speed of 300 miles (480 kilometers) per hour (category EF5) hits objects with a pressure force of 404 pounds per square foot (1,950 kilograms per square meter). Most homes are designed to withstand pressure of only 50 pounds per square foot (244 kilograms per square meter). Scientists who studied tornadoes that occurred in the United States from 1985 to 1997 found that nearly two-thirds of tornado-related deaths occurred in houses or mobile homes. That number remained about the same in the first decade of the 2000's.

The most severe tornadoes from 1950 to 2005—categories F3, F4, and F5—amounted to fewer than 2 percent of all tornadoes. However, these violent twisters caused nearly two-thirds of the 4,716 tornado-related deaths. Around 81,000 people were injured by tornadoes.

What will the future bring?

Scientists cannot say whether climate change will cause an increase in the number and severity of tornadoes. Although they believe that global warming has contributed to heavier rain and flooding, by 2012, they did not yet have enough data to understand how such changes may affect the formation of tornadoes. Nevertheless, it stands to reason that as the U.S. population increases and urban centers grow larger, more and more people in the future will find themselves in the path of powerful and deadly twisters. Knowing how to stay safe in such circumstances will be key.

Workers clear debris from the remains of St. Joseph's Catholic Church, one of a number of buildings in Ridgway, Illinois, destroyed by a tornado on Feb. 29, 2012. The twister, part of a tornado outbreak that swept across the South and Midwest, left at least a dozen people dead.

Meltdown: Climate Change in the Arctic

By Edward Ricciuti

Warming in the Arctic is profoundly affecting this region's landforms, plant and animal life, and human residents.

The supertanker *Vladimir Tikhonov* made a record-breaking voyage through the Arctic Ocean to the Pacific in August 2011. It steamed from Murmansk in northwest Arctic Russia to the Bering Strait—a distance of more than 4,800 kilometers (3,000 miles)—in only seven and a half days. In doing so, the *Tikhonov* plied open waters well north of Siberia that had historically been clogged by polar ice, even in summer. The ship also made news as the largest tanker ever to sail this offshore water route linking Europe with the Pacific Basin, known alternately as the Northern Sea Route or the Northeast Passage. Previously, only a few small ships, aided by icebreakers, made it through, and then only by hugging the coast of Siberia.

Meanwhile, on the opposite side of the Arctic icecap, the Northwest Passage was fully navigable without an icebreaker in 2007. This sea route through the Canadian Arctic and around Alaska links the Atlantic and the Pacific oceans. The thawing of the passage's waters has permitted populations of Atlantic and Pacific bowhead whales, previously separated, to mingle. Scientists speculate that these distinct populations may eventually interbreed.

TERMS AND CONCEPTS

Albedo: The proportion of sunlight that a surface reflects.

Arctic: The polar region that includes the Arctic Ocean and the far northern regions of North America and Eurasia that surround it.

Boreal forest: Evergreen forest common to subarctic regions of the Northern Hemisphere; also known as *taiga.*

Climatologist: A scientist who studies climate.

Feedback loop: A sequence of events in which an occurrence establishes conditions favorable for it to repeat.

Pack ice: The ice that forms on the surface of polar seas.

Permafrost: Ground that remains frozen for two or more years.

Plankton: Masses of tiny organisms that drift at or near the surfaces of oceans and other bodies of water.

Tundra: Treeless Arctic plains with stunted vegetation.

The author:

Edward Ricciuti is a free-lance author based in Killingworth, Connecticut.

New sea routes and the mixing of species are examples of dramatic changes that are occurring across the Arctic due to global warming. The Arctic encompasses the Arctic Ocean, which surrounds Earth's North Pole, and the landmasses of far northern Eurasia and North America, which surround this ocean. Before the 1990's, "normal" conditions in the Arctic—that is, climatic patterns observed over hundreds of years—were largely determined by freezing air temperatures and ground and sea ice, with a very brief summer respite in some areas. Where summer did occur, it was not long or warm enough to clear surface ice from bodies of water or to thaw more than the top surface layers of *permafrost* (ground that stays frozen for two or more years). In particular, the sea ice covering most of the Arctic Ocean—called pack ice—remained largely intact, a situation that exerted a profound year-round cooling effect on the region.

However, since the early 1990's, a "new normal" climate regime has emerged in the Arctic, according to *climatologists* (scientists who study climate). Temperatures are now warm enough to melt thousands of square kilometers (miles) of Arctic sea ice and to turn permafrost on many land areas into quagmires. These changes, scientists predict, will in turn create conditions favorable for further warming.

Global warming

The warming trend observed in the Arctic in recent decades is part of the larger phenomenon of global warming, climatologists assert. Temperatures worldwide have increased by about 0.74 Celsius degrees (1.3 Fahrenheit degrees) since the late 1800's, according to the National Climatic Data Center of the National Oceanic and Atmospheric Administration (NOAA), an agency of the United States government. Most scientists attribute this long and persistent period of warming, at least in part, to the introduction into the atmosphere of carbon dioxide and certain other gaseous by-products of industry and transportation over the past 200 years. These gases, dubbed greenhouse gases, trap warmth from the sun's rays in the atmosphere. As greenhouse gases build up, atmospheric temperatures rise.

Recent climate data suggest that global warming is accelerating. According to the United Nations (UN) World Meteorological Organization (WMO), the 13 warmest years on record have all occurred since 1997. Data analyzed by scientists with NASA's Goddard Space Flight Center in Greenbelt, Maryland, indicate that 2010 was 0.51 Celsius degree (0.92 Fahrenheit degree) warmer than the average annual temperature from 1951 to 1980. The data also indicate that 1998, 2002, 2003, 2005, 2006, 2007, and 2009 were about as warm as or even warmer than 2010.

ARCTIC PASSAGES

The Arctic consists of the Arctic Ocean and the lands in Eurasia and North America that surround it. The Arctic icecap expands and shrinks with the seasons, falling to its yearly minimum in late summer. Global warming and the long-term shrinking of the icecap are opening new shipping lanes through the Arctic Ocean. The Northwest Passage, a long-sought marine route from the North Atlantic to the Pacific Ocean, first opened for several weeks in August 2007. This route winds through Baffin Bay to the Bering Sea. A second route, called the Northern Sea Route or Northeast Passage, skirts the Arctic coast of Russia. Since 2000, shrinkage of the icecap has opened a wide, relatively ice-free passage along this route for a time in summer.

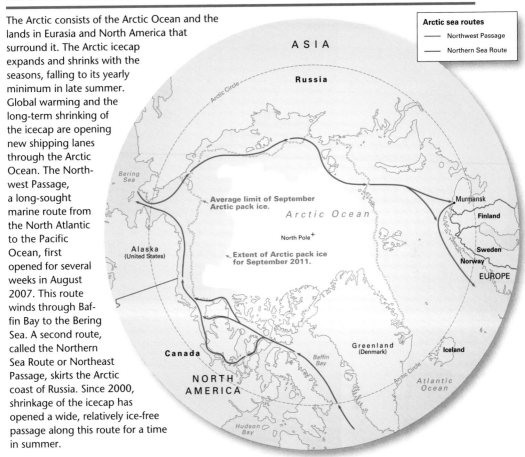

Arctic hotbox

Scientific analyses of weather and climate data demonstrate that the Arctic is warming far more rapidly that most other regions. According to the Union of Concerned Scientists, average annual surface air temperatures in Alaska and Siberia have increased from 2 Celsius degrees (3.6 Fahrenheit degrees) to 3 Celsius degrees (5.4 Fahrenheit degrees) since the early 1960's. (The Union of Concerned Scientists is a nonprofit association of scientists and laypersons concerned about climate change, based in Cambridge, Massachusetts.) In a 2011 study, scientists led by climatologist Margareta Johannson of Sweden's Lund University reported that the period from 2006 to 2010 was the warmest five-year period in the Arctic since 1900. (Before that date, records are not complete enough to make any comparison.) Several factors may be contributing to the Arctic warmup, but the most significant, most scientists say, is the

SHRINKING POLAR ICECAP

Images made by Earth-orbiting satellites have revealed that the Arctic polar icecap has shrunk dramatically during the summers of the early 2000's. Sea ice covers most of the Arctic Ocean in winter, then shrinks during the summer months. It reaches a minimum extent in September before beginning to re-form. In 1980, the icecap, even at the summer minimum, covered most of the Arctic Ocean between North America and Siberia (eastern Russia). In 2007, the year with the lowest summer minimum to date, summer shrinkage of the icecap left the western third of the Arctic Ocean ice free. The summer minimum in 2011 was only slightly greater than that of 2007, again with large areas of the western Arctic Ocean ice free.

shrinking of the Arctic icecap, which allows the Arctic Ocean to absorb more and more sunlight.

Scientists contributing to the "Arctic Report Card 2011" stated that "record-setting changes are occurring throughout the Arctic environmental system." (The Arctic Report Card is an NOAA-funded annual report on climate change in the Arctic filed by international scientists with specialties in Arctic studies.) Indeed, climate-related changes can now be observed throughout the Arctic.

The Arctic Ocean's polar icecap

Until the very end of the 20th century, a thick layer of sea ice, forming the Arctic polar icecap, covered most of the Arctic Ocean year-round between Greenland, Canada, and Alaska on one side, and Siberia on the other. However, in recent years, the icecap has shrunk significantly because of summer melting, retreating far from the coasts of Alaska and Siberia. The record low for summer ice minimum occurred in 2007. In September of that year, scientists determined that Arctic Ocean ice coverage was about 40 percent less than the average coverage measured for the years 1979–2000. Climatologists reported that the minimum ice coverage measured in September 2011 was only slightly above the 2007 record low.

The extent of summer ice in the Arctic Ocean is not merely a curiosity. Ice has a high *albedo* (reflection index), which means that a high percentage of sunlight striking it gets reflected back into space. Sea ice reflects from 60 to 80 percent of incoming sunlight, depending upon such factors as the age of the ice and amount of snow cover. By contrast, open seawater has a low albedo, reflecting only 10 percent of incoming sunlight. In

THE ALBEDO EFFECT

Earth's surface features absorb or reflect varying percentages of incoming sunlight. The percentage of reflection from a particular kind of surface is known as the albedo. Ice and snow have a high albedo, meaning that they reflect most sunlight back into space and absorb little energy. Such surfaces as bare ground and open seawater have a relatively low albedo—that is, they reflect little sunlight and absorb much energy. The albedo effect strongly influences the amount of solar energy absorbed by Earth.

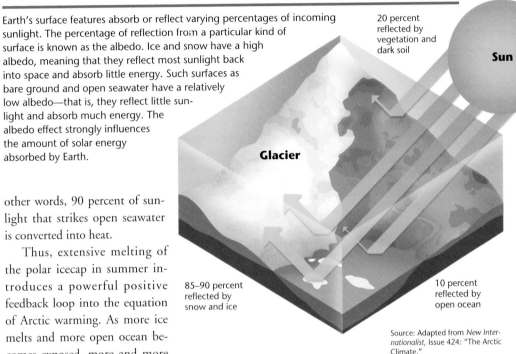

20 percent reflected by vegetation and dark soil

Sun

Glacier

85–90 percent reflected by snow and ice

10 percent reflected by open ocean

Source: Adapted from *New Internationalist,* Issue 424: "The Arctic Climate."

other words, 90 percent of sunlight that strikes open seawater is converted into heat.

Thus, extensive melting of the polar icecap in summer introduces a powerful positive feedback loop into the equation of Arctic warming. As more ice melts and more open ocean becomes exposed, more and more sunlight is absorbed and converted to heat. This heat gain prompts yet more melting of Arctic ice, and the cycle repeats.

One of the biggest questions in Arctic climate studies concerns when the Arctic Ocean will be entirely ice-free in summer. Most scientists estimate that the ocean's first iceless summer will occur sometime this century, though some experts predict ice-free summers as early as 2020 or even before then. However, all climate scientists agree that the loss of summer ice cover in the Arctic Ocean will accelerate Arctic—and global—warming.

The Greenland icecap

Another Arctic phenomenon that is showing signs of change is the vast icecap on the island of Greenland, a landmass nearly as large as the combined areas of Texas and Alaska. The lens-shaped icecap covers 80 percent of the island and is 3.2 kilometers (2 miles) thick near its center.

Climatologists contributing to the "Arctic Report Card 2011" noted that five of the six most extensive melt years for the Greenland icecap—determined by measuring the surface area of liquid water—occurred after 2000; the exception is the year 1998, which scientists have confirmed to be the warmest year of the 20th century. Data for surveillance of the

Climate change in the Arctic is creating opportunities for such species as the red fox to extend its range northward. In doing so, the red fox is coming into competition with the native Arctic white fox. Scientists speculate that the larger, stronger red fox may push the Arctic fox out of some of its habitat.

icecap come from satellites, which have been routinely monitoring Arctic ice patterns since the 1970's. A number of individual glaciers emerging from the icecap or on nearby islands also exhibit long-term melting and retreat. Shrinkage of some of these glaciers is documented by photographs or field measurements dating as far back as the 1930's.

The melting of the Greenland icecap has implications far beyond the Arctic. As much as 10 percent of the Earth's fresh water is locked up in the icecap. Scientists calculate that if Greenland's icecap were to melt completely, world sea levels would rise by 66 meters (about 217 feet). Although a total meltdown is extremely unlikely in the foreseeable future, the consequences of significant warming could be serious to catastrophic for many low-lying coastal regions on Earth.

Permafrost

The strong warming trend in Arctic lands is also thawing extensive tracts of permafrost. Since the 1970's and 1980's, scientists have measured steadily rising underground temperatures at many locations in Alaska, northern Canada, and Russia. These warmer ground temperatures mean that summer thawing of permafrost is penetrating more deeply than before and that areas with year-round permafrost are shrinking.

Rapid thawing of permafrost has important implications for residents of the Arctic and for industrial activities there. Houses and other struc-

tures built on permafrost become destabilized when excessive warming leads to deep thawing. Engineers who maintain pipelines, highways, and other infrastructure frequently find it necessary to shore up supports as thawing ground shifts.

However, many scientists believe there is a potentially more serious, global implication of melting permafrost. They theorize that rapid thawing would decompose billions of tons of carbon from the long-accumulated remains of plants and animals in the upper layers of permafrost. Studies suggest that melting permafrost would release vast amounts of carbon dioxide in the atmosphere, accompanied by methane, a greenhouse gas known to be 20 times as effective at trapping heat as carbon dioxide. Thus, widespread thawing of permafrost could contribute yet another positive feedback loop to global warming.

A polar bear struggles to find solid footing in warming seawaters in which ice floes are breaking up and melting. Polar bears depend on ice floes to hunt their chief prey, seals. The Arctic warming trend threatens polar bear populations in many parts of the region.

Challenges for Animals, Plants, and Other Organisms

A warming climate poses many challenges to Arctic life, from microscopic plants and animals in Arctic waters to polar bears and great whales—and to people. Disruptions in long-established natural cycles benefit some species but put others at a disadvantage.

Great sweeps of Arctic seawater harbor vast populations of plankton, masses of tiny organisms that drift at or near the surfaces of oceans and other bodies of water. (Indeed, some planktonic creatures thrive in

icy waters just beneath the Arctic pack ice.) *Blooms* (sudden rapid growth) of certain kinds of plankton now occur 50 days earlier in spring than 30 years ago, according to scientists reporting in the "Arctic Report Card 2011." Plankton-feeding bowhead whales, year-round northern residents, benefit from the early plankton bounty. However, gray whales, which migrate seasonally into Arctic waters from the Pacific Ocean, lose out because the plankton blooms now occur before they arrive.

Scores of walrus occupy a small ice floe in sea-waters off the northwest coast of Alaska. The animals require periods out of the water on ice floes or beaches to breathe, rest, and give birth. Jammed into too-small areas, walrus mothers sometimes injure or suffocate their young. A diminishing pack ice in summer poses serious challenges for these populations.

Hunters on the ice

Animals that depend on Arctic pack ice for hunting and birthing are especially threatened by Arctic warming. Walruses, seals, and polar bears are all dependent in various ways on the pack ice.

In summer, walrus mothers and young typically rest on in-shore ice floes. These also serve as platforms from which the animals can easily graze on bottom-dwelling sea creatures in shallow waters. In 2011, ice receded so early and so far from Alaska's northwest coast that thousands of walrus were forced to haul themselves onto a rocky ribbon of shore for rest periods. Many pups were crushed by the jam-packed adults.

Trees in a "drunken forest" in interior Alaska skew away from the vertical. The cause of this bizarre effect is deep melting of permafrost below the trees' roots. As the permafrost melts, the forest's solid foundation is transformed into a quagmire. As a result, trees begin to lean and tip. Scientists report extensive melting of permafrost in Arctic regions as the climate there warms rapidly.

Seals give birth, raise their pups, and rest on ice floes. Adult seals spend much of their time swimming underwater searching for fish, but they cannot stay submerged indefinitely. The increasing scarcity of summer sea ice threatens Arctic populations of this marine animal.

Shrinking pack ice also diminishes the hunting grounds that polar bears roam in search of seals, their chief food supply. Data gathered from scientific observation indicate that some populations of polar bears are declining. Scientists have grouped polar bears into 19 subpopulations, based upon geography. Reporting in the "Arctic Report Card 2011," the scientists noted that statistics sufficient to estimate population trends were available for only 12 of the 19 subpopulations. Of these 12 groups, 3 populations appear to be remaining stable or growing slightly. The other nine populations are declining.

A different threat is coming from the south. In 2010, biologists affiliated with New York City's American Museum of Natural History reported that grizzly bears had been sighted in Wapusk National Park in Manitoba, Canada, almost every year since 2000, and that three grizzlies were sighted there in 2009. No grizzlies had ever been seen in the park before 1996. Wapusk is just southeast of Churchill on western Hudson Bay, a region that has long been a prime habitat of polar bears.

MARCHING NORTH

Changes in the density of ground plant vegetation in Canada's Arctic northern Quebec are obvious in satellite photos taken in 1986 and 2004. Low shrublike plants from farther south have become more common in areas that were previously dominated by lichens and other tundra plants as the climate has grown warmer.

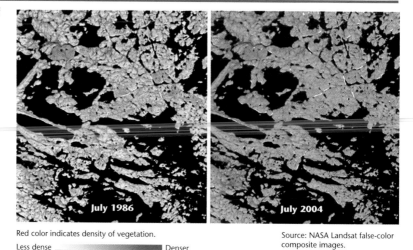

July 1986

July 2004

Red color indicates density of vegetation.

Less dense ▬▬▬▬▬ Denser

Source: NASA Landsat false-color composite images.

The scientists speculated that the Arctic warming of the past 25 years has created opportunities for grizzlies to move northward. In a study financed by the National Science Foundation and reported in the online journal *PLoS ONE* in November 2010, scientists compared the jaws and teeth of polar bears and grizzly bears. They determined that grizzlies have bigger teeth and much stronger jaws than polar bears. This anatomical difference allows grizzlies to eat a varied diet, including not only prey but also such vegetable matter as plant leaves, stems, and berries. The weaker jaws of polar bears are suited to tearing and chewing meat—but little else. The scientists speculated that if grizzlies spread into polar bear habitat and opportunities for the polar bears to hunt seals are diminished, the invading grizzlies could eventually outcompete the polar bears for available food.

Other animals native to the Arctic face challenges from invaders from the south. Field observations indicate that red foxes, native to lands south of the Arctic, have invaded some Arctic regions, which are home to Arctic foxes. Because red foxes are larger and stronger than Arctic foxes, they are likely to possess a competitive edge, scientists surmise.

Changes in vegetation

Vegetation characteristic of the subarctic and temperate zones is also inching northward. NASA scientists announced in December 2011 that shrubs and grasses have spread into Arctic northern Quebec. The scientists analyzed satellite data captured between 1986 and 2010. The data indicate that tracts of Arctic *tundra* (treeless Arctic plains with stunted vegetation) are slowly being transformed into denser, mixed-vegetation coverage typical of subarctic regions.

Also in December 2011, NASA's Jet Propulsion Laboratory (JPL) in Pasadena, California, revealed a computer-modeling study that predicted major shifts in plant communities in the Northern Hemisphere. The scientists projected that *boreal forests* (evergreen forests common to subarctic regions of the Northern Hemisphere, also known as taiga) will slowly shift northward. As a result, formerly treeless areas of the Arctic will begin to support trees. At the same time, deciduous forests common to temperate zones will inch northward into the boreal forests, the study predicts. In the long term, the scientists say, this gradual change will reduce habitat for many organisms adapted to Arctic conditions.

People in a warming Arctic

People native to the Arctic, such as the Inuit, are likely to be increasingly affected by climate change. Open water and thawing bogs are impeding their travel and access to seals, whales, caribou, and other traditional food sources.

In northern Eurasia, the Arctic warming trend is disrupting age-old patterns of reindeer herding. In 2009, scientists with the European Space Agency announced that they were providing satellite data about snow cover to Sami (formerly know as Lapp) herders in northern Scandinavia to guide them to appropriate pastures. The herders need snow-covered pastures without an icy crust to graze their animals. A crust, caused by rain or thawing temperatures, makes it difficult or even impossible for the reindeer to paw through the snow cover to eat the edible lichens and mosses beneath.

On the other hand, persistent warming may be making new sources of food available to some Arctic residents. In parts of southern Greenland, the warming trend has led to the recent cultivation of turnips and potatoes, crops not historically raised on that island. Higher summer

A house on Alaska's Bering Sea coast slides off its foundations to the water's edge after a severe autumn storm. According to climatologists, delayed formation of coastal pack ice, due to global warming, is exposing Alaska's coastline to punishing waves in autumn. Without protective inshore ice, the waves tear away chunks of shoreline.

Farmers harvest potatoes on a strip of land along the southwest coast of Greenland. The Arctic warming trend is enabling farmers to plant and harvest crops in areas previously too cold for such agriculture.

temperatures could allow people of the Arctic to grow more of their own food and thus reduce expenses associated with importing food.

Rising temperatures are opening up previously icebound reserves of natural resources. A rush is on to exploit gold, silver, uranium, and fossil fuels in Canada's Nunavut Territory. Geologists estimate that this Arctic territory may hold up to 75 billion barrels of oil and 8.5 trillion cubic meters (300 trillion cubic feet) of natural gas. Greenland is issuing licenses to oil companies for exploring adjacent seas that, until recently, were ice-covered. The United States Geological Survey estimates that a quarter of the world's petroleum and gas reserves may lie under the Arctic.

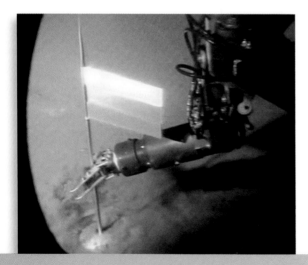

The mechanical arm of a submersible vehicle plants the Russian national flag on the sea bottom at the North Pole in August 2007. Members of a Russian Arctic expedition in two submersible vehicles descended 4,267 meters (14,000 feet) below the ocean surface to perform the action, which other nations with Arctic interests regarded as provocative. The highly publicized event underscores growing international competition for Arctic resources.

The *indigenous* (native) peoples of the Arctic have a front-row view of climate change. During 2011, the United States Geological Survey (USGS) publicized a study documenting changes that natives of the Yukon River Basin in central Alaska have observed and experienced.

The USGS coordinated interviews with elders of the Yupik Inuit people in two villages. The Yupik people told interviewers that the length of the ice season has shortened by several weeks in recent years, and that frozen rivers and lakes harbor many treacherous weak spots during warm spells. Local people use these frozen waterways as winter highways. Several interviewees cited the names of people who had fallen through the thin ice and drowned.

The Yupik also noted that changes in vegetation in recent years have disrupted age-old routines of food gathering. Moose and other animals the natives hunt have moved from their normal ranges due to vegetation changes. Salmonberries, an important food source for the Yupik, ripen earlier than before.

The declining spring snowmelt impacts daily life, too. Melting snow floods rivers, carrying logs downstream. With a reduced winter snow cover, the spring flood diminishes and rivers transport fewer logs. Traditionally, the Yupik people have collected the logs in spring and summer to serve as winter fuel. However, many now find it necessary to purchase expensive fossil fuels to heat their homes.

Armed with a rifle and a long walking stick to probe weak holes in the ice, two Yupik Inuit hunters make their way along shore ice in northwest Alaska as they search for seals. These hunters, like many of their Arctic neighbors, know to be cautious on ice that sometimes becomes treacherous in during thaws. Such thaws are becoming characteristic of a rapidly warming Arctic climate.

As access to rich resources opens up, nations are scrambling to stake claims. In 2007, a Russian expedition planted that country's flag, by means of a submersible vehicle, on the Arctic seabed. The feat advertised Russia's claim to ownership of almost half the Arctic sea floor—a claim that Canada, the United States, Denmark, and other nations dispute. Such competition for Arctic resources could well spark serious international tensions. Harvesting newly available resources could also expose the region to environmental problems. These threats underline the precarious situation that rapid Arctic warming has created.

For most of the world's people, the Arctic seems impossibly remote. However, climatologists increasingly assert that what happens there will have a profound impact on the rest of the world. The Arctic is, indeed, the main stage on which the drama of climate change is unfolding.

The Burj Khalifa, the world's tallest building in 2012, soars more than 800 meters (2,700 feet) above the desert city of Dubai in the United Arab Emirates. Its sleek, tapering design is characteristic of a new class of "megatall" skyscrapers.

Sky-High Tech

By Jeffrey Rubenstone

A new architectural superstar took center stage on the world's urban skyline in 2010. Named the Burj Khalifa, the slender, tapering tower in the United Arab Emirates grabbed the title of the world's tallest building, held since 2004 by the Taipei 101 in Taipei, Taiwan. The Burj Khalifa, designed for mixed commercial and residential use, soars 828 meters (2,716 feet) above the desert city of Dubai. But even as the Burj Khalifa was breaking the height record, officials in Jiddah, Saudi Arabia, were announcing plans for the Kingdom Tower, a massive spire that would rise more than 1 kilometer (3,280 feet) into the sky.

The geographic proximity of these two supertall buildings on the Arabian Peninsula is not a coincidence—16 of the 20 tallest buildings in the world in 2012 were located in the Middle East or Asia. That number jumps to 19 out of 20 when taking into account buildings that are still in the design or construction phase. The construction of skyscrapers has always been closely linked to economic boom times and, since the 1990's, economies in the Middle East and southeast and east Asia have surged.

More than a century ago, buildings soared skyward, thanks to innovative engineering. Today, advances in engineering and materials are pushing structures even higher.

The author:

Jeffrey Rubenstone is a free-lance writer based in Sparkill, New York.

TERMS AND CONCEPTS

Buttressed core: A design for tall buildings consisting of a highly reinforced core, a three-sided footprint, and a tapering ascending form.

Damper: A suspended weight whose side-to-side movement helps stabilize a structure.

Lateral (horizontal) load: The sideways push and pull of such forces as wind and earthquakes on a structure.

Masonry skyscraper: A tall building supported by very thick *masonry* (brick and stone) walls at its lowest levels.

Megatall: Describes a building that is at least 600 meters (1,968 feet) tall.

Skyscraper: An informal descriptor for any tall building.

Steel frame: A design for tall buildings based on a steel superstructure that carries the loads.

Superstructure: The structural elements that support the loads in a tall building.

Supertall: Describes a building that is from 300 to 600 meters (984 to 1,968 feet) tall.

Tube frame: A design for tall buildings that relies on a core tube and a perimeter tube, each consisting of closely spaced steel or concrete columns, to carry the loads.

Vertical load: The downward pull of gravity on a structure.

The skyscraper has been a status symbol since architects and engineers first developed it more than 100 years ago, and any new attempt to build the tallest building usually triggers a flurry of competition. The current round of one-upmanship arguably began in 1998, with the completion of the 452-meter (1,483-foot) Petronas Towers in Kuala Lumpur, Malaysia. These twin towers dethroned the 442-meter (1,450-foot) Sears Tower (now Willis Tower) in Chicago as the world's tallest building, a title it had held since 1974. In turn, the Petronas Towers were eclipsed in 2004 by the 508-meter (1,667-foot) Taipei 101.

The Petronas Towers and Taipei 101 are actually classified as "supertall" buildings by the Council on Tall Buildings & Urban Habitat (CTBUH), an international architectural resource organization. Supertall buildings are more than 300 meters (984 feet) tall. The term *skyscraper,* in contrast, has no formal definition; it is a colloquial term first used by the public and the press to describe the steel-framed buildings of 10 stories or taller erected in American cities in the late 1800's. In 2011, the CTBUH introduced a new category for tall buildings—megatall. Such buildings are at least 600 meters (1,968 feet) tall. So far, only the Burj Khalifa and the Mecca Royal Clock Tower in Saudi Arabia rate megatall status.

Advances in engineering have also played a part in the recent skyscraper boom. Megatall buildings, in particular, are technologically feasible because of the development of high-performing reinforced concrete and innovative structural designs.

Although the process of designing tall buildings is quite complex, the chief goal is simply to overcome gravity. The higher a building goes, the more it weighs, and the stronger the supporting structure must be. This gravity-induced dead weight, known as *vertical load*, must be accounted for in the design, or the building will simply collapse in on itself. Another major concern is the *lateral* (horizontal) *load*. This force includes the pressure of wind striking the structure, as well as side-to-side vibrations caused by earthquakes.

Skyscrapers with steel framing

Until the late 1800's, "tall" buildings were usually 10 to 12 stories. They were generally constructed of masonry and stone, with structural walls thick and robust enough at lower levels to bear the load of the building's upper floors. A superb example of a masonry "skyscraper" is the Monadnock Building in Chicago, designed by the architectural firm of Burnham and Root. In the Monadnock Building, the deep window wells at ground level clearly reveal the extraordinary thickness of the lower structural walls—1.8 meters (6 feet) on the ground floor.

Chicago's Monadnock Building (left) is an example of a masonry skyscraper, in which structural loads are carried by thick, robust brick and stone walls. The thickness of these supporting walls can be seen in the window wells (above) at ground level.

Many experts regard the 10-story Home Insurance Building in Chicago, designed by William LeBaron Jenney and completed in 1884, as the world's first skyscraper. It was the first structure to incorporate a load-bearing steel structural frame, though some of the building's load was supported by stone and brick elements. Because of its steel frame, the Home Insurance Building weighed only one-third as much as a comparable masonry building. Jenney said he got the idea for the structural steel frame when he saw his wife place a heavy book on a wire birdcage, which held the load without buckling. This use of a robust "superstructure," or independent support frame, is the basic principle behind all modern skyscrapers.

Another structural engineering innovation of the late 1800's was a foundation of piles driven deep into the earth. Directly connecting the vertical columns of the superstructure to a firm foundation stabilizes the

New York City's iconic Empire State Building (right) was constructed with a massive skeleton of steel beams held together with steel rivets and bolts (above). Steel frame construction is very strong. However, today's open floor plans are impossible in such structures because of the many interior columns.

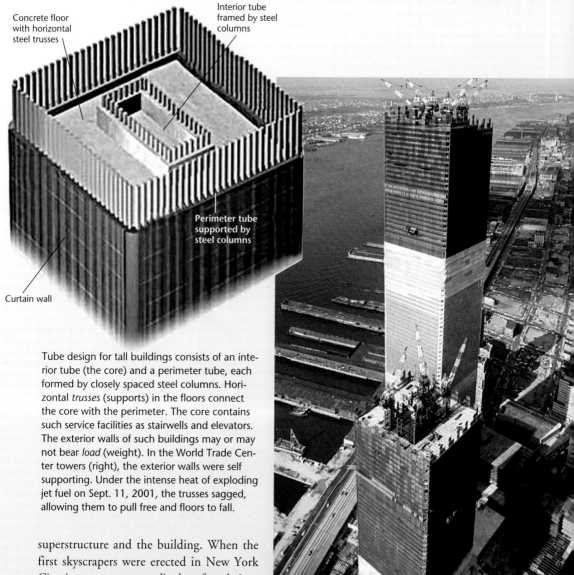

Concrete floor with horizontal steel trusses

Interior tube framed by steel columns

Perimeter tube supported by steel columns

Curtain wall

Tube design for tall buildings consists of an interior tube (the core) and a perimeter tube, each formed by closely spaced steel columns. Horizontal *trusses* (supports) in the floors connect the core with the perimeter. The core contains such service facilities as stairwells and elevators. The exterior walls of such buildings may or may not bear *load* (weight). In the World Trade Center towers (right), the exterior walls were self supporting. Under the intense heat of exploding jet fuel on Sept. 11, 2001, the trusses sagged, allowing them to pull free and floors to fall.

superstructure and the building. When the first skyscrapers were erected in New York City, it was necessary to dig deep foundations so the piles could be rooted in the solid bedrock beneath Manhattan Island. This was not possible in Chicago, however, which was built on soft soils along the banks of Lake Michigan. The solution was to dig a deep foundation pit and pour in layer upon layer of concrete until a stable pad was formed into which the piles could be driven.

New York City's iconic, Art Deco Empire State Building is perhaps the most famous example of the steel-frame superstructure plan. Designed by the architectural firm of Shreve, Lamb & Harmon and completed in 1931, the 381-meter (1,250-foot) tower employed a steel-frame design with 210 steel columns. Twelve of the columns run the entire structural height of the building. The first building to ever exceed 100 stories (it has 102 floors), the Empire State Building was the tallest building in the world from 1931 to 1972.

Chicago's Willis Tower (formerly Sears Tower) embodied a bundled-tube concept of skyscraper design (below). Engineered by Fazlur Khan of the Chicago architectural firm of Skidmore, Owings and Merrill (SOM), the building incorporated the tube-frame plan—an SOM innovation—into a bundled system of "tube" sections of staggered height, anchored by a central, two-tube bundle. Like a rubber-banded bundle of rolled-up newspapers, the bundled-tube system provides great strength to the composite structure. Willis, completed in 1974, was the tallest building in North America in 2012.

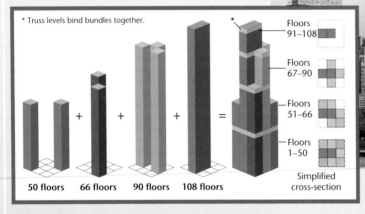

* Truss levels bind bundles together.

Floors 91–108
Floors 67–90
Floors 51–66
Floors 1–50

Simplified cross-section

50 floors   66 floors   90 floors   108 floors

Tube frame—a revolutionary design

Although steel-framed buildings are still being built today, the tube frame is considered its successor in tall-building engineering. The tube frame consists of a tightly arrayed core of vertical steel or concrete columns at the center of a building. The columns are connected with horizontal steel beams to closely aligned support columns along the building's outer skin. The central core accepts most of the vertical load but transfers some of the weight of the building to the outer tube, distributing the core's load across a wider footprint.

The tube-frame design was first developed in the 1960's by Fazlur Khan and J. Rankine of the Chicago architectural firm Skidmore, Owings and Merrill (SOM) for use in the DeWitt-Chestnut Apartment Building in Chicago, which Khan engineered. In contrast to the traditional steel-grid system, the steel tube design allows for more open interiors as well as less boxy exteriors.

One disadvantage of the early tube designs, however, was the need to closely space support columns along the building's perimeter, thus reducing available window space. Two of the best-known tall buildings to employ the tube-frame plan were Tower One and Tower Two of the former World Trade Center in New York City, designed by Minoru

Reinforced concrete involves melding steel reinforcing rods with concrete. The technique endows structures with greater strength than either steel or concrete alone. Reinforced concrete was used in the Petronas Towers, in Kuala Lumpur, Malaysia. It was both cheaper than imported steel and a technique familiar to local contractors.

Yamasaki. (These buildings were destroyed in the terrorist attack of Sept. 11, 2001.) Completed in 1972, Tower One of the "Twin Towers" reigned as the tallest building in the world until 1974, when it was surpassed by Chicago's Sears (now Willis) Tower, designed by SOM.

Variations on the tube frame

Since the 1960's, architects and engineers have made many improvements to the popular tube-frame design. Some of these advances came from Khan himself, as seen in the John Hancock Center in Chicago. The building, designed by SOM and completed in 1969, employs diagonal bracing in the perimeter walls to allow for a more open, glass-clad exterior than earlier tube-frame skyscrapers could offer.

For the design of the Sears Tower, Khan developed what became known as the bundled-tube design. The bundled frame consists of nine cores of varying heights connected by horizontal *trusses* (supports). Although only two of the cores rise through the entire 110 stories of the building, the vertical and horizontal loads are distributed among all nine.

Another recent example of innovation in tube design is the high-strength, reinforced concrete tube superstructure of Kuala Lumpur's Petronas Towers, designed by the U.S. architectural firm of Cesar Pelli & Associates. The buildings' core walls and columns are made of a super-high-strength reinforced concrete, with no structural steel columns

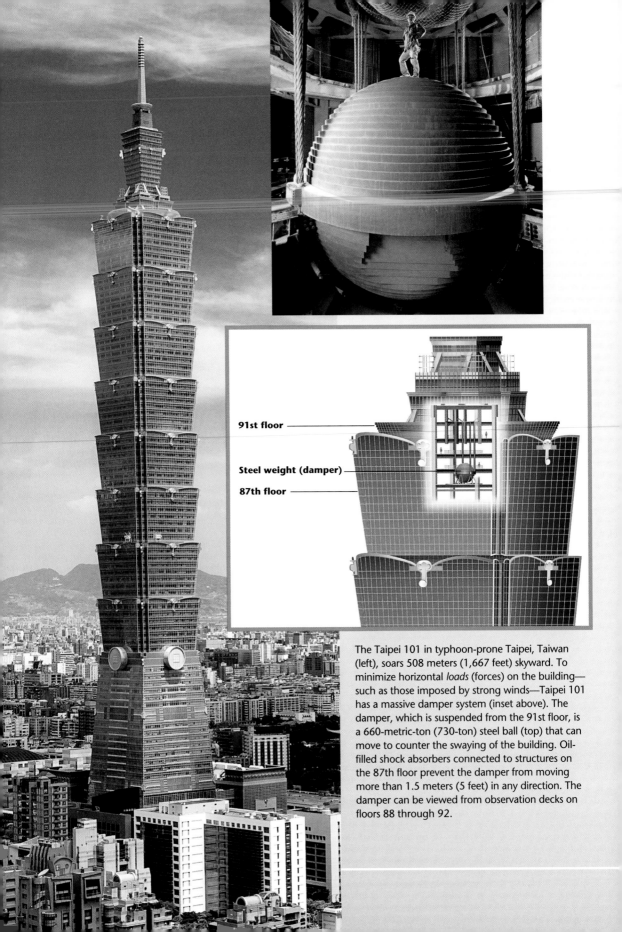

91st floor

Steel weight (damper)

87th floor

The Taipei 101 in typhoon-prone Taipei, Taiwan (left), soars 508 meters (1,667 feet) skyward. To minimize horizontal *loads* (forces) on the building— such as those imposed by strong winds—Taipei 101 has a massive damper system (inset above). The damper, which is suspended from the 91st floor, is a 660-metric-ton (730-ton) steel ball (top) that can move to counter the swaying of the building. Oil-filled shock absorbers connected to structures on the 87th floor prevent the damper from moving more than 1.5 meters (5 feet) in any direction. The damper can be viewed from observation decks on floors 88 through 92.

at all. Keeping to the basic principles of the tube design, each tower has a 23.8-meter by 23.8-meter (75-foot by 75-foot) central concrete core. An outer ring of widely spaced reinforced concrete columns along the perimeter is connected to the inner core. The strength of these perimeter columns allows for wider spacing between the structural supports.

The decision to use high-strength reinforced concrete in the Petronas Towers was driven by the high cost of importing steel to Malaysia and the familiarity Asian contractors had with concrete construction. A reinforced concrete tube superstructure also permits less *lateral deformation* (swaying from side to side) than a steel tube, allowing for the Petronas Towers' distinctive skybridge, which links the two towers at the 41st floor. This design would not have been possible without the high-strength concrete developed in recent decades.

Another building that pushes the classic tube design to its limits is the Taipei 101 tower in Taipei, Taiwan. This distinctive supertall skyscraper, with its Chinese-inspired, pagoda-like profile, was designed by C. Y. Lee and Company of Taipei. The second-tallest building in the world (as of 2012), Taipei 101 sits near several active earthquake faults and is regularly battered by seasonal typhoons. Both of these site conditions had to be taken into account in the building's design.

Taipei 101's structural system is essentially tube frame but with some significant innovations. The architects designed a perimeter of "megacolumns" to help the core support the vertical load. Each of the eight megacolumns is a hollow steel tube filled with high-performance, reinforced concrete. The perimeter megacolumns are not in the outer wall but are embedded within the structure near the outer walls. This design was necessary to accommodate the slanting profile of the pagoda-inspired exterior. Strongly reinforced horizontal steel trusses link the inner tube columns and the outer megacolumns at every eighth floor, which was designed to be an equipment- and mechanicals-support level.

The tower's structural system was put to the test in 2002, when a 6.8-magnitude earthquake struck Taiwan. Construction cranes on the unfinished tower fell to the street below, but the building withstood the quake without significant structural damage.

Tall buildings are designed to sway in the wind, but too much horizontal loading can overload the structure—or, at the very least, cause uncomfortable conditions for building occupants. The Taipei region is subject to powerful typhoons, which can produce gusts of up to 241 kilometers (150 miles) per hour, exerting profound horizontal loading. One technology used to restrain this horizontal movement in Taipei 101 is a damper.

The basic principle of a damper involves suspending a large weight from the interior superstructure near the top of the building, where it is allowed to swing like a pendulum. This weight is also connected to the superstructure via oil-filled shock absorbers. In Taipei 101, the main damper is a 660-metric-ton (730-ton) steel weight that is suspended in the middle of the building's 89th floor. When Taipei 101 starts to sway during a typhoon, the damper begins to swing. This movement is then "dampened" by the shock absorbers, which essentially soak up the energy of the moving weight, steadying the entire building.

Terrorism and design

The structural engineering community has seen much debate over whether the design of the World Trade Center towers contributed to their structural failure and collapse on Sept. 11, 2001, several hours after terrorists crashed two passenger jets into the towers.

In 2005, the National Institute of Standards and Technology (NIST), a U.S. agency, completed an in-depth review of the collapse. The experts concluded that the intense heat of the planes' burning jet fuel caused the horizontal steel trusses on the affected floors to soften and sag. The sagging floors pulled the perimeter columns inward, which "led to the inward bowing of the [wall] and failure of the south face of WTC 1 and the east face of WTC 2, initiating the collapse of each of the towers." Once the perimeter columns were no longer supporting their share of the load, the tube design was compromised and each tower failed in turn.

The NIST study concluded that the design of the towers was not at fault, as the unprecedented scale of the attacks inflicted damage far beyond any that the designers could have reasonably anticipated. Still, the report recommended that high-rise buildings review the fireproofing of their structural systems. It advised that designs of future tall buildings

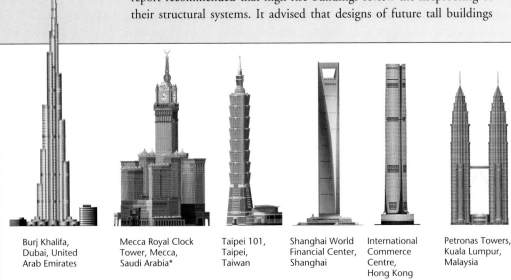

| Burj Khalifa, Dubai, United Arab Emirates | Mecca Royal Clock Tower, Mecca, Saudi Arabia* | Taipei 101, Taipei, Taiwan | Shanghai World Financial Center, Shanghai | International Commerce Centre, Hong Kong | Petronas Towers, Kuala Lumpur, Malaysia |

Source: Council on Tall Buildings and Urban Habitat.
*Scheduled for completion in 2012.

should have "improved performance to delay or prevent building collapse …" as well as strongly reinforced stairwell enclosures.

Despite predictions at the time of the attacks that security and safety concerns would stifle enthusiasm for new tall buildings, the pace of tower construction barely paused. One factor may be that the tube design utilized in the World Trade Center had been greatly improved in building design prior to 2001. At the same time, innovative structural systems were on architects' and engineers' drawing boards.

Superskyscrapers, or the rise of the megatalls

The Burj Khalifa embodies a structural system quite different from the classic tube structure. This innovative type of structure emerges from a Y-shaped, *tripodal* (three-legged) footprint—an inherently stable shape. At the heart of the structure is a reinforced concrete *hexagonal* (six-sided) core. Extending from the sides of the core are three highly reinforced stacked corridors that form tripodal "wings." As the building rises, the three reinforced wings buttress the massively built core. Periodic setbacks taper the ascending profile. All of these factors endow the structure with stability as well as a certain amount of flexibility. In engineering terms, the robust core with the buttressing supports the massive vertical load and, at the same time, resists the horizontal load of strong winds at higher levels with enough flexibility to minimize disturbing sway on upper floors.

The design for Saudi Arabia's Kingdom Tower, the next megatall record-breaker, has occasioned much comment and much comparison to the design of the Burj Khalifa. (Contractors began groundwork for construction of Kingdom Tower in early 2012.) Although the final

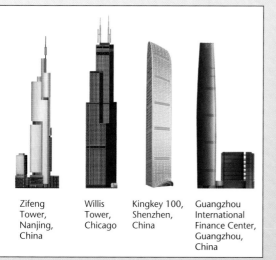

Zifeng Tower, Nanjing, China

Willis Tower, Chicago

Kingkey 100, Shenzhen, China

Guangzhou International Finance Center, Guangzhou, China

Skyscrapers in Asia and the Middle East dominate the "top ten" list of the world's tallest buildings (as of mid-2012). The Council on Tall Buildings and Urban Habitat (CTBUH) maintains a database of tall buildings and ranks their height according to specific criteria. For example, spires that are part of the building's architectural design are included in the official height, but add-ons—such as the antennas atop Willis Tower—are not. A tall-building boom underway in parts of Asia and the Middle East since the end of the 1990's shows no sign of slowing. The world's tallest building, the Burj Khalifa in Dubai, United Arab Emirates (far left), is likely to hold the title until at least 2017, when the Kingdom Tower in Jiddah, Saudi Arabia, was scheduled for completion.

height is a closely guarded secret, spokespersons for Saudi Arabia's Kingdom Holding Company, the project's owner, have confirmed that the sleek tower will soar more than 1 kilometer (0.62 mile or 3,281 feet) when completed. It will have more than 530,000 square meters (5.7 million square feet) of space for offices, residential apartments, and recreational facilities.

It is also known that the Kingdom Tower will be three-sided, converging at a single point with multiple spires along its height. With its tripodal footprint, reinforced concrete core, and tapering profile, Kingdom Tower promises to be an exemplar of the buttressed-core plan—the same structural concept used in the Burj Khalifa. In the designs of these remarkable megatalls on the Arabian Peninsula, some architectural critics detect influences from American architect Frank Lloyd Wright. In 1956, the great American architect unveiled a design for the mile-high Illinois Tower (also called Illinois Sky City) in Chicago, which was never built. That design, if realized, would also have produced a sleek, tapering, megatall tower based on a tripodal footprint.

The use of similar structural designs for the Burj Khalifa and Kingdom Tower suggests that the buttressed-core structural system may represent the wave of the future for the world's megatall contenders. But the plan for Kingdom Tower indicates that this megatall standout will have a few innovations of its own. Among the more innovative design elements are a vertical series of notches on all three sides of the building. The notches create pockets of shade that reduce surface heat gain in the hot, sunny Arabian climate. Such design elements are evidence of the architectural creativity and imaginative engineering being applied to megatall buildings. As far as tall buildings are concerned, the future is wide open.

An architect's rendering of Kingdom Tower (right) reveals the projected structure's soaring, sleek profile, punctuated with notches to deflect hot sunshine. When completed later in this decade, this megatall building on the edge of the Arabian Sea in Jiddah, Saudi Arabia, will shatter previous height records. It will top out at more than 1 kilometer (0.62 mile) high. The architects envision an observation terrace on the 157th floor (below).

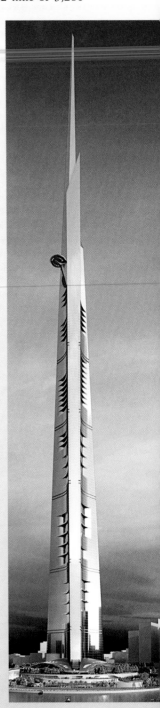

Widely viewed as one of the most important figures in American design history, architect Frank Lloyd Wright (1867–1959) is perhaps best known for his revolutionary domestic architecture embodied in the prairie-style house. However, Wright authored several innovative designs for skyscrapers. His most radical design for a tall building was that of the Illinois Tower, publicized in 1956 as part of his visionary, large-scale urban plan called Broadacre City. Illinois Tower, which was never built, would have soared 1,600 meters (1 mile) above Chicago, making it twice as tall as the Burj Khalifa—completed more than 50 years later.

Wright's structural concept for the Illinois Tower was of a massively built tripodal column, firmly embedded in the earth, with floors cantilevered from a central core. (In a cantilever, a rigid structural element extends horizontally without any support on its freestanding end. Making this possible is a balancing downward force applied to the end that is attached to the structure.) Wright, a lifelong proponent of "organic architecture"—that is, architecture arising from forms found in nature—compared this tall-building structural design to a massive tree trunk with underground roots, a soaring trunk, and branches growing from the trunk.

Although the Illinois Tower was never built, Wright did see his ideas for skyscrapers worked out in steel and concrete in the H. C. Price Company Tower, a 19-story skyscraper in Bartlesville, Oklahoma, that opened to the public in 1956. Today the structure houses the Price Tower Arts Center and enjoys protection as a national historic landmark. The Price Tower stands as testament to Wright's uncanny vision of the future of tall buildings. In pioneering the firmly anchored, solidly built core as the structural essence of the skyscraper of the future, Wright anticipated the astonishing megatowers of the contemporary scene.

Renowned architect Frank Lloyd Wright presents his design for the Illinois Tower, a visionary skyscraper of unprecedented height, at a press conference in Chicago in October 1956. Although never built, the Illinois Tower embodied principles used recently by architects in their designs of megatall buildings. During his lifetime, Wright saw his innovative design for the Price Tower in Bartlesville, Oklahoma (inset above), executed in a completed skyscraper.

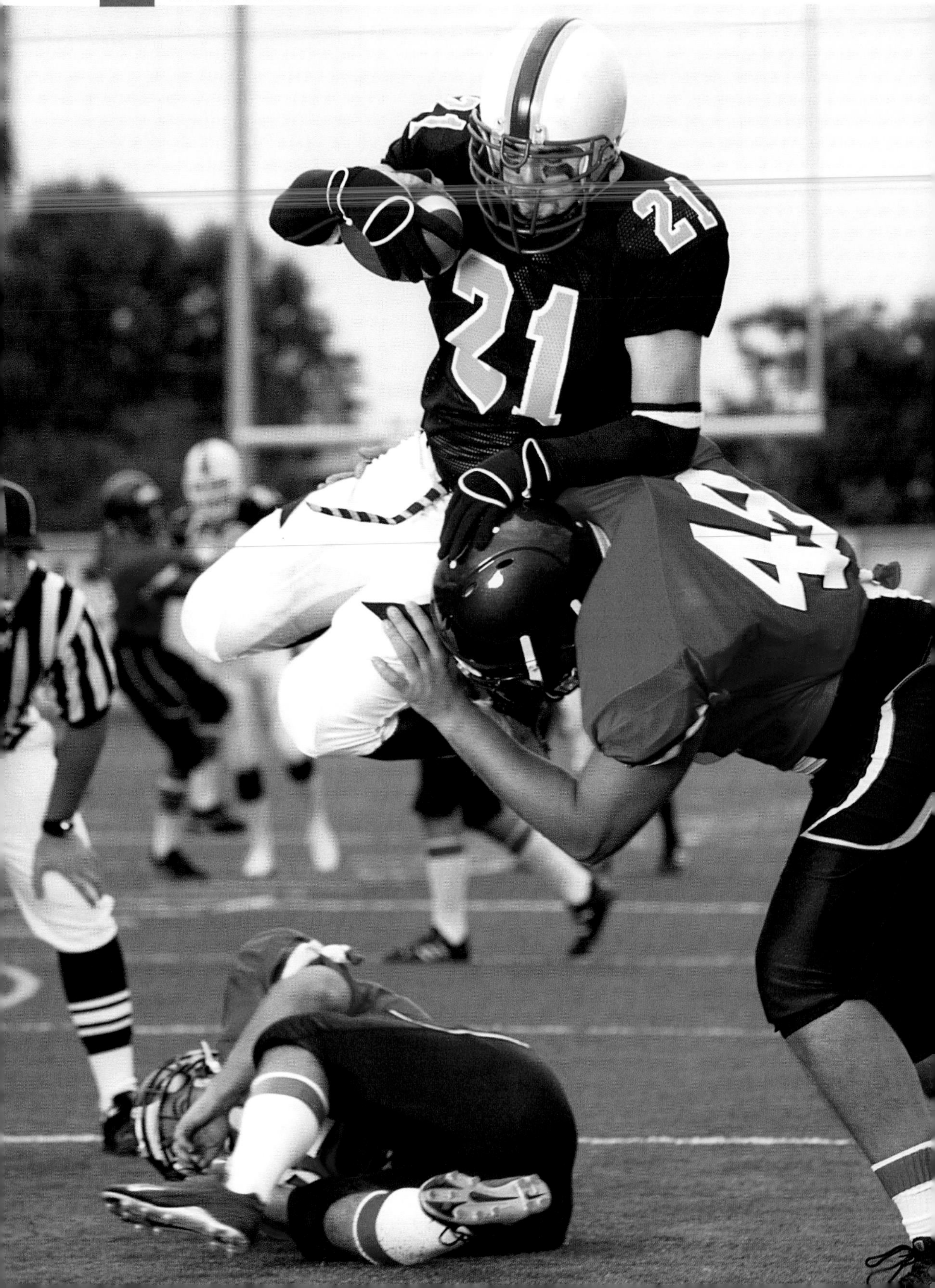
21
21
44

Knocking Heads: The Dangers of Concussions

By Scott Witmer

Concussions among professional athletes highlight dangers faced by children playing sports.

When former Chicago Bears safety Dave Duerson committed suicide in February 2011 at age 50, he left a note that read, "Please, see that my brain is given to the NFL's brain bank [a center for concussion-related research partly funded by the National Football League (NFL)]." Duerson had sustained numerous concussions during his playing career and had suffered from declining physical and psychological health for years. An autopsy of his brain tissue revealed that he had severe brain abnormalities that many scientists believe are caused by repeated concussions. These abnormalities have also been found in the brains of many other deceased football players, as well as athletes from other sports.

By mid-2012, more than 3,300 former football players and families of players had filed some 80 lawsuits against the NFL, accusing the organization of hiding information about the link between football-related concussions and permanent brain damage from players. In June, the lawsuits were combined into one mega-lawsuit. According to the lawsuit—and numerous researchers—repeated con-

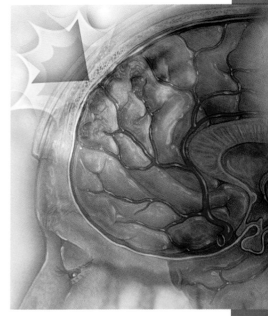

A hard blow to the head, such as that sustained in a football tackle, can lead to a concussion or other traumatic brain injury.

TERMS AND CONCEPTS

Amyloid precursor protein: Protein that normally regulates connections between nerve cells.

Cerebral cortex: The brain's outer layer of "gray matter."

Chronic traumatic encephalopathy: Chronic condition similar to dementia that may be caused by repeated concussions.

Computed tomography: X-ray system used to produce three-dimensional images of various parts of the body.

Concussion: Temporary disturbance of brain function caused by a sudden blow to the head or a sudden change in movement.

Dementia: Decline in intellectual capacity that reduces a person's ability to carry out everyday activities.

Hemorrhage: Bleeding inside the body.

Magnetic resonance imaging: Technique used to produce images of tissues inside the body, based on magnets and radio waves.

Neuron: Nerve cell in the brain.

Tau: Protein that helps to keep the microtubules of *axons* (nerve fibers) intact.

Traumatic brain injury: Damage to the brain resulting from any of various injuries, such as concussion or whiplash.

The author:

Scott Witmer is a free-lance writer based in Chicago.

cussions can result in a condition called chronic traumatic encephalopathy (CTE), the symptoms of which are similar to those of Alzheimer's disease and other forms of *dementia* (decline in intellectual capacity that reduces a person's ability to carry out everyday activities).

For many years, concussions were considered only minor, *acute* (short-term) conditions with no lasting severe effects. Symptoms were often ignored by athletes, coaches, and even team physicians as "dings" or "getting your bell rung." Recently, however, concussions are being seen as a serious health hazard for professional and amateur athletes—including children—especially in such high-contact sports as football and hockey. According to the Centers for Disease Control and Prevention (CDC) in Atlanta, hospitals in the United States reported a 60-percent increase in emergency-room visits from 2001 to 2009 for children and adolescents with head injuries. The CDC attributed this jump primarily to an increased awareness among parents and coaches of the potentially serious consequences of concussions. Although concussions can range from mild to severe, they are classified as a mild type of traumatic brain injury (TBI). Other types of TBI's include such penetrating injuries as shrapnel from an explosion entering the skull as well as whiplash (which can be associated with concussions) from automobile accidents.

The CDC estimates that 1.6 million to 3.8 million people experience a sports-related or recreation-related concussion or other TBI in the United States each year. Hundreds of thousands of other TBI's each year are caused by such incidents as falls or crashes involving automobiles, motorcycles, or bicycles, as well as assaults and work-related accidents. In addition, concussions and other TBI's are considered the "signature wound" of the wars in Iraq and Afghanistan, making up 22 percent of all U.S. casualties and 59 percent of all U.S. explosion-related injuries associated with those conflicts. In 2012, studies of how concussions affect the brain led neuroscientists, sports specialists, and physicians to explore more effective forms of diagnosis, treatment, and prevention.

What is a concussion?

Although the precise definition of "concussion" varies depending on the source, most physicians and researchers consider it a temporary disturbance of brain function caused by a sudden blow to the head or a sudden change in movement. In a concussion, the brain moves and hits the inside of the skull, injuring the *cerebral cortex* (the brain's outer layer of "gray matter") and disrupting the cortex's normal functions of regulating memory, thought, and movement.

When many people think of a concussion, they picture an athlete knocked unconscious by a head-on collision. However, not all con-

After a concussion, an individual typically is confused and has difficulties with memory and concentration. Other symptoms may include balance problems, blurry vision, dizziness, headache, nausea or vomiting, and sensitivity to noise or light.

Physicians strongly recommend that individuals rest for several days after sustaining a concussion. Activities that are mentally or physically demanding, such as playing video games, may aggravate symptoms. Resting helps prevent or limit swelling and further injury, as does the application of an ice pack. Pain can be relieved with an over-the-counter medication, such as acetaminophen. However, such blood-thinning and anti-inflammatory medications as aspirin or ibuprofen should be avoided because they may increase the risk of bleeding. Alcohol should also be avoided, because it slows recovery and increases the risk of further injury.

Symptoms should be closely monitored for at least 24 hours. Asking simple questions every two or three hours, such as "What is your name?" is a useful way to monitor the individual's alertness. In most cases, symptoms improve within 7 to 10 days. However, individuals who have worsening or prolonged symptoms should follow up with a physician.

Possible Symptoms of Concussion

- Bleeding from nose or ears
- Blurred vision
- Confusion
- Difficulty concentrating
- Dizziness
- Drowsiness
- Headache
- Memory loss
- Nausea or vomiting
- Seizures
- Sensitivity to noise or light
- Slurred speech

cussions result in loss of consciousness. Some concussions are not so obvious, with individuals experiencing them differently for unknown reasons. In a milder concussion, such as a bump on the head, an individual may experience temporary confusion but no memory loss or unconsciousness. In a more serious concussion, such as a head-to-head slam in a football tackle, an individual may lose consciousness and, upon regaining consciousness, experience memory loss and disorientation for a prolonged period. Other possible symptoms of concussion include blurry vision, ringing in the ears, headache, dizziness, trouble concentrating, exhaustion, and nausea. Concussions sometimes lead to changes in behavior that can manifest as anger, frustration, impulsiveness, insomnia, irritability, or mood swings. Concussion symptoms may last for hours, days, weeks, or even months, depending on the individual and the nature of the injury.

The general name for prolonged symptoms experienced by some people after sustaining a concussion is postconcussion syndrome. Scientists are not sure why symptoms last longer in some people than in others. Research suggests that the severity of injury is apparently not the reason for differences in symptom length.

Concussion symptoms may be difficult to predict, in part, because of the complexity of changes that can occur in the brain during and after a concussion. After the brain sustains an impact, *neurons* (brain nerve cells) may become damaged, leading to changes in the neurons' production of proteins, chemical imbalances in the brain, and other abnormalities in

WHAT HAPPENS IN A CONCUSSION

A concussion results from the sudden movement of the brain in the skull because of a blow to the head. If the blow occurs at the front of the head, the frontal region of the brain knocks against the bony inner surface of the front of the skull. The head is then jarred backward, causing the head and neck to become *hyperextended* (extended beyond the normal range). The head may quickly recoil, causing the head and neck to become *hyperflexed* (flexed beyond the normal range) and the back of the brain (the occipital region) to hit the inner surface of the back of the skull. The impact of the brain on the skull triggers a series of chemical reactions in the *cerebral cortex* (the brain's outer layer) that interfere with memory, thought, and movement.

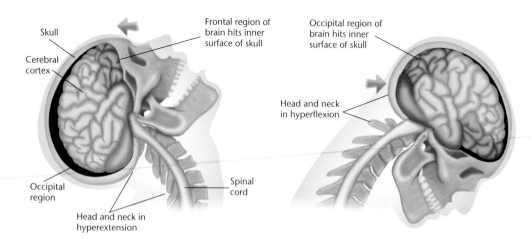

Skull

Cerebral cortex

Frontal region of brain hits inner surface of skull

Occipital region of brain hits inner surface of skull

Head and neck in hyperflexion

Occipital region

Spinal cord

Head and neck in hyperextension

brain *metabolism* (the biochemical processes that occur in an organism). In addition, various degrees of *hemorrhage* (internal bleeding) and *edema* (swelling) can occur as blood and other circulatory fluids build up in brain tissues. The particular combination of brain abnormalities resulting from a concussion causes the symptoms experienced by an individual.

Repeated concussions

Given time and plenty of rest, an injured person's brain has a natural ability to heal these problems. However, if the brain sustains another concussion or other impact injury before the damage from the first injury has healed, it is possible that the problems may be cumulative—that is, the second concussion may worsen the problem sustained in the first concussion. In such cases, severe brain edema or herniation can result. In brain herniation, parts of the brain bulge outward and squeeze against structures in the skull, often resulting in death. Some researchers classify the potentially fatal problems caused by repeated concussions within a short time as second-impact syndrome—a term first proposed by neurosurgeon Richard Saunders and neurologist Robert Harbaugh in 1984.

A series of shocking fatalities of amateur football players, many of them teenagers, brought much public attention to the dangers of repeated concussions in the 1980's. In 1981, Cornell University freshman football player Enzo Montemurro received a head-impact injury during a game. Initially considered minor, the injury caused a swollen brain that led to Montemurro's death. In an autopsy of Montemurro's brain, Saunders and Harbaugh discovered that the fatal jolt had occurred on top of existing damage from an impact that had been sustained days earlier.

Saunders and Harbaugh used the term second-impact syndrome to describe the effects of a mild second concussion being more dangerous than the effects of the first concussion—even fatal—if the brain has not yet healed. The identification of this syndrome raised concerns about the lingering effects of undiagnosed concussions, especially for children, whose developing brains are particularly vulnerable to damage. However, some physicians and researchers doubt whether such a fatal syndrome truly exists, noting that evidence for it is rare.

According to a number of researchers, multiple concussions or other impact injuries over a lengthy period—as in the cases of some professional athletes—can result in CTE, a more common condition. Symp-

BRAIN DAMAGE IN A CONCUSSION

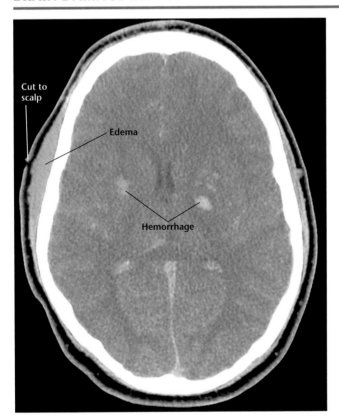

Cut to scalp

Edema

Hemorrhage

A computed tomography (CT) scan of the brain of a teenager injured in an automobile accident while not wearing a seatbelt shows several types of brain damage that may occur in a concussion. This damage includes *edema* (swelling) caused by ruptured blood vessels in the right temporal region (blue). The scan also reveals two areas of *hemorrhaging* (severe internal bleeding) in the basal ganglia, structures that help control body movement.

CHRONIC TRAUMATIC ENCEPHALOPATHY

Chronic traumatic encephalopathy (CTE) is a progressive disease that has been found in the autopsied brains of individuals who have had numerous concussions and other brain injuries. In CTE, *neurons* (nerve cells in the brain) become severely damaged. The *axons* (nerve fibers that carry messages) may twist and stretch to abnormal lengths. The axons may then tear, spilling proteins called amyloid precursor protein and tau. As the leaking neurons die, the proteins form tangles, or plaques. In autopsied brain tissue (inset at right), the CTE plaques appear as brownish areas.

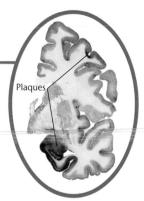

Plaques

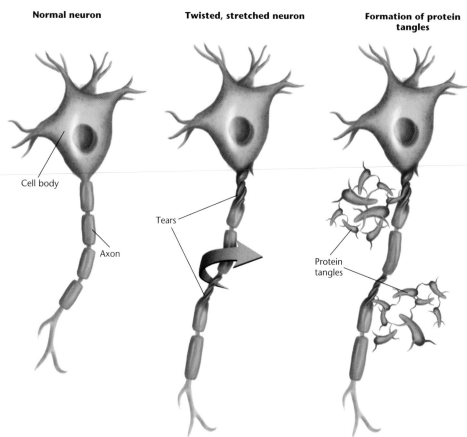

Normal neuron

Cell body

Axon

Twisted, stretched neuron

Tears

Formation of protein tangles

Protein tangles

toms linked to CTE include impaired judgment, impulse control problems, aggression, depression (sometimes leading to suicide), and dementia. These symptoms mimic those of other forms of dementia, including Alzheimer's disease and certain types of Parkinson disease, because the biochemical processes responsible for the conditions appear to be similar.

The repeated concussions and other impact injuries that may lead to CTE can impair the brain's axons, the fibers of neurons that carry electrochemical information from one neuron to another. The axons may become twisted and stretched to abnormal lengths. Axons are made up of tiny channels, called microtubules, that transport nutrients when prompted by electrochemical signals. When neurons stretch or break, these microtubules are pulled open and spill their nutrients. Among the nutrients in these spills are amyloid precursor protein (APP), which normally regulates connections between nerve cells, and tau, a protein that helps to keep the microtubules intact. The leaked APP piles up at the site of the damaged axon and chemically breaks down into a smaller protein called amyloid beta.

Accumulations of leaked amyloid beta and tau, called tangles or plaques, are signs of dying brain cells and are seen in the autopsied brains of many people who have had multiple concussions. In fact, CTE can be definitively diagnosed only in autopsies, by using high-powered microscopes to identify the characteristic protein tangles in slides of brain slices stained with special dyes. Such tangles are also a sign of Alzheimer's disease. In both Alzheimer's disease and CTE, the cerebral cortex has gradually *atrophied* (wasted away).

Growing awareness of CTE

Many of the symptoms that are today associated with CTE were originally associated with a condition first known as dementia pugilistica ("punch-drunk syndrome"). This condition gained attention in medical circles in the 1920's, when physicians observed slurred speech, slowed thinking, memory problems, balance problems, and tremors in many older boxers who had experienced repeated blows to the head.

By the early 1980's, computed tomography (CT) scans had revealed various degrees of irreversible atrophy of the cerebral cortex in boxers who had sustained repeated concussions. Some of these individuals had not yet displayed obvious symptoms, while others showed signs of dementia. In 1984, a study by the American Medical Association (AMA) based on CT scans and neurological examinations found brain damage in an alarming 87 percent of boxers. The evidence that multiple concussions caused brain damage in boxing was strong enough to lead the AMA to call for an end to the sport. The most famous boxer to be struck with a serious medical condition likely related to repeated concussions, retired heavyweight champion Muhammad Ali, was diagnosed at age 42 with a form of Parkinson disease, in which cells are destroyed in regions of the brain responsible for body movements.

By the early 2000's, autopsies of the brains of a number of NFL players who had each sustained multiple concussions revealed details of the biochemical basis of CTE. In 2002, an autopsy performed by Pittsburgh neuropathologist Bennet Omalu on the brain of the late NFL player Mike Webster revealed the protein tangles surrounding damaged neurons that are characteristic of dementia. During the final years of his life, Webster had often been depressed, angry, and confused. By the time he died, the dementia brought on by CTE had left Webster homeless and alienated from family and friends.

With the assistance of Chris Nowinski, a researcher and former college football player and professional wrestler whose athletic career was cut short by concussions, Omalu acquired brain tissue from a number of deceased football players for examination. Omalu founded the Brain Injury Research Institute on the campus of West Virginia University in Morgantown in 2002. Nowinski partnered with neuropathologist Ann McKee of Boston University School of Medicine to form the Center for the Study of Traumatic Encephalopathy (CSTE) in 2008. The CSTE has received substantial financial support from the NFL for concussion-related research (and it is the "NFL's brain bank" referred to in Dave Duerson's suicide note). As of early 2012, scientists at the CSTE had diagnosed CTE in the autopsied brains of more than 60 deceased athletes, including Duerson.

Concussion diagnosis and assessment

Although CTE can be definitively diagnosed only in autopsies, a clinical diagnosis of concussions and an assessment of concussion severity in living patients can be performed with standardized testing. Neuropsychologist Mark Lovell of the University of Pittsburgh Center for Sports Medicine developed one of the first tests to assess concussions in patients in the early 1990's while working with the Pittsburgh Steelers NFL team. Concussion victims are typically confused and unreliable at gauging their own symptoms. Thus, a standardized diagnostic test of cognitive impairment was necessary not only to measure the severity of the concussion, but also track a patient's recovery.

Lovell's test, which evolved into an evaluation tool called Immediate Postconcussion Assessment and Cognitive Testing (ImPACT), involves verbal and visual memory exercises performed on a computer. Now the standard in postconcussion assessment used with thousands of professional and amateur athletes (as well as many nonathletes), ImPACT measures responses based on accuracy and speed. An athlete takes the test at the beginning of each season to establish a baseline score, then again after a concussion to determine neurological effects on the brain and time needed to recover.

The Standardized Assessment of Concussion (SAC) is an evaluation of cognitive impairment in the areas of orientation, concentration, immediate memory, and delayed recall memory. The SAC test, designed

Neuropathologist Ann McKee holds the brain of a deceased athlete at the Center for the Study of Traumatic Encephalopathy (CSTE) in Boston. As of early 2012, autopsies performed at the CSTE had revealed evidence of chronic traumatic encephalopathy in the brains of more than 60 athletes.

At Super Bowl V in 1971, Baltimore Colts tight end John Mackey caught a pass that had flown through the hands of two other players. He then ran the ball 75 yards down the field to score his team's first touchdown of the game. Mackey's spectacular play contributed to the Colts' 16-to-13 defeat of the Dallas Cowboys. In a storied career that lasted from 1963 to 1972, Mackey's 75-yard touchdown would remain one of his proudest moments.

By the time Mackey died in July 2011, his life would also be remembered for another reason. In 2000, he was diagnosed as having frontal temporal dementia. The early onset of the disease, at age 60, suggested that it may have been caused by multiple concussions sustained while playing football. In one such incident, during an exhibition game in 1965, Mackey crashed head-first into a goal post, causing him to wander in a daze to the opposing team's huddle before taking a seat on their bench. The incident also resulted in the repositioning of goal posts from the goal line to the back of the end zone.

Mackey's dementia meant that, in the last several years of his life, he could no longer consistently recall much of his football career, nor recognize many of his closest friends and former teammates. He even had trouble remembering how to do simple daily tasks. His personality also changed. He became listless, moody, and easily angered. By age 65, he was residing in an assisted-living facility.

Thanks to the efforts of Mackey's wife, Sylvia, the NFL established a fund in 2007 that covers up to $88,000 per year in medical expenses for retired players suffering from dementia. The amount was chosen in honor of Mackey's jersey

Baltimore Colts tight end John Mackey is tackled by Karl Kassulke of the Minnesota Vikings in 1965, during Mackey's days as a star player in the National Football League. During his career, from 1963 to 1972, Mackey sustained a number of concussions. When he was 60 years old, he was diagnosed as having dementia, which may have been caused by the multiple concussions.

number, 88. Within its first four years, the "88 Plan" had assisted 166 players.

Mackey's brain was donated to researchers at the Boston University School of Medicine's Center for the Study of Traumatic Encephalopathy for studies to investigate whether his dementia was linked to injuries sustained playing football.

for a quick evaluation of mental function after a concussion, can be performed by a clinician with minimal experience in neuropsychological testing, such as a team's athletic trainer on a football field sideline.

Other tests have been developed to measure the physical coordination of people recovering from concussions. For example, researchers at the University of North Carolina's Sports Medicine Research Laboratory developed the Balance Error Scoring System (BESS) in the late 1990's. This test requires the individual to stand with eyes closed while maintaining a balanced posture in several different stances on flat or foam surfaces for 20-second periods. Individuals are scored based on the number of stumbles or errors they make during each trial—mistakes that are representative of the brain damage characteristic of concussions. BESS can be used to determine when athletes with brain injuries can safely return to play.

Not all concussion-related injuries appear on such clinical brain scans as CT or magnetic resonance imaging (MRI). Although CT and MRI scans show the overall structure of the brain (including major structural damage to the cerebral cortex), they do not reveal axon damage or other internal biochemical changes that are signs of multiple concussion injuries and CTE. By contrast, positron emission tomography (PET) scans allow brain specialists to view the function of the brain and, thus, these scans are more likely to reveal biochemical signs of concussions.

Positron emission tomography scanners trace weakly radioactive *glucose* (blood sugar) that has been injected into the arm of the patient. After the circulatory system carries the glucose into the brain, the radiation highlights chemical activity in particular regions of the brain as the glucose is consumed in chemical reactions. Individuals with repeated concussions or other TBI's typically have less chemical activity in vital cognitive areas of the brain—similar to the reduced cognitive activity observed in patients who are in comas.

Functional MRI (fMRI), which shows blood flow in the brain, can indicate areas where the brain is working to repair an impact injury. Another technology, diffusion tensor imaging, can be used with fMRI to view water flow in the brain. Such advanced forms of medical imaging help highlight areas, including the frontal lobes of the brain, in which normal functioning has been disrupted because of impact-caused axon damage. After an appropriate diagnosis is made, treatment of the patient can begin.

IMMEDIATE POSTCONCUSSION ASSESSMENT AND COGNITIVE TESTING

A young student athlete uses Immediate Postconcussion Assessment and Cognitive Testing (ImPACT), an evaluation of cogntive abilities involving verbal and visual memory exercises performed on a computer. This test is used by many professional and amateur athletes—at the beginning of a season and again after a concussion—to determine the severity of concussion-caused neurological effects.

TESTING FOR A SAFE RETURN TO PLAY

An athlete who has suffered a concussion attempts to maintain a balanced posture in a series of stances included in the Balance Error Scoring System (BESS), a tool that can help clinicians determine whether injured athletes can safely return to play. The BESS includes six different stances on firm or foam surfaces that must be maintained for 20-second periods.

Single-leg stance
on firm surface

Tandem stance on
firm surface

Double-leg stance
on foam surface

Treating patients with concussions

Basic, initial treatment for a concussion includes rest, use of a pain-relieving medication, application of an ice pack to relieve swelling, and close monitoring of the patient's condition. In addition, a thorough medical evaluation may be needed if symptoms worsen. The main goal of treatment is to allow the brain to heal before the patient returns to normal activities.

Many investigations into new treatments for patients with multiple concussions and possible CTE focus on blocking degenerative biochemical conditions in the brain. For example, Mark Burns, a neuroscientist at Georgetown University in Washington, D.C., and his colleagues have experimented with mice to develop a drug that blocks the production of amyloid beta protein following brain injuries. In 2009, Burns and his team reported that the amyloid beta-blocking drug that they developed improved the ability of mice with concussion-type brain injuries to balance on a beam.

Although much more research must be conducted, physicians were hopeful in 2012 that drugs that alter biochemical problems in the brain may eventually speed recovery in patients suffering from the effects of concussions.

Improving safety

In 2009 and 2010, members of the U.S. House of Representatives held hearings on the dangers of football-related concussions. Although NFL representatives argued that head injuries could not be definitively linked to dementia in football players, the hearings led to stricter NFL policies regarding recovery times for injured players, enhanced enforce-

HEAD IMPACT TELEMETRY SYSTEM

Sports medicine researcher and athletic trainer Kevin Guskiewicz, director of the Matthew Gfeller Sport-Related Traumatic Brain Injury Research Center at the University of North Carolina-Chapel Hill, displays part of the Head Impact Telemetry (HIT) system that he developed for football helmets (right). The HIT system uses small sensors inside players' helmets (opposite page) to track hits to the head. A helmet with a version of the HIT system is tested in a laboratory (below) for Riddell Sports Inc., of New York City, a leading manufacturer of equipment for amateur and professional football teams.

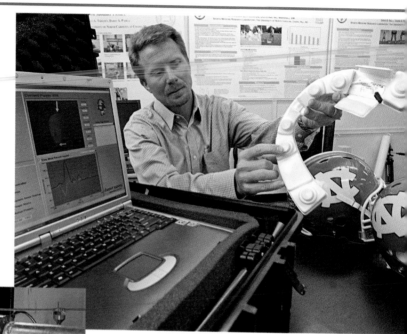

ment of rules for safety violations (such as purposeful helmet-to-helmet hits), and greater attention by the NFL to helmet technology that could help prevent concussions. Public health advocates hoped that the new NFL standards would inspire greater concussion awareness among younger athletes, especially children.

For many school and other amateur athletic programs, concussion safety is mainly a matter of proper diagnosis and guidelines regarding how long a concussed player should be sidelined before being allowed to return to play. Some state legislatures have passed laws designed to protect young amateur athletes from concussions. For example, the Zackery Lystedt Law, which was signed by the governor of Washington in 2009, is named for a 13-year-old football player who was disabled by a second concussion in 2006. The law requires coaches to remove players suspected of having concussions and requires players to be cleared by a health care professional before returning to play.

Some colleges and high schools use special helmet technology to monitor the safety of their athletes. Kevin Guskiewicz, director of the

Matthew Gfeller Sport-Related Traumatic Brain Injury Research Center at the University of North Carolina-Chapel Hill, developed a system of small sensors inside players' helmets to track dangerous or frequent hits to the head. This system, known as Head Impact Telemetry (HIT), is used in some school programs. The HIT system relies on data from *accelerometers* (electronic devices that measure acceleration or vibrations). The data can be incorporated into computer models to teach coaches and players about safer blocking and tackling techniques, such as rotating their heads away from direct contact.

Tradition vs. safety

Despite a growing recognition of the dangers of concussions in 2012, these injuries remained a high risk for many athletes. Within football, hockey, and other sports, some coaches, athletes, and fans are reluctant to see the traditionally violent aspects of their sport altered in the interests of safety. For people who consider the risks and dangers of sports to be fundamental to the excitement of the game, concussions and their long-term effects will remain a reality.

Meanwhile, scientists continue to learn more about the effects of concussions and other TBI's on the brain and to investigate advanced technologies for obtaining a clearer picture of these effects. Scientific research and closer attention to concussion diagnoses on the part of physicians, coaches, and athletes will hopefully lead to more effective treatments to prevent serious complications of concussions.

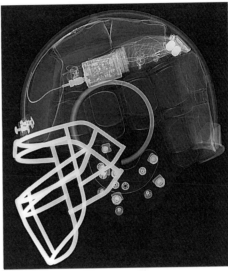

An X-ray image of a football helmet reveals the hidden sensors of the HIT system, including a data encoder and *accelerometers* (electronic devices that measure acceleration or vibrations). Data from these sensors are incorporated into computer models to teach coaches and players about safer blocking and tackling techniques.

■ FOR ADDITIONAL INFORMATION

Book

Carroll, Linda and Rosner, David. *The Concussion Crisis: Anatomy of a Silent Epidemic.* New York, NY: Simon & Schuster, 2011.

Websites

Boston University School of Medicine's Center for the Study of Traumatic Encephalopathy
http://www.bu.edu/cste/about/
Brain Injury Association of New Jersey, Inc.—Sports Concussion
http://www.sportsconcussion.com/
Centers for Disease Control and Prevention—Concussions and Mild Traumatic Brain Injuries
http://www.cdc.gov/concussion/

The Dog Who Came in from the Cold

By Robert N. Knight

How have the brains, bodies, and behavior of dogs been shaped by their long association with human beings?

Danielle was in love. The object of her affection was a fluffy, floppy-eared, bright-eyed puppy that she had adopted from a nearby shelter. At work, Danielle found herself counting down the minutes in anticipation of being greeted by "Duchess," barking and wagging her tail, at her apartment. After a few moments of pandemonium, Danielle would say "sit," and Duchess would settle on her haunches and adopt a lady-like demeanor appropriate to her name.

Adoring, devoted, loyal, obedient—these were all adjectives that Danielle used to describe Duchess. Millions of other dog owners feel the same way about their canine companions. But what is Duchess—or Spot or Maestro—really thinking, and what are his or her true motives? That is, how much of a dog's behavior is conditioned by nature and how much by the thousands of years during which dogs and humans have shared destinies? As a result of some remarkable research, we are finally getting scientific answers to these questions.

What is a dog?

Advances in genetics technology have enabled scientists to determine that all modern dog breeds have descended from the gray wolf. This conclusion is based on evidence from analyses of DNA, the molecule that makes up genes, from various species of *canines* (dogs and such dog-like animals as wolves and foxes). The human-guided behavioral and anatomical transformation of wild wolves into tame dogs—a process called domestication—is largely lost in time. However, archaeological clues, including the unearthed remains of ancient dogs, as well as genetics studies are helping scientists understand this process.

For many years, archaeological evidence suggested that dogs became domesticated approximately 14,000 years ago. However, in August 2011, a Russian-led team of scientists reported finding a 33,000-year-old canine skull in a cave in Siberia's Altai Mountains. The skull has some characteristics that are typical of a wolf (such as large teeth) and others that are typical of a domesticated dog (such as a shortened snout). The mixture of traits led the scientists to propose that the skull was evidence of early canine domestication.

In October 2011, archaeologists led by Mietje Germonpre of the Royal Belgium Institute of Natural Sciences reported finding the 31,500-year-old remains of three dogs in what is now the Czech Republic. One dog skull had a mammoth bone lodged between its jaws, suggesting that humans at the site shared meat with the dogs. The scientists also speculated that the bone was placed in the dog's mouth as part of a ritual burial of the canines. Evidence that the dogs' brains had been removed through holes in their skulls provided additional evidence for this idea. The researchers further proposed that the dogs may have served the humans as beasts of burden for hauling meat, bones, and tusks from mammoth kills.

The author:

Robert N. Knight is a free-lance writer.

Some geneticists have suggested that the domestication of dogs may have begun more than 100,000 years ago. They base this idea on studies of canine mitochondrial DNA (mtDNA), which is DNA found only in cellular structures called mitochondria. Most of a cell's DNA is found in the nucleus, the membrane-bound central structure. Unlike nuclear DNA, which is inherited from both parents, mtDNA is inherited from only the mother and does not get recombined during sexual reproduction. Because of this relative simplicity of inheritance, geneticists can use the tools of mathematical probability to estimate how many generations it would take for one mtDNA *genetic sequence* (order of chemical units called bases) to *mutate* (change) into another. By comparing wolf mtDNA with dog mtDNA, geneticists have estimated that differences would require anywhere from 40,000 to 135,000 years to develop.

However, in May 2012, an international team of researchers, reporting in *The Proceedings of the National Academy of Sciences,* questioned the reliability of both mitochondrial DNA studies and as well as the interpretations of archaeological sites dating much earlier than 14,000 years ago. The researchers also discounted backward projections derived from the highly manipulated DNA of modern breeds.

Fossil evidence of dog domestication

Fossils provide some of the earliest evidence of the domestication of dogs. A mammoth bone found between the jaws of a 31,500-year-old dog skull (arrow, right), discovered in what is now the Czech Republic, may have been placed there by a human companion as part of a ritual burial. A 33,000-year-old canine skull (right bottom) found in a cave in Siberia shows a combination of typical wolf-like traits—such as large teeth—and typical domesticated dog-like traits—such as a shortened snout. However, other scientists disagree with this analysis.

They concluded that the only way to settle the controversy about when dogs were first domesticated would be to extract and analyze DNA from a number of ancient wolf/dog fossils.

Exactly how the process of canine domestication began is a matter of conjecture. One idea long been favored by scientists is that certain wolves became "camp followers" of human hunter-and-gatherer communities, lured by the attraction of trash piles. The wolves that entered the human encampments were likely less skittish than other wolves about approaching people. People may have allowed the friendlier wolves to remain in or near the encampments, perhaps as "watch dogs." People may have also adopted and raised orphaned and unusually friendly wolf cubs, which, after reaching maturity, may have been bred by the humans. In time, increasing numbers of friendly wolves oriented toward humans would have become permanent companions of the human population. From humans, these animals derived such benefits as a steady food supply, protection from inclement weather, and a secure place to give birth to and raise young.

After many generations of breeding—with people actively selecting animals for certain preferred characteristics—domesticated dogs became physically and genetically distinct from gray wolves. In time, people bred dogs for characteristics useful to important types of work, including catch-

Cooperative wolves assist prehistoric human hunters in an attack on an auroch (an extinct type of cattle), in an artist's illustration. Such cooperation between wolves and people may have been among the first steps leading to the behavioral and physical transformation of wild wolves into domesticated dogs.

ing vermin, hauling animal kills, or herding. Within the past few centuries, breeders have produced a number of distinct types of dogs with widely varying characteristics. Some of these breeds were created for hunting or other types of work; others, purely for companionship or appearance.

Nature vs. nurture

A unique multidecade breeding experiment with foxes in Siberia has shed light on the process of domestication in dogs. In 1959, Russian biologist Dmitri Belyaev obtained more than 100 silver foxes from fur farms and began breeding them in a facility near the Siberian city of Novosibirsk. From each generation of foxes, Belyaev and his colleagues selected those foxes that exhibited the greatest affinity for people. Over multiple generations, the selected foxes became increasingly tame.

These personality characteristics in the Novosibirsk foxes eventually extended to physical traits seen in many domesticated dogs, though breeders had not specifically selected for these traits. Within a few generations, many of the foxes had floppy ears instead of the characteristic

Dog-like foxes

Physical characteristics commonly found in certain breeds of modern dogs, including floppy ears (right), have appeared in silver foxes being bred for their ability to interact with people (far right) in an ongoing study by scientists at the Institute of Cytology and Genetics in Russia. As successive

generations of foxes have become increasingly tame, the foxes have begun to look more like dogs. Many of the foxes have also developed *piebald* (spotted) markings and now curl up their tail in response to seeing a person (left). The scientists speculate that the genes that control personality traits in the animals also affect physical traits in complex ways that remain largely unknown.

pricked-up ears of foxes. Many foxes also had *piebald markings* (large spotting patterns) on their coats. Further along the generational line, the foxes developed tails that curled up in response to seeing a human. Still later generations of animals exhibited shorter tails with fewer *vertebrae* (bones of the spinal column). As their physical traits changed, successive generations of foxes became friendlier and more responsive to people.

Although foxes are not ancestral to dogs, many researchers regard the Novosibirsk experiment as a useful model for understanding dog domestication. Scientists speculate that the experiment, while selecting for genes controlling personality traits, had "dragged along" genes for physical traits as well. Thus, the inheritance of the body genes is apparently linked to the inheritance of the personality genes. The fox breeding experiment prompted scientists to wonder if domestication is mainly a process of nature rather than nurture—that is, if the basic, natural mechanisms of genetic inheritance largely control the physical changes that occur during domestication.

Geneticists suspect that many genes are associated with domestication and that these genes interact in many complex ways. Much information about the complexities of dog genetics became available in 2005, when geneticists at the Broad Institute of Harvard University and the Massachusetts Institute of Technology, both in Cambridge, Massachusetts, published the entire sequence of the dog *genome* (total set of genetic instructions in a species). The scientists found that the dog genome consists of 39 *chromosomes* (the structures that carry genetic information) containing some 19,300 genes. (Humans have 23 chromosomes with about 25,000 genes.) However, the specific functions of most of the dog genes remain unknown.

Geneticists are investigating the functions of dog genes as well as comparing dog genes with the genes of other animals. The goals of such research are varied, including an improved understanding of dog breeds, domestication, and diseases. Analyses of dog genes, along with comparisons with the wolf genome, have allowed scientists to group dog breeds into different "clusters" based on genetic similarities and the age of a particular breed. Surprisingly, some of the oldest breeds—and, thus, the breeds most closely related to wolves—bear little resemblance to wolves. They include the Afghan hound, Pekingese, shar-pei, and shih tzu.

How intelligent are dogs?

Dog owners often talk about the "intelligence" of their canine companions. But dog intelligence can be better understood by examining the evolutionary relationship between dogs and human beings. Dogs and people belong to the *class* (large group of related species) known as Mammalia (mammals)—as do other animals in which females have *mammary* (milk-producing) glands. Other examples of mammals include

All present-day breeds of domestic dog have descended from a single species—the gray wolf (right). People began domesticating dogs anywhere from 40,000 to 135,000 years ago in East Asia, according to studies of dogs' genes, the material that determines heredity. Additional research has revealed that the appearance of a breed of dog may have little relationship to its evolutionary history. Scientists at the National Human Genome Research Institute in Bethesda, Maryland, and the University of California at Los Angeles reported that existing breeds can be divided into four genetic groups, or clusters.

Many of the oldest breeds—those most closely related to the gray wolf—actually bear little resemblance to wolves. The dogs in the oldest cluster, most of which are Asian, include the chow as well as the Afghan, Akita, lhasa apso, Pekingese, saluki, shar-pei, shih tzu, and Siberian husky. The next-oldest cluster, Cluster B, includes the boxer, bulldog, German shepherd, mastiff, and rottweiler. The herding dogs of Cluster C are more recent. Among these are the collie, greyhound, Saint Bernard, and Shetland sheepdog. The most recent—and largest—cluster, Cluster D, includes breeds associated with hunting, companionship, or other purposes. They include chihuahuas, beagles, border collies, Great Danes, poodles, retrievers, spaniels, and terriers.

apes, cats, elephants, horses, pigs, and whales. People are closely related to apes (especially bonobos and chimpanzees) but only distantly related to dogs. Most scientists believe that the common ancestor of dogs and humans lived during the time of the dinosaurs, perhaps 80 million to 100 million years ago. By contrast, the common ancestor of humans and chimpanzees lived less than 10 million years ago.

Researchers have demonstrated that apes can make simple tools and learn sign language. Like humans, apes have large brains—or more precisely, the ratio of their brain weight to body weight is large. Such animals would be expected to exhibit levels of intelligence beyond that of most other animals. However, research has revealed that some animals with smaller ratios of brain weight to body weight—including dogs—have substantial *cognitive* (thinking) abilities. However, dogs have a different type of intelligence than that found in apes. Demonstrations of dogs' cognitive abilities have been primarily based on the way they interact with humans.

Since 2000, a number of researchers have investigated the way that dogs interpret gestures, such as pointing, by people. Scientists who have conducted pointing experiments with dogs include Brian Hare, an evolutionary anthropology at Duke University in North Carolina; Michael Tomasello, a developmental psychologist with the Max Planck Institute for Evolutionary Anthropology in Germany; and Jozsef Topal, an *ethologist* (scientist who studies animal behavior) at Eotvos University in Hungary. According to these researchers, dogs from even an early age will follow a person's pointing gesture to a hidden treat, which suggests that the ability is inborn. Other researchers propose that this behavior may not be inborn, but rather quickly and easily learned by dogs.

Cluster A: Chow

Cluster C: Borzoi

Cluster B: Mastiff

Cluster D: Beagle

Further research has compared the behavior of dogs in response to pointing with that of human babies, chimpanzees, and wolves. Babies respond in much the same way as dogs do—that is, they seem to have an inborn ability to look in the direction of a pointed finger. However, chimpanzees and wolves will follow pointing and other gestures by humans only after they have learned such skills through intensive training. These findings suggest that both dogs and babies have a genetic tendency toward understanding human pointing. This genetic tendency in dogs may have developed through the process of domestication.

Scientific evidence that dogs respond physically to human signals was reported in May 2012 by researchers at Emory University's Center for Neuropolicy. The study involved dogs that were trained to respond to hand signals indicating that they either would or would not receive a treat. The scientists then scanned the brains of the dogs while making the signals. They found that the same region of the brain associated with rewards in humans became active in the dogs when the dogs saw the hand signal for treats. This region remained unchanged when the "no-treat" signal was made. The Emory scientists predicted that their canine brain-scanning technique would lead to other revelations about how dogs think.

In another study reported in 2010, investigators led by veterinary scientist

A puppy follows a researcher's pointing gesture to a treat hidden under a cup. Some researchers argue that dogs, like human babies, are born with an understanding of the human pointing gesture.

Daniel Mills of the University of Lincoln in the United Kingdom examined the way that dogs' eyes move when they look at people. Using specially designed eye-tracking equipment mounted on the dogs' heads, the researchers discovered that dogs' eyes "read" the human face differently than they read another dog's face. When dogs look at the faces of other dogs, they glance randomly either left or right. But when dogs look at human faces, their eyes lock on the middle of the face, then track to the left (that is, to the right side of the human face). According to Mills, this behavior reflects a keen skill for reading human emotions, because the right side of the human face tends to be more expressive of emotions than the left side. The eyes of humans move in the same way when looking at one another's faces. This emotion-reading ability—like the ability to understand pointing—apparently developed in dogs during domestication. These findings, as well as other research, suggest that dogs have a profound and unique ability to communicate with people and gauge their emotional states—giving them a type of social intelligence that, in some ways, trumps the greater cognitive abilities of apes.

The "genius" dogs

Researchers have described several border collies that seem to be "geniuses" among dogs. Dogs, like people, appear to exhibit a wide range of intelligence levels. However, in general comparisons of dog breeds, border collies rank among the more intelligent and quickest-learning breeds. In 2004, scientists at Germany's Max Planck Institute reported that a border collie named Rico had been taught a "vocabulary" of at least 200

Rico, a border collie with an impressive "vocabulary," poses with one of the toys he was able to fetch after receiving a specific command. Researchers in Germany reported in 2004 that Rico, who died in 2008, understood the meanings of at least 200 words—all proper nouns that represented particular objects.

nouns. When the researchers prompted Rico with the word for a toy or other object, the dog would run into another room to retrieve that object. The investigators theorized that Rico had learned the more than 200 words as proper nouns—that is, each word meant a specific physical object, the way the word *Chicago* represents a specific city. In January 2011, retired psychologist John W. Pilley of Spartanburg, South Carolina, published a report claiming that his border collie, named Chaser, had a vocabulary of more than 1,000 proper nouns.

Perhaps the most impressive "genius" dog is Betsy, a border collie owned by a family in Vienna, Austria. In 2008, Juliane Kaminski, a cognitive psychologist with the Planck Institute, reported an experiment in which, after training, Betsy was shown color photographs of numerous objects and then prompted to fetch the actual objects. Kaminski reported that Betsy performed the task flawlessly. These results, Kaminski argued, indicate that dogs can make the mental leap from a two-dimensional image of an object to the real-life object—suggesting, in turn, that dogs possess an understanding of symbolic concepts. Such an understanding was previously demonstrated only in humans, apes, and dolphins.

Despite such canine accomplishments in the laboratory, many scientists believe that the overall cognitive abilities of dogs are limited by their lack of a so-called "theory of mind." This term describes the ability of an individual to figure out what others are thinking.

In 2009, psychologist William Roberts of the Animal Cognition Lab at Western Ontario University in London, Ontario, reported the results of an experiment testing dogs for a theory of mind. In the experiment, 24 dogs were presented with a choice of two buckets positioned on the ground some distance from the dogs. Both of the buckets smelled like food, but only one contained food (a hot dog). The researchers then conducted a series of trials with each dog. In some trials, a person directed the dog to the bucket containing the hot dog. In other trials, a different person directed the same dog to the empty bucket. Many of the dogs, after many trials, learned to distrust the person who "lied" to them, refusing to obey that person's bucket directions.

Did this experiment prove that the dogs figured out that the deceptive person was lying to them and that the dogs possessed a theory of mind? Not exactly, Roberts explained, noting that if the dogs truly had a theory of mind, they would have figured out that the deceptive person was lying about the bucket more quickly than they did.

The coevolution of humans and dogs

Scientists have reported several study results about how the coevolution of dogs and humans may have shaped dog intelligence and behavior. One tantalizing finding, about the development of barking in dogs, was reported in 2005 by researchers in Hungary. Wolves rarely bark, and then main-

About 400 kinds of dogs have been bred to perform various tasks, provide companionship, and please the human eye. Hunting, herding, and providing protection were among the first uses of domesticated dogs. In addition to serving as watchdogs, modern dogs work with police to track criminals and to sniff out illegal drugs and hidden explosives. Dogs also assist people with visual problems and other disabilities.

ly as a warning, but dogs bark often, for a number of reasons. The researchers, led by ethologist Adam Miklosi of the Hungarian Academy of Sciences, recorded barks in six behavioral situations involving dogs and people: the presence of a stranger, aggression against an enemy, going for a walk, being left alone, seeing a ball, and playing a game. An analysis of the sound-wave frequencies of the barks proved that the barks recorded in each situation had unique characteristics.

The scientists then played the bark recordings for hundreds of human subjects, asking the subjects to classify each bark into one of five emotional states: aggressiveness, despair, fearfulness, happiness, or playfulness. The results showed that most people could distinguish the different barks and largely agreed about the meaning of the barks. Miklosi and colleagues concluded that over time, a sensitivity to dog barking evolved in humans as the barking behaviors evolved in dogs.

Other research has uncovered a biochemical basis for the emotional bond between dogs and people. In 2010, researchers with the Karolinska Institute in Sweden discovered that levels of oxytocin, a *hormone* (a substance produced in the body that controls the activity of cells or tissues), increase in the blood of both people and dogs as they interact. Oxytocin released in milk by mammal mothers encourages bonding with their newborns by reducing heart rate, blood pressure, and stress levels in newborns. The researchers surmised that a similar oxytocin-caused bonding response evolved in dogs and people during their cohabitation.

But the mutually evolved relationship between people and dogs can lead to a misinterpretation of dogs' motives. For example, many people may think, "My dog loves me so much that he will selflessly put himself forward in dangerous situations to protect me." However, the dog's real motives lie elsewhere, according to ethologists. They argue that the dog is merely behaving according to its inherited wolf-pack mentality by protecting the dominant member of the pack. Nevertheless, such arguments may fail to convince dog owners that their pets do not feel love for them.

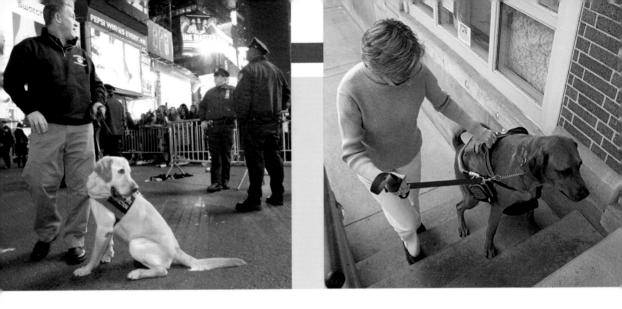

The uniqueness of dogs

Duke University's Brian Hare describes the unique dog-human relationship as follows: "People are superimportant [to dogs], and dogs can solve almost any problem if they rely on people." Hare's statement summarizes the fundamental reality of dogs as a species: They have become the creatures they are through tens of thousands of years of intimate association with humans. Dogs' ability to respond to cues from their human masters stems from their willingness to accept humans as social companions throughout the dogs' lives.

The effects of domestication on dogs were starkly demonstrated in an experiment devised by scientists at Budapest's Eotvos University. These scientists hand-reared newborn puppies and wolf cubs simultaneously. They lived with the animals, lavishing equal attention on both litters. At eight weeks of age, the puppies engaged fully with their human caregivers, gazing at their faces and readily responding to their instructions. By contrast, the wolf cubs refrained from looking into their caregivers' faces. In fact, the wolf cubs responded no differently to strangers than they did to their caregivers. Differences became even more pronounced as the animals grew older, with the wolf cubs becoming increasingly aggressive and destructive in the presence of their caregivers. The researchers argued that the experiment conclusively showed that the dog is a unique animal attuned to the presence of human beings—not simply a socialized wolf.

Perhaps the most important insight arising from canine scientific research is that many of the qualities we value most in dogs have become encoded in their DNA during the long process of domestication. This is not to say that nature obliterates nurture. A dog with the potential of becoming a loyal, obedient partner can be turned into a snarling, threatening beast by an abusive master. However, a puppy—unlike a wolf cub—is highly predisposed toward becoming a devoted partner to its human companion. And that is the true wonder of dogs.

CONSUMER SCIENCE

Topics selected for their current interest provide information that the reader as a consumer can use in understanding everyday technology or in making decisions—from buying products to caring for personal health.

Heads in the Cloud

The client's deadline was approaching, and Ramón was sweating it out. He had promised to deliver the report on time, but everything was going wrong. First, he received an e-mail from the vendor of his word processing software instructing users to install a *patch* (a segment of computer code) in the program to plug a security hole. Ramón feared that if he ignored the notice, his computer might become vulnerable to *hackers* (computer experts who break into computers or computer systems) or *viruses* (destructive programs that spread from computer to computer). So he downloaded the patch and installed it. Suddenly, he couldn't open the program—and couldn't access his work. He spent hours on the telephone with tech support to fix the problem.

Then Ramón dropped the flash drive he used for *backing up* (copying) his work into his coffee cup. So off he went to the office supply store for a new one.

In the middle of the project, Ramón decided to spend a week at the lake as a working vacation. But he changed his mind, because he knew he would have to transfer huge amounts of data between his desktop and his laptop—and back again—and then *synch* (synchronize) the desktop version with the laptop version. That

seemed risky, considering the size of the job and the tight deadline.

Ramón's frustrations are familiar to millions of people who run small businesses as well as to home computer users. To maintain computing services, users must perform an occasionally bewildering variety of computer tasks—and pay any associated costs. Users must purchase and load software and periodically download patches or *upgrades* (software updates). They must back up their data to such separate storage media as flash drives (also known as stick drives) or writeable CD's and DVD's. But backups are useful only if made on a regular basis, and many users forget to copy their data—or ignore backups altogether. Users must manage their computer's hardware, too. For example, it may be necessary to expand the computer's internal memory to improve performance.

Computer users also bear the responsibility of managing e-mail and such other computer-related services as streaming entertainment and photo-sharing services, and social media. (*Streaming* involves the real-time transmission of videos, music, or other content.) Finally, users must remain vigilant regarding security threats and take appropriate action to defend against them.

For frustrated computer users,

How the Cloud Works

The cloud is actually an enormous pool of computing resources in data centers scattered across the globe. Linking these resources to the computing mass market is the Internet. Clients subscribe to and use cloud-based resources through their broadband Internet connections. Such resources include devices that provide massive data storage; super-computers that generate mega-computing power; and the *servers* (computers) that manage these systems and communications with clients. Clients range from individual users of smartphones and personal computers to medium-sized companies.

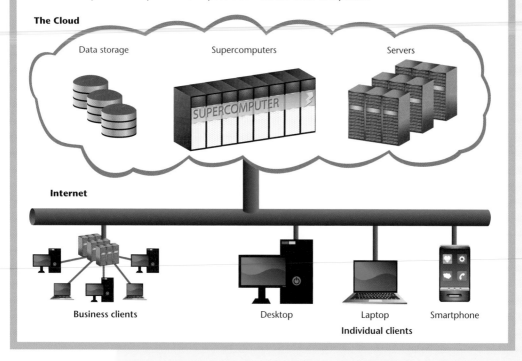

there is hope. That hope resides in "the cloud." The cloud is a vast array of computer-based services that users can access over the Internet. It is a model of mass computing emerging in the marketplace, and technology analysts predict that it will eventually overtake the more traditional model of self-contained computing. In the latter model, dominant since the dawn of personal computing in the 1970's, computer users maintain most of their computing resources on their personal devices. In the cloud model, individuals use their computers and mobile computing devices to access a variety of remotely managed, Internet-based computing resources.

These Internet-based services "in the cloud" actually reside on thousands of vendor-maintained servers in large data centers across the globe. Users of cloud services access such services online through a *broadband*

(high-volume) connection. However, the process is fully transparent, meaning that computing activities look and feel as if everything is still taking place on your own device.

To advocates of cloud computing, deciding to transition to the cloud is a "no-brainer" because the list of potential benefits is so long. Cloud computing clients can access their data on multiple devices—home computers, mobile phones, laptops, tablet computers—from anywhere these devices travel. And they can do so without any worries that the data will get out of synch, because cloud-based services synchronize all the data in one place. This type of service is sometimes referred to as file synchronization.

In the cloud, users can access up-to-date computer programs, confident of getting the latest versions. Users of cloud services can do their computing free of worry about security breaches or lost data. The cloud vendor defends its aggregated servers and associated equipment with resources above and beyond what any individual user or small business could likely muster. The vendor also automates the chore of making regular backups and provides expansive data storage.

Technology experts predict that widespread cloud computing will eventually reduce computing costs. Users will no longer have to devote significant time and resources to computer management and maintenance responsibilities. They will not have to purchase media and equipment to make backups. Moreover, as users move more and more computer functions to the cloud, they will probably opt to purchase low-cost, stripped-down machines rather than performance-packed stand-alones. In 2011, Google introduced one such device to the market—the Chromebook. The Chromebook looks like a *netbook* (ultra-thin laptop) and is essentially a window for a *browser* (program that accesses Internet content). It is a lean device, conceived and designed to get users to the Internet quickly.

With full-scale cloud computing, most or all of the *crunch* (rapid, high-volume) computing will occur in the cloud. Cloud vendors, rather than end-users, will invest in the devices and technology necessary to generate this computing power.

As of 2012, mass-market cloud vendors were offering various "bundles" of cloud computing services; not all were offering the full range of services described above. Some cloud companies are involved in niche-market cloud computing—offering services targeted to particular industries. Other companies are primarily vendors of data storage and file synchronization services.

Most vendors of cloud services offer a basic suite of services for a nominal monthly fee. Users who need levels of service beyond the basic package pay extra fees.

Users' access to mass-marketed cloud services may be linked to the purchase of a particular company's *proprietary* (brand name) devices or of devices running a specific *operating system* (OS—the software that manages a computer or other device). For example, Apple offers a full package of cloud services only to users of its computers and other proprietary devices. Google and Amazon support devices running the Android operating system, which is used on many smartphones other than the Apple iPhone. Microsoft offers cloud services to users of its Windows operating system.

At least in the short term, consumers are likely to select cloud services based on the devices they use. However, some computing experts believe that, over the long term, cloud computing services will become less proprietary and more open-market than they generally are now.

Some companies that specialize in a particular subset of cloud-based services support a wider range of platforms. For example, Box.net, Dropbox, and SugarSync offer data storage and file synchronization services on most commercially available computers and devices.

Cloud computing as a product for the mass market is quite new. In June 2011, Apple Inc. launched the Apple iCloud, amidst much publicity. By then, Apple's major, mass-market cloud competitors—Google, Amazon, and Microsoft—also had marketed various cloud-based products. These vendors are all large corporations with deep pockets; developing the infrastructure for cloud computing—the large data centers with various product support—is costly. For example, then-Apple CEO Steve Jobs, at his June 2011 press conference announcing the iCloud, highlighted the company's $1-billion data center in North Carolina, then nearing completion.

Vendors of cloud services are rapidly expanding their offerings. Analysts with Forrester Research of Cambridge, Massachusetts, predict that revenues from cloud computing services will increase from an estimated $41 billion in 2011 to $241 billion by 2020.

However, not everyone has gone "cloud crazy." Some computer users

A massive data center (also known as a server farm) in California is one of numerous sites established to support cloud computing services. These climate-controlled facilities are staffed by computer experts, technologists, and other support staff.

have difficulty letting go of their data and express concerns about security. Users may also worry that a high degree of dependence on their broadband connection could make them vulnerable, for the quality of a cloud service is only as good as the connection that accesses it.

By moving to the cloud, consumers relinquish ultimate control and oversight of their data to a service provider. Security is a big issue for cloud vendors; they take it seriously and devote considerable resources to it. Nonetheless, some members of the computing public—and even some computing experts—suspect security vulnerabilities in cloud computing.

In June 2011, the cloud-based file synchronization service Dropbox suffered a security glitch when the updating of some computer code inadvertently disarmed security protections. As a result of the flaw, users could then access other users' accounts by entering *any* password during a window that lasted for several hours. The company quickly discovered and repaired the glitch, and it reached out to consumers to help them identify any possible file tampering. Dropbox later reported that fewer than 100 accounts had been broken into and no data damage was discovered—but the inci-

dent underlined the potential for security breaches in the cloud.

According to many security experts, the activities of hackers may pose the greatest danger to the security of cloud-based data. Several widely publicized, damaging hacks into allegedly secure databases underscore this threat. In May 2011, hackers broke into a database owned by Sony Online Entertainment, a subdivision of Sony Corporation. That same month, hackers broke into a database of consumer data owned by the New York City-based banking corporation Citigroup. In both instances, hackers stole thousands of credit card numbers.

The bottom line is that cloud-based computing is only as secure as the protections put in place by providers. Computer experts encourage cloud service consumers to demand evidence of good security practices and enforcement from providers. Experts also note that the high financial stakes in this emerging industry and the power of negative publicity may serve as swift correctives to any security lapses.

Another concern for consumers of cloud services is the long-term stability of their vendors, especially in an environment where so much is new. Because many cloud services are device and OS-dependent, consumers may not enjoy a wide range of vendor choices. However, where users can pick and choose, experts advise them to check out the company's history as well as its track record in security and service outages. The Internet and magazines about computers and computing are good places to look. And of course, there is always word of mouth.

The cloud is here, and it is already changing the way millions of people do their computing. Many experts believe that it is the next logical—and inevitable—step in the evolution of personal computing. As this technological and commercial transition proceeds, the decision confronting computer users is, "Do I want to soar to the clouds—or stay grounded in my own computer for now?"

■ Robert N. Knight

The "Skinny" on Gluten

You want to diet? How about gluten free? It's the latest word in dieting, according to popular magazines and social and broadcast media. Among the celebrities who have endorsed gluten-free diets are talk-show host and cable TV entrepreneur Oprah Winfrey, actor Gwyneth Paltrow, and National Football League quarterback Drew Brees. The goal of these diets is to eliminate gluten, a complex of proteins in wheat that makes it possible for yeast bread dough to rise and pizza dough to stretch. Gluten is also abundant in rye and barley.

Celebrity advocates of gluten-free diets claim that eliminating gluten makes them feel more energetic and helps them lose weight. In fact, highly publicized endorsements by celebrities have recently helped boost sales of gluten-free food products. In the United States, product sales in 2011 amounted to about $6.3 billion—a 17-percent increase over 2010 sales, according to SPINS, a market research firm based in Schaumburg, Illinois.

Doctors and nutritionists originally designed the gluten-free diet not for general-purpose dieting or wellness programs but for people with celiac disease. A serious digestive disorder, celiac disease—also known as sprue—occurs when a person's immune system mistakenly identifies gluten consumed in food as a foreign invader and attacks it inside the small intestine. In the process, the lining of the small intestine may become damaged. Such damage interferes with the body's ability to absorb nutrients from food.

Most people do not have an allergic sensitivity to gluten. However, about 2.2 million people in the United States—somewhat less than 1 percent of the nation's population—cannot tolerate gluten and suffer from celiac disease, according to a study by researchers at the University of Maryland. Some medical experts suspect that many other people experience a level of gluten intolerance below the threshold that is detectable using currently available medical tests. Long-term celiac disease can lead to serious illness and even death.

For people with celiac disease, a gluten-free diet is the only effective treatment—and a potential lifesaver. But can adherence to a gluten-free diet benefit people who do not have celiac disease? Can a gluten-free diet be harmful if taken up casually or without expert guidance? Medical professionals and nutritional experts are beginning to provide guidance on these issues.

At first glance, it may appear that an individual could avoid gluten simply by eliminating bread and such flour-based foods as rolls, cake, pastry, and crackers. However, this is just the start. Gluten is in many processed foods and even in such nonfood products as some toothpaste, mouthwash, and lip balm. People with celiac disease are advised to avoid even these products.

Lesser-known varieties of gluten-rich grains must also be eliminated. For example, semolina, spelt, and kamut are varieties of wheat. Processed forms of gluten-rich grains are also off the table; for wheat, this restriction applies to graham flour and *farina* (cream of wheat). Malt, a widely used derivative of gluten-rich grains, is also rigorously excluded. Most beers contain malt derived from barley. Malts, which are also processed from wheat and rye, are present in malted vinegars, malted shakes and other milk-based processed drinks, and in a variety of processed foods.

In addition, gluten is a component of such commonly used food additives as dextrin and maltodextrin. These products, derived through industrial processes from grain, are used in many processed foods as a flavoring or as a stabilizing and thickening agent. For example, ketchup, salad dressings, sausage, ice cream, and many other foods often contain dextrin. It is even used in such nonfood products as cosmetics, envelope glue, and over-the-counter and prescription drugs.

As a result, most experts acknowledge that eliminating gluten from the diet is nearly impossible. Therefore, the aim of a gluten-free diet is to reduce the amount of gluten ingested or encountered to the lowest levels possible.

Attaining even this goal is challenging in the absence of comprehensive federal guidelines in food packaging. The federal Food Allergen Labeling and Consumer Protection Act of 2004 requires that producers of processed foods must identify on their food labels any of eight specific food allergens; wheat is one of the eight. However, the regulation does not require labeling for rye or barley. Furthermore, there is no industry-wide standard to define "gluten-free." Congress has directed the Food and Drug Administration (FDA) to establish such a standard, but, as of mid-2012, FDA action was still pending.

Another difficulty involved in identifying gluten-containing products is due to limitations inherent in food processing and distribution. For example, most nutrition experts consider oats to

Thick plumes of seed clusters top quinoa plants growing near Cusco, Peru. Quinoa seeds can be eaten whole or ground into flour, providing a gluten-free alternative to such gluten-rich grains as wheat, barley, and rye. Long cultivated in the highlands of Peru and Bolivia, quinoa is now spreading to other parts of the world.

Gluten-Rich and Gluten-Free Grains

Americans typically consume significant amounts of such gluten-rich grains as wheat, barley, and rye. These grains are commonly found in bread products, sauces, food coatings, snack foods, and many processed foods. Fortunately, a number of gluten-free substitutes are available for people with celiac disease and others on a gluten-free diet. Both corn and rice are gluten free. Less widely known gluten-free grains include millet, sorghum, and teff. Other substitutes are derived from noncereal crops, including seed-bearing flowers, tubers, and beans. Although oats are gluten free, they usually become contaminated with gluten during harvesting or processing. As a result, most experts recommend excluding oats from a gluten-free diet.

Gluten-rich	Gluten-free	Gluten-free grain substitutes[1]
Barley	Corn	**Amaranth** Seeds from a flowering plant native to Central and South America
Rye	**Millet** A cereal grain long cultivated in parts of Asia and Africa	**Arrowroot** Starch from the tubers of a flowering plant originally cultivated in the Americas
Wheat	Rice	**Buckwheat** Seeds from a flowering plant first cultivated in Southeast Asia
Malts Grains processed to develop sugar content—most commonly barley, but also wheat and rye. Malts are used in beer and as additives in many processed foods.	**Sorghum** A cereal gain used both as livestock feed and as a nutritious food for people	**Chickpea** Beans from a plant first cultivated in the Middle East
Oats Commonly used cereal grain that typically becomes contaminated with gluten during harvesting or processing	**Teff** A cereal grain long cultivated in Ethiopia	**Quinoa** Seeds from a flowering plant native to South America
		Soy Beans from a plant first cultivated in East Asia

[1]Flour made from these grain substitutes can be used in bread and other baked goods.

be gluten-free. However, medical and nutritional professionals generally counsel celiac patients against consuming oats. The reason is not the oats themselves; it is that oats and wheat are often grown side by side in fields; weighed and distributed in the same grain elevators; milled using the same equipment; transported using the same containers; and processed in the same food factories. Oats handled and processed in this way inevitably become contaminated with gluten.

Accessing gluten-free grains and grain products to replace the more common, gluten-rich grains can be challenging. Cereal grains that are gluten-free include corn (maize), millet, rice and wild rice, sorghum, and teff. Millet is a grain long cultivated in Asia and Africa; sorghum is a grain commonly cultivated in the United States as a livestock feed and grown elsewhere for human consumption; teff is a cereal grain long cultivated in Ethiopia.

Gluten-free grain substitutes include amaranth, buckwheat, and quinoa—all foods derived from seeds of various species of flowering plants. Other substitutes include arrowroot, a starch derived from the *tubers* (starchy enlarged roots) of a plant; and flours and other products derived from soybeans and chickpeas. Almond flour and other flours derived from nuts are gluten-free as well.

As the public has become more aware of gluten-free diets and celiac disease, many individuals not diagnosed with celiac disease have adopted gluten-free diets as a way to lose weight or boost energy levels. In fact, overindulging in such gluten-rich foods as beer, pizza, white bread, pancakes, and high-fat baked goods often results in weight gain.

However, most experts agree that the culprit is not gluten. Instead, it is either the highly refined, calorie-packed carbohydrates or the fats in such foods. Removing gluten does not necessarily remove these high-calorie ingredients. In fact, many "gluten-free" processed products actually substitute fat and sugar for gluten to make the products more appealing.

Nutrition experts recognize the psychological appeal of "elimination diets," in which a dietary "villain" is identified and removed. Most of these experts assert, however, that gluten is a villain only for people suffering from celiac disease and that it is harmless for the nonceliac population. These experts also point out that claims of improved health and vigor by nonceliac individuals on a gluten-free diet have not been substantiated by scientific studies.

Many medical and nutritional experts counsel nonceliac individuals against adopting a gluten-free diet, because of the difficulty of ensuring an adequate intake of fiber and certain other nutrients. Grains—a source of healthful complex (unrefined) carbohydrates, fiber, vitamins, and minerals—are an important component of a well-balanced diet. Dietary guidelines issued by the U.S. Department of Agriculture (USDA) and the FDA in 2010 include grains as one of the five essential food groups, with an emphasis on whole grains over highly processed grain foods. (The other four food groups are fruits; vegetables; dairy; and such protein foods as meat, fish, and beans.) Moreover, flours refined from grains are often fortified with such minerals and vitamins as iron, calcium, thiamin, riboflavin, niacin, and folate.

Following a gluten-free diet in the absence of professional supervision can lead to deficiencies in iron, calcium, B vitamins, vitamin D, and fiber, which is essential for healthy digestion. That is why medical professionals urge individuals to adopt a gluten-free diet only under the supervision of a medical or nutritional professional.

For many people, a greater challenge may be the expense of gluten-free products. In 2008, Canadian researchers reported that, on average, gluten-free products cost approximately three times as much as their non-gluten-free equivalents. For people with limited means, there is no reason to incur the added expense of a gluten-free diet, experts note, unless it is recommended by a doctor for the treatment of celiac disease.

For people who suffer from celiac disease, the verdict is in: A gluten-free diet is highly beneficial and, indeed, a critical component of treatment. For everyone else, the jury is out.

Adherence to a gluten-free diet may convey some benefits, but there are also significant risks. A majority of medical and nutritional experts agree that no one should try to go "gluten free" without input from a medical or nutritional professional and careful attention to the balance of nutrients in one's diet plan. ■ Rebecca J. Fiala

SCIENCE NEWS UPDATE

Contributors report on the year's most significant developments in their respective fields. The articles in this section are arranged alphabetically.

◼ AGRICULTURE

Record amounts of harvestable adult shrimp can be produced with relatively small amounts of water using a system of stacked tanks, according to a report published in September 2011 by Addison Lawrence, a scientist at the Texas AgriLife Research Mariculture Laboratory Port Aransas, Texas. The new system represents a major innovation in shrimp *aquaculture* (the controlled raising of aquatic animals and plants).

For several decades, shrimp producers have been using raceways—large rectangular tanks with levels of water at least 1 meter (3 to 4 feet) high—to raise shrimp indoors. The technique is biologically successful, but its productivity is limited by the amount and weight of water required. Lawrence's innovation was to grow shrimp in a much shallower container, allowing producers to stack the tanks and significantly improve productivity per cubic unit of water.

The new system is known as a "super-intensive stacked raceway." The tanks are filled with 15 to 20 centimeters (6 to 8 inches) of circulating water and stacked seven containers high. Baby shrimp are added to the top tank. As they grow, the shrimp are moved progressively through lower raceways until they reach a harvestable size. Constant monitoring of the tanks by computers and the continuous adjustment of such inputs as nutrients and oxygenated water make it possible to culture shrimp in such small volumes of water.

Some shrimp sold in the United States are caught in the wild, but more are raised in aquaculture ponds, with harvests taken about twice yearly. In the standard type of shrimp aquaculture, the average annual production is about 22,000 kilograms per hectare (20,000 pounds per acre) of water. With Lawrence's system, shrimp can be harvested 12 times per year, yielding an annual production of as much as 1,120,000 kilograms per hectare (1 million pounds per acre) of water.

SEE ALSO   CONSUMER SCIENCE
THE "SKINNY" ON GLUTEN
PAGE 101

Lawrence applied for a United States patent on his shrimp-farming process in 2008. A Texas-based seafood company, Royal Caridea, is licensed to use the technique.

Analysts speculated that the stacked raceway technology would enable the United States to sharply reduce its shrimp imports. According to seafood industry analysts, some 90 percent of the shrimp consumed in the United States is imported, with the largest volumes coming from Thailand, Indonesia, Vietnam, China, Ecuador, and Mexico. In 2011, U.S. companies imported a total of $5 billion worth of shrimp,

FILL 'ER UP

A crane drops a load of waste from corn crops into a collection bin at a biofuels factory in Emmetsburg, Iowa. The owner of the facility, energy company POET, received a $105-million loan guarantee from the U.S. Energy Department in July 2011. The loan was an incentive for the Sioux Falls, South Dakota-based energy company to convert its pilot cellulosic ethanol program to a viable commercial enterprise. Most ethanol in the United States is made from corn kernels, rich in sugar-producing starch that can be fermented into ethanol. Cellulosic ethanol is processed from such materials as corn *stover* (parts of the corn plant left over after harvest) and other plant wastes. Unlike corn kernels, stover and other plant wastes must be pretreated with a variety of chemicals to make the *cellulose* (the fibrous substance that forms a major part of the plant's mass) yield its starch. Chemists with POET are seeking ways to streamline the process and reduce production costs. Agriculture experts cite several potential advantages of cellulosic ethanol: Corn harvests could be reserved for use as food, and agricultural waste could be recycled.

the U.S. Department of Agriculture (USDA) reported.

Aquaculture companies could build the super-intensive stacked raceway systems anywhere there is an adequate water supply. For instance, facilities could be built near such inland cities as Denver or Chicago that do not have easy access to fresh shrimp. In addition, this technology could be used in areas where food is scarce and expensive. Boosting shrimp production could lower prices of this high-protein food.

Shining a light on antioxidants. Exposing carrots to a quick dose of ultraviolet (UV) light increases their antioxidant level. That finding was reported on March 14, 2012, by scientists with the Agriculture Research Service (ARS) Western Regional Research Center, a division of the USDA based in Albany, California. The research team was led by food technologist Tara McHugh and included ARS scientists Roberto Avena-Bustillos, Andrew Breksa, and Wen Du. Their research appeared in the online edition of the *Journal of the Science of Food and Agriculture.*

Antioxidants are a group of chemical compounds in food. Eating foods rich in antioxidants may prevent certain kinds of cell damage, including those that can lead to cancer, heart disease, and other diseases associated with aging. Fruits and vegetables are rich sources of dietary antioxidants.

Carrots naturally contain antioxidants. The research conducted by the ARS scientists showed that it is possible to artificially boost the levels of antioxidants. The researchers placed whole, baby, and sliced carrots under intense UVB light for 14 seconds. (Scientists separate ultraviolet light into three categories—UVA, UVB, and UVC—based on *wavelength* [the distance between the crest of one wave and that of the next wave]). The treated carrots had levels of antioxidants that were double or triple those of untreated carrots.

Scientists have long known that exposing

AGRICULTURE continued

plants to UVB light causes abiotic stress, a response in plant tissue to environmental factors not associated with living things. Stress caused by UV exposure prompts cells in the plant to increase the production of certain enzymes that boost antioxidant levels.

The scientists said that the UV exposure was too brief to cause the carrots to heat up or dry out. They reported that the treated carrots were indistinguishable by taste or texture from the untreated carrots. Incorporating the UV technology into standard food processing procedures would be relatively easy, the scientists speculated.

The carrot project was inspired by an earlier research project at the ARS center in Albany in which mushrooms were exposed to UVB light to increase their vitamin D content. Monterey Mushrooms, a California-based producer of mushrooms, has been using the UV technology and marketing the vitamin D-enriched mushrooms since 2008. McHugh reported that her group was also testing the effects of UVB light on radishes and other vegetables.

Oranges in livestock diets. A team of ARS scientists reported in October 2011 that adding pellets of compressed orange peel to feed for cattle or sheep can reduce the risk of bacterial contamination of meat products from these farm animals. The research team consisted of microbiologist Todd Callaway, with the ARS Food and Feed Safety Research Unit in College Station, Texas; animal scientist Jeffery Carroll, with the ARS Livestock Issues Research Unit in Lubbock, Texas; and animal scientist John Arthington of the University of Florida in Ona. The ARS researchers were assisted in the study by bacteriologist Steven Ricke and food scientist Philip Crandall of the University of Arkansas at Fayetteville.

The research appeared in the October 2011 issue of *Foodborne Pathogens and Disease*. It also appeared in the November/December 2011 issue of the USDA's *Agricultural Research*.

Farmers and ranchers near orange-producing areas have long used shredded orange peel as an additive in livestock feed. Animals can obtain fiber and vitamins from the peel, which is a discarded by-product of orange juice processing. Noting that crushed peels are bulky and difficult to transport, ARS scientists developed pellets from the orange waste to make the additive feasible for cattle and sheep operations located far from orange processing plants.

The researchers fed the orange-peel pellets to sheep whose intestinal waste had previously been tested for populations of harmful *Salmonella* and *E. coli* O157:H7 (also known as Shiga toxin-producing *E. coli*—or STEC). After an eight-day feeding period, the scientists retested the animals' waste. They detected a tenfold reduction in populations of these *pathogens* (disease-causing bacteria).

The ARS scientists discovered that essential oils in the orange peels kill *Salmonella*, STEC, and other harmful bacteria naturally found in the intestines of cattle and sheep. The scientists identified the essential oil D-limonene as an especially effective *antimicrobial agent* (material that can kill bacteria and other microscopic organisms).

Not all gut bacteria in cattle and sheep are harmful, but such bacterial strains as *Salmonella* and STEC can sicken people, often seriously, when they swallow them in food. Because these bacteria naturally inhabit the digestive systems of live cattle and sheep, the harmful bacteria may enter the food supply when the animals are slaughtered and processed.

The U.S. Centers for Disease Control (CDC) estimated that around 1 million people in the United States became ill from *Salmonella* in 2011, leading to the death of more than 300 people. Infection by STEC consumed in food is far rarer, but the hospitalization rate and the death rate are much higher. Speculating that rates of these foodborne illnesses could be substantially reduced by reducing the number of pathogens living in the animals' bodies, the ARS researchers announced further studies to test other compounds in citrus fruits for antimicrobial properties.

■ Sara Schafer

AGRICULTURE

A Big Stink on the Farm

In late spring, the swarms begin to feed. As the summer progresses, they mar or destroy valuable crops of grain, fruit, and vegetables. At the onset of cool autumn weather, the insect hordes invade homes near cropland, overwhelming residents by their sheer numbers. *Halyomorpha halys*, better known as the brown marmorated stink bug, has quickly established itself as a seemingly unstoppable scourge in the eastern United States. In 2012, the U.S. government, university researchers, concerned farmers, and homeowners continued to search for the means of battling this invasive pest.

Although North America is home to around 250 species of stink bug, the brown marmorated variety is not native to this continent. It was first discovered in Allentown, Pennsylvania, in 1998, though it likely arrived a few years earlier aboard a shipping container from Asia. Originally native to China, the insect is also long established in Japan, South Korea, and Taiwan.

The brown marmorated stink bug is classified as a "true bug"—that is, an insect belonging to the *order* (large scientific grouping) *Hemiptera*. Bugs in this order have a *proboscis* (elongated beak-like mouthpart) that enables them to suck fluid from food. The brown marmorated stink bug uses its strong proboscis to pierce such crops as tree fruit, vegetables, and soybeans in order to extract nourishing juice.

Like other stink bugs, the brown marmorated variety has a shield-shaped shell. Adult bugs are approximately 17 millimeters (⅝-inch) long, colored in shades of brown. Brown marmorated individuals can be distinguished from other species of stink bug by the alternating dark and light bands near the end of their antennae and along the rear edge of their abdomen. Although they have wings and can fly, these bugs are especially adept "hitchhikers," known to travel on clothes, produce, or other forms of conveyance.

Stink bugs get their name from the odor emitted from scent glands on their body surfaces. The smell has been described as a skunklike blend of cilantro, rubber, and dirty socks. The bug uses the odor as a defense mechanism against predators or other threats.

From June to August, females lay multiple clusters of 20 to 30 pale yellowish eggs on the undersides of leaves. Eggs hatch in several days. Hatchlings grow through five *nymphal instars* (immature stages). Progressive stages of nymphs range in length from 2.4 millimeters (⅒-inch) to 12 millimeters (⅖-inch).

During warm months, brown marmorated stink bugs forage on some 300 varieties of plants, including tree fruits, vegetables, *legumes* (peas and beans), and ornamental plants. Damaged orchard fruits display brownish surface spots or craters. Stink bug damage to such vegetables as peppers and tomatoes appears as cloudy whitish spots. Farm produce injured by stink bugs is unmarketable because of its appearance, though it's still edible if the damaged parts are cut away.

Stink Bugs— Just Hatched

Baby brown marmorated stink bugs hatch out of shiny white eggs deposited by an adult female on the underside of a leaf. The bugs emerge as orange, black-banded first instar nymphs —the first stage of development in the insect's life cycle. The immature stink bugs progress through four more stages before attaining adulthood—some five to six weeks after hatching. The adult insect is approximately six times larger than the first instar nymph. Adults and all nymphal instars feed on leaves, fruits, and other parts of plants.

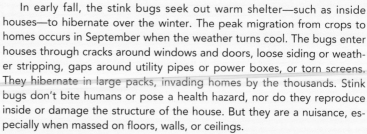

AGRICULTURE

CONTINUED

Crop Damage by Stink Bugs

Adult stink bugs feed on a ripening tomato on a commercial farm in Maryland. Greenish-white blotches indicate damage inflicted by the insects. In 2011, the Pennsylvania Department of Agriculture reported losses of up to 25 percent of the apple and peach crops in that state during 2010. In 2011, agricultural experts in New Jersey estimated losses of 30 to 60 percent of the state's tomato, pepper, apple, and peach crops. Also in 2011, authorities reported significant stink bug damage to peach crops in Virginia's Shenandoah Valley.

In early fall, the stink bugs seek out warm shelter—such as inside houses—to hibernate over the winter. The peak migration from crops to homes occurs in September when the weather turns cool. The bugs enter houses through cracks around windows and doors, loose siding or weather stripping, gaps around utility pipes or power boxes, or torn screens. They hibernate in large packs, invading homes by the thousands. Stink bugs don't bite humans or pose a health hazard, nor do they reproduce inside or damage the structure of the house. But they are a nuisance, especially when massed on floors, walls, or ceilings.

As a first line of defense, experts recommend that home owners seal potential entry points with silicone-latex caulk or insulating foam. Stink bugs have also been known to enter through air conditioners and exhaust fans; these can be covered with a bug-proof screen.

Homeowners can use pyrethrum dust and aerosol foggers to kill the bugs inside their houses. (Pyrethrum is a plant-derived insecticide that is generally not harmful to people and breaks down quickly in the environment.) However, the dead bugs themselves may become a food source for carpet beetles or other pests. Vacuum cleaners are effective in sucking up stink bugs, but the bugs' odor may linger in the device for some time. Once caught, stink bugs can be finished off by dropping them into a bucket filled with soapy water.

Exasperated homeowners often turn to exterminators for help. Insecticides applied on the outside of the house by a licensed pest control specialist can provide temporary relief from an infestation. However, experts note that the compounds used by professional exterminators are likely more toxic and long-lasting than the pyrethrum you would use inside your house. Furthermore, they say, the effectiveness of insecticides applied outside tends to diminish over time, because sunlight typically breaks down the insecticidal chemicals.

Stink bugs are certainly annoying to homeowners, but the spread of these pests is a far more serious concern for farmers. Unlike the native varieties of stink bug, the brown marmorated insect has no significant natural enemies in North America. This factor has enabled populations to increase rapidly. As of 2012, the U.S. Department of Agriculture (USDA) reported sightings of the bug in 36 states, with massings of the insects observed in at least 20 states. The invasive stink bugs are most well established in the Middle Atlantic States, though specimens have been reported as far west as Oregon and as far south as Florida.

By 2010, populations of the brown marmorated stink bug had grown out of control in Pennsylvania, Maryland, Virginia, and West Virginia. That year, brown marmorated stink bugs caused extensive damage to crops in the Middle Atlantic States. The bugs destroyed $37 million worth of apple crops alone.

Damage to crops actually decreased in 2011. Residents in the Middle Atlantic States also reported fewer bugs entering their homes that year. Scientists speculated that flooding in the eastern United States caused by Hurricane Irene and Tropical Storm Lee may have drowned many of the bugs and eggs.

Meanwhile, government officials and university research scientists continued to develop long-term plans to manage the brown marmorated stink bug. In 2011, the USDA's Specialty Crops Research Initiative granted $5.7 million to a three-year research project aimed at studying stink bug behavior and developing methods of control. The research task force focused on integrated pest management (IPM), a methodology that emphasizes control methods other than pesticides. In any event, many pesticides widely used in commercial agriculture have proved ineffective against the brown marmorated stink bug, agriculture experts reported.

In 2011, researchers at Pennsylvania State University and the Pennsylvania Department of Agriculture collaborated on the development of an online monitoring tool. The free web-based tool (http://stinkbug-info.org) provides farmers with information on brown marmorated stink bugs in their region and long-term management strategies.

Scientists have also developed chemicals that mimic *pheromones* (scents sprayed by males to attract mates) to lure and trap the bugs at the edges of croplands. However, pheromone-scented traps have had limited success in orchards, according to a 2010 study by *entomologist* (scientist who studies insects) Tracy Leskey of the USDA Appalachian Fruit Research Station in Kearneysville, West Virginia. Stink bug nymphs responded to the traps all season long, but adult bugs responded only later in the season.

Above all, entomologists hope to find a predator species to control populations of the brown marmorated stink bug. In its native China, roughly two-thirds of the brown marmorated population was killed off by the *Trissolcus halyomorphae*, a parasitic wasp. This wasp lays its eggs inside stink bug egg clusters. After the wasp larvae hatch, they devour the eggs. Scientists have studied four species of the Trissolcus wasp at the USDA laboratory in Newark, Delaware, to determine whether they can be introduced into the wild.

Before an invasive insect can be considered for release, its impact on other native species must be studied to ensure it will attack only the target pest. Research entomologist Kim Hoelmer of the USDA Agricultural Research Service estimated that the study would take until at least 2013 to figure out if the predatory wasps are safe for release in the United States.

Meanwhile, there is no immediate end in sight to the invasion. In 2011, USDA experts estimated that crops in 33 states with a potential value of $21 billion were either already subject to brown marmorated insect activity or could soon be threatened by the bugs. If populations of these invasive stink bugs continue to surge and threaten cropland, consumers could soon be faced with higher grocery prices. Scientists hope that the patience of farmers, homeowners, and consumers can hold out long enough for researchers to find an ecologically sustainable solution to the troublesome invasion.   ■ Scott Witmer

Get Them Out!

A homeowner, accompanied by his apprehensive toddler, vacuums up stink bugs on a porch. The insects, seeking winter cover, can invade porches and other areas of houses by the thousands during the autumn months. Experts advise homeowners to use a shop vac (bucket-sized vacuum cleaner without a bag) to remove the insects; then to fill the shop vac with soapy water to kill the bugs; and finally, to dump the dead insects outdoors. The experts also caution homeowners to avoid crushing the bugs, if possible—to avoid releasing the stink bug's "stink."

ANTHROPOLOGY

The discovery of a 3.4-million-year-old fossil foot from Ethiopia indicated, contrary to previous beliefs, that more than one *hominid* (human or human ancestor) species existed at that time and in that place, according to a March 2012 report. A team led by paleoanthropologist Yohannes Haile-Selassie of the Cleveland Museum of Natural History in Ohio made the discovery at a location called Waranso-Mille, in the Hadar region of Ethiopia. The scientists noted that the foot is structurally different from that of the only other hominid known to exist in the East African woodlands at that time—*Australopithecus afarensis* (nicknamed "Lucy" since the discovery of its fossils in 1974).

The eight bones of the newly discovered foot include *metatarsals* (bones of the middle foot) and *phalanges* (toe bones). The shapes of the bones of the big toe suggest that the toe extended outward from the foot, rather than lying alongside the other toes as in *Au. afarensis* and later hominids. The outward orientation of the big toe suggested to the researchers that it was more useful for grasping branches and climbing trees than for "toeing off" during a human-like walking gait. The foot more closely resembles that of *Ardipithecus ramidus*, a hominid that lived in East Africa about 1 million years earlier, than that of *Au. afarensis*.

According to the researchers, some of the foot's features, including a *transverse arch* (across the ball of the foot) and details of the toe joints, indicate that the foot was equally adapted to life on the ground and in the trees. However, the owner of the foot would have walked with a different gait than Lucy and may have spent more time in the trees than its better-known cousin.

Scientists did not plan to assign a scientific name to the species represented by the foot until teeth or skull fragments of the species are found and examined. Nevertheless, the foot discovery showed that hominid evolution between 4.4 million and 3.4 million years ago was more complex than many anthropologists had suspected. While the *lineage* (line of descent) of *Au. afarensis* was

evolving in the direction of full-time life on the ground, at least one other lineage was living alongside *Au. afarensis* with more *arboreal* (tree-dwelling) adaptations.

New hominid in China. A previously unknown type of hominid lived in what is now southwestern China as recently as 11,500 years ago—long after modern-type human beings were assumed to have replaced all of their *archaic* (pre-modern) relatives. This conclusion was reported in March 2012 by archaeologist Darren Curnoe of the University of New South Wales in Australia and a team of Chinese and Australian colleagues.

The researchers based their conclusion on fossils from two caves in southwestern China. At Longlin Cave, a partial skull with an almost complete face and isolated bones and teeth were dated to 11,500 years ago. At Maludong Cave, the dates for the top of a skull and other bones and teeth ranged from 14,310 to 13,590 years ago. The team reported that the skulls have a unique combination of features found in other hominids.

Like modern-type human beings, the people from Longlin and Maludong had high, strongly curved foreheads, and the frontal lobes of their brains were enlarged. Their faces were relatively flat like ours, though somewhat shorter. However, their faces were more broad than those of living humans or any fossil hominid. Their large cheekbones flared out from the top to the bottom. Their skulls, too, were exceptionally broad and thick, yet they were pinched in behind the eyes like the skulls of *Homo erectus*, believed to have last existed about 400,000 years ago. The skull shape suggested that the parietal lobes, which comprise most of the sides and top of the brain, were expanded in a way that resembled those of Neandertals. Also like Neandertals, the Longlin and Maludong people had prominent brow ridges, large noses, and deep projecting jaws.

According to the researchers' analyses, the peculiar combination of features of the newly found fossils indicated that the bones may represent a species or subspecies of human different from any previously described.

The scientists speculated that the hominid may have belonged to a late-surviving population of archaic human beings. Alternatively, they proposed, the hominid may represent one of multiple waves of migrations of human beings from Africa into Eurasia. Archaeologists and geneticists planned on conducting additional research to clarify the position of the Chinese fossils within the human lineage.

Neandertals not fire makers? Archaeologists and anthropologists have known for many years that Neandertals could use fire, but the authors of a study published in July 2011 questioned whether these early humans could have purposefully started a fire. A team led by archaeologist Dennis M. Sandgathe of Simon Fraser University in British Columbia and the University of Pennsylvania in Philadelphia conducted new excavations in two limestone caves in southwestern France. Fossil evidence shows that Neandertals used these caves for shelter between roughly 100,000 and 40,000 years ago. The researchers examined ash deposits from prehistoric fires, as well as animal bones and other objects that had been burned in the fires.

The oldest layers of ash in the caves were produced when Europe's climate was fairly warm and moist, and the area had many forests and forest-dwelling animals. Examination of these deposits suggested that Neandertals at the time used fire frequently. The remains of burned bones showed that they sometimes roasted meat. As time passed, Earth slipped into an ice age, and Europe's climate became cold and dry as massive glaciers covered most of the northern part of the continent. The investigators found that ash-deposit evidence for Neandertals' use of fire during this long cold period is rare in the caves.

Sandgathe and his colleagues concluded that Neandertals rarely used fire after the widespread forests and warm, moist climate of northern Europe gave way to the coldest and driest periods of the Ice Age. According to Sandgathe, Neandertals had probably obtained fire from such natural sources as forest fires started by lightning. But after the climate cooled and dried—and lightning-caused forest fires became less common—Neandertals were unable to use fire because they could not start it on their own.

European Neandertals were adapted to a cold climate in many ways. They

EVIDENCE OF PREHISTORIC HUMAN INTERBREEDING

Prehistoric humans known as Denisovans, named for a cave in Siberia (right) where their bones were first found, left their "genetic footprints" in the *genomes* (genetic makeup) of modern-day people from Southeast Asia and Oceania. That finding was reported in October 2011 by researchers at Uppsala University in Sweden. The genetic evidence, including material obtained from a Denisovan tooth (inset), indicates that ancestors of modern-day humans interbred with Denisovans on the Asian mainland sometime between 20,000 and 40,000 years ago. Denisovans were closely related to Neandertals. Previous research has suggested that our ancestors also mated with Neandertals.

ANTHROPOLOGY continued

were short and powerfully built, with relatively short arms and legs to help conserve body heat. They had large noses, which may have helped warm the air they breathed. But if Neandertals survived during the Ice Age without fire, their *physiology* (body functions) must have differed substantially from that of modern-type humans, who started and used fire during the Ice Age.

Secret of our success. Our species, *Homo sapiens*, has adapted to life in every corner of the planet. In an effort to identify just why we have been so successful, anthropologists and cognitive scientists led by Lewis G. Dean of the University of St. Andrews in Scotland conducted an experiment comparing 18 capuchin monkeys, 74 chimpanzees, and 35 children (aged 3 or 4 years) performing the same task. The researchers published their conclusions in March 2012.

Human beings constantly innovate and improve. For example, the Wright brothers' biplane led eventually to the development of the space shuttle. This progressive development of knowledge is called cumulative culture. Other species do not "piggy back" on the inventions of others to produce even better tools.

Some scientists believe that humans are the only species with a cumulative culture because we have certain key *cognitive* (mental) abilities, including language, teaching, and *prosociality* (the tendency to actively share information with one another). Other researchers have suggested that monkeys and apes lack a cumulative culture because of certain social barriers, not because they lack certain cognitive abilities. For example, dominant individuals in a group of apes may seize the best food for themselves, even if they are terrible tool users. In addition, any innovative acts by low-ranking apes are likely to be ignored.

The researchers built puzzle boxes that monkeys, apes, and human children could all theoretically "solve" in three steps to obtain rewards, each one more desirable than the previous. The rewards—foods for the monkeys and apes and stickers for the children— were hidden behind a sliding door in the puzzle boxes. Pushing the door revealed the first reward. If a button was pushed, the door would open farther, revealing the second, more desirable reward. Finally, turning a dial opened the door all the way, revealing the best reward. All test subjects, working in groups of the same species, were allowed to imitate the actions of others and to share information.

The researchers found no evidence that the behaviors of dominant monkeys or apes affected the behaviors of the others operating the puzzle boxes. Nor were low-ranking individuals of these species ignored or pushed aside. Neither the capuchins nor the chimpanzees showed each other what to do, shared rewards, or even seemed interested when another individual was manipulating the puzzle box. After 30 hours, only one chimpanzee figured out how to get the best reward. In 50 hours of manipulating the puzzle box, not a single capuchin reached the best reward.

By contrast, the children immediately approached the puzzle box in a group. Individual children shared information, used words and gestures to show others what to do, and shared rewards. The children actively watched and imitated each other. The researchers observed many cases in which one child actively taught another. Although the children spent only two-and-a-half hours with the puzzle box, 15 of the 35 children reached the best reward. All 15 of those children had received some form of teaching from others.

Dean and his colleagues reported that the absence of a cumulative culture in monkeys and apes is not due to such adverse social factors as bullying behavior by dominant individuals or ignoring the clever acts of low-ranking individuals. Unlike the children, the monkeys and chimps paid little attention to the behaviors of others and did not share rewards. Thus, the investigators concluded that our cumulative culture is made possible by the distinctively human cognitive abilities of language, teaching, sharing, and prosociality. ■ Richard G. Milo

See also **ARCHAEOLOGY.**

ARCHAEOLOGY

The earliest apparent use of fire by human beings was pushed back hundreds of thousands of years by a discovery in a South African cave reported in April 2012. Anthropologist Michael Chazan of the University of Toronto in Canada and archaeologist Francesco Berna of Boston University were among a group that analyzed burnt bones and ash in a spot deep within Wonderwerk Cave, on the edge of the Kalahari Desert. The burning activity, which may have involved cooking, was dated to approximately 1 million years ago. The age of the new fire evidence is 300,000 to 400,000 years earlier than the oldest evidence for human-used fire from other sites.

Wonderwerk Cave extends about 140 meters (459 feet) into a hillside. Within the massive cave are deposits, some as deep as 7 meters (23 feet), consisting of natural sediment as well as burnt animal bones, engraved stones, and other artifacts. Analyses of the deposits suggested that humans occupied the cave extended over a 2-million-year span. Archaeologists attribute the earliest human-related deposits to *Homo erectus*, a species of human being that lived from about 1,900,000 to about 400,000 years ago.

In deposits about 30.5 meters (100 feet) into the cave and dating to some 1 million years ago, the investigators uncovered evidence of repeated fires, including animal bones, pollen grains, wood charcoal, and pieces of ash. They determined that the fires were not natural phenomena caused by ashes blown into the cave by the wind. As seen under a microscope, the ash pieces had jagged edges, which likely would have been smoothed out had the ash been carried by wind or water. Microscopic analyses of the animal bones revealed mineral crystals that had changed shape, signs of being heated to temperatures of more than 400 °C (750 °F), as in a fire.

The researchers noted that although they found no evidence of formal *hearths* (fireplaces), the broken and burnt animal bones and microscopic bits of ash, as well as fire-fractured stone, were all signs that humans had cooked at the site. They added that the prehistoric people may have also used the fire for warmth and light. However, the scientists found no evidence that the human species of the time—*H. erectus*—purposefully made the fires. Rather, they proposed that the cave inhabitants used burning wood from natural fires to start their own fires.

Butchered giant ground sloth. In the early 1900's, a large fossil bone was found in an Ohio swamp and documented as a *femur* (upper leg bone) from a giant ground sloth.

MAMMOTH OR MASTODON "ART" FROM ICE AGE AMERICA

An etching of a mammoth or mastodon on a fragment of 13,000-year-old bone is the oldest—and only known—depiction of an animal with a trunk from the Americas. The discovery of the Ice Age etching was announced in June 2011 by researchers at the Smithsonian Institution in Washington, D.C., and the University of Florida in Gainesville. The etching is about 7.6 centimeters (3 inches) long and 4.4 centimeters (1 ¾ inches) tall. The bone, which likely came from a mammoth, mastodon, or giant sloth, was discovered by amateur fossil hunter James Kennedy in what is now Vero Beach, Florida. All three of those large mammals became extinct in North America from 12,000 to 10,000 years ago.

ARCHAEOLOGY continued

These animals were long-haired, bearlike mammals that ate vegetation. This femur rested in an Ohio museum for decades until analyzed by archaeologist Haskel Greenfield of the University of Manitoba in Canada. In March 2012, Greenfield and his team reported that they had identified more than 40 incisions in the bone that had been made by stone tools. The evidence showed that human beings butchered and ate giant ground sloths (which they may have hunted) in North America some 13,500 years ago.

Giant ground sloths became extinct, along with mammoths, mastodons, and other huge mammals in North America, at the end of the Pleistocene Epoch (often called the Ice Age) more than 10,000 years ago. The species known as the Jefferson ground sloth was the largest North American ground sloth, standing about 3 meters (10 feet) tall.

Greenfield's team estimated that the bone of the Jefferson ground sloth that they examined was 13,435 to 13,738 years old. They arrived at this estimate using radiocarbon dating, a technique based on measuring the amount of carbon 14 in an object. Microscopic examinations of the cuts revealed that the marks were likely left by stone tools. However, the researchers could not determine whether the cuts were made by people while processing an animal they had killed or while scavenging a carcass.

According to the archaeologists, the butchering marks on the sloth femur may represent activities by some of the earliest immigrants to North America. Archaeological evidence of the Clovis people, the earliest widely studied inhabitants of North America, has been dated to about 11,200 years ago. Greenfield's team proposed that the butchered femur may be a "pre-Clovis" find. The age of the femur was in line with a number of pre-Clovis campsites, dating from 13,000 to 16,000 years ago, that have been found across North and South America.

Gobekli Tepe. In a June 2011 review of more than 15 years of excavation and research, archaeologist Klaus Schmidt of the German Archaeological Institute discussed his conclusions about Gobekli Tepe, a huge

MAJOR ARCHAEOLOGICAL FIND IN AUSTRIA

The discovery of a large, well-preserved school for Roman gladiators in what is now Austria was announced in September 2011 by an international team of archaeologists. The remains of the school, at a site east of Vienna, were found through the use of ground-penetrating radar imagery. The school was part of a Roman city, Carnuntum, that was an important military and trade outpost 1,700 years ago. The radar images reveal a walled compound with training and bathing areas and 40 small sleeping cells for the gladiators. Archaeologists have not yet begun excavations of the school, which is part of a site so large that less than 1 percent of it has been excavated, though digging began in 1870.

A virtual re-creation of a gladiator school found on the site of an ancient Roman city of some 50,000 people

mound in southeastern Turkey marked by massive stone sculptures and architectural structures. Schmidt believes that the site, which dates from the early Neolithic era (late Stone Age), some 12,000 years ago, may be the world's oldest religious complex.

According to Schmidt, the site, which is far from any evidence of settlement or agriculture, indicates that the urge to worship by hunters and gatherers helped give rise to agriculture and cities. This theory challenges a widespread belief that the development of agriculture by settled people helped give rise to organized religion. In his review, Schmidt also suggested that Gobekli Tepe was used by a cult of the dead.

Schmidt's excavations at Gobekli Tepe have uncovered 4 of the site's 20 known round architectural structures, each of which is 10 to 30 meters (33 to 98 feet) in diameter. In the center of each structure are the remains of two pillars, which may have served as roof supports. The walls of each structure included as many as eight pillars, the remains of which are decorated with carved reliefs. Unworked vertical stones lie between the decorated pillars. Archaeologists describe the stone pillars as "megalithic" because each is so massive—with a height up to 3 meters (10 feet) and a weight ranging from 9 to 45 metric tons (10 to 50 tons). Although the stone was quarried nearby, researchers estimate that as many as 500 people were required to move each stone to the hilltop site.

Animal motifs, including those of such large mammals as bulls, donkeys, and gazelles, dominate the carvings on the pillars. The carvings also include large felines thought to be lions as well as snakes and other reptiles, birds, and even insects. Carvings of vultures are notable, because these scavenger birds are linked to disposal of the dead, suggesting that the site may have been used by a cult of the dead. Such vulture carvings can be seen in other Neolithic sculptures elsewhere. Carvings of human arms and hands and stylized human bodies depicted at Gobekli Tepe may be additional evidence of a cult of the dead.

No contemporary evidence for agriculture or dwellings has been found near Gobekli Tepe. The round pillared structures and massive stones predate the invention of pottery, agriculture, and animal domestication.

Schmidt argued that hunter-gatherer communities likely built an early phase of Gobekli Tepe, which was expanded by later hunter-gatherer groups. He believes that pilgrims visited the site from throughout the region.

Much remains unknown about the nature of the Neolithic peoples who built the site. Were they organized by priests or other religious leaders? Was there an "elite class" in charge of the workers? Additional excavations were expected to generate new ideas about the rise of civilization and religion during the Neolithic era.

Beneath the Pyramid of the Sun. Located about 65 kilometers (40 miles) north of Mexico City, the massive archaeological site of Teotihuacan is dominated by the Pyramid of the Sun. This flat-topped pyramid rises 64 meters (210 feet) above the valley floor and is 213 meters (699 feet) wide at its base. The

HUMAN PORTRAIT FROM BENEATH THE PYRAMID OF THE SUN?

A jade (greenstone) mask that was excavated from beneath the Pyramid of the Sun, at the archaeological site of Teotihuacan in Mexico, may have been a portrait of an actual individual, according to a December 2011 report by archaeologist Alejandro Sarabia of Mexico's National Institute of Anthropology and History. Other artifacts discovered at the site included seashells, projectile points, and pottery vessels. Sarabia proposed that the mask and other artifacts may have been placed as offerings to commemorate the beginning of construction approximately 1,800 years ago. Also found at the site were the bodies of seven people, who may have been sacrificed at the start of construction.

ARCHAEOLOGY continued

AGONY OF THE DEAD IN HELL

A scene of naked dead people—seemingly crying in agony with outstretched arms—is part of a 9th-century painting of hell found in central Sudan, described in November 2011 by a team of archaeologists led by Bogdan Zurawski of the Institute of Mediterranean and Oriental Cultures of the Polish Academy of Sciences. The painting is from one of several medieval churches found at Banganarti and Selib, two sites along the Nile River. Most of the churches were built from the 500's to the 1000's. During much of this period, the region was part of a Christian kingdom called Makuria. Other artwork found in the remains of the churches depicts kings, saints, pilgrims, and a female demon named Sideros being trampled by a horse ridden by St. Abbakyros. The researchers noted that the style of the art revealed a strong European influence.

Pyramid of the Sun, the construction of which may have begun 1,800 years ago, dominated Teotihuacan as the city grew in size and influence. In December 2011, archaeologist Alejandro Sarabia of Mexico's National Institute of Anthropology and History announced discoveries beneath the pyramid's center that included two groups of ceremonial offerings, known as caches, and seven human burials. The burials included the bodies of infants, children, and adults sacrificed as work began on the pyramid.

For decades, archaeologists dug tunnels into the pyramid to investigate its internal structure. The ancient inhabitants of Teotihuacan had also tunneled into the pyramid, which they believed was linked to the forces of the underworld. From 2007 to 2011, archaeologists led by Sarabia began to expand an exploratory tunnel that had originally been excavated in the 1930's. The team also dug tunnels from the interior to the exterior sides of the pyramid. This research program had the goal of learning what was beneath the pyramid—mainly to determine what had been at the site before pyramid construction started in about A.D. 200.

The smaller of two artifact caches discovered by Sarabia and colleagues contained a small jade (greenstone) mask about 11 centimeters (4.3 inches) long. This item was carved as a human face, which archaeologists believe may be an actual portrait. Other artifacts included a human figure chipped from *obsidian* (volcanic glass), seashells, and projectile points. A second, larger cache included 11 pottery vessels, which may have been dedicated to a rain god, according to the researchers. Within these vessels were flint and obsidian tools, projectile points, and the bones of an eagle, a feline, and a canine.

Excavations suggested that prior to the pyramid's construction, the area had been used for three different ceremonial buildings, in addition to a plaza. The details of the artifact caches indicated to Sarabia's team that the pyramid was associated with a rain god who was eventually transformed into the powerful god of rain, lightning, and thunder known as Tlaloc.

Viking boat burial. An undisturbed Viking boat burial more than 1,000 years old was excavated on the western coast of Scotland, reported archaeologists Hannah Cobb of the University of Manchester and Oliver Harris of the University of Leicester, both in the United Kingdom, in October 2011. The remains constituted the first known intact Viking burial uncovered in that region. The site of the discovery, overlooking the sea on the remote Ardnamurchan Peninsula, had previously yielded a Neolithic-era burial (about 6,000 years old) and a Bronze Age (2500-800 B.C.) burial mound.

While excavating the Neolithic burial in

2008, the archaeologists noted a nearby low mound. When they returned later to excavate the mound, the archaeologists were able to outline a small boat with sides, pointed prow, and stern, indicated only by small scraps of wood and hundreds of metal rivets. The outline revealed that the vessel had been about 5 meters (16.4 feet) long and l.5 meters (5 feet) wide. The relatively small size of the boat suggested that it was used to travel the short distance between Ireland and Norway.

The boat had been filled with large rocks, like those found in many other Viking boat burials. When the researchers removed the rocks, they discovered a man's teeth and scattered bones, along with many objects that probably belonged to him. These artifacts included a whetstone (used for sharpening knives), a sword with a silver-inlaid hilt, a shield, an axe, and a drinking horn with bronze tip. Smaller items found in the burial included a bronze pin

and fragments of pottery styled in the Viking ceramic tradition.

The burial suggested to the scientists that a previously unknown Viking settlement may have existed on the Ardnamurchan Peninsula. Project members planned to search for other evidence of this settlement in 2013. They speculated that the buried man, likely a warrior, may have come from Viking villages on the nearby Hebrides islands.

Coronado Cibola expedition. The discovery of numerous metal artifacts from a famous Spanish expedition in the mid-1500's to what is now the southwestern United States was reported in March 2012 by Matthew Schmader, city archaeologist for Albuqerque, New Mexico. The expedition, known as the Coronado Cibola expedition was led by Spanish explorer Francisco Vasquez de Coronado. Schmader made the discovery at a site in New Mexico known as Piedras Marcadas. The artifacts, including pieces of armor, dag-

WAS THE PREHISTORIC SPOTTED HORSE REAL OR IMAGINARY?

A 25,000-year-old painting of a white horse with black spots in a cave in Spain (below) may have depicted an actual animal, according to a November 2011 report by geneticists Arne Ludwig of the Leibniz Institute for Zoo and Wildlife Research in Germany and Michael Hofreiter of the University of York in England. Researchers had long suspected that numerous prehistoric paintings of spotted horses in Europe represented an imaginary animal, because such horses were not developed through breeding until sometime within the past 5,000 years. However, analysis of the DNA of the remains of more than 30 horses found in Europe and Siberia and dating as far back as 20,000 years revealed genetic characteristics in six horses that correspond to spotting in modern horses. Thus, the geneticists concluded that spotted horses could have lived in Europe when the cave paintings were made.

ARCHAEOLOGY continued

gers, and crossbows, indicated that a battle between the Spaniards and the native population had occurred at the site.

From 1540 to 1542, Coronado, his soldiers, and a vast entourage of wives, children, slaves, and American Indian allies searched—unsuccessfully—for the fabled Seven Cities of Cibola, said to be rich in gold and other treasures. During the expedition, Coronado's group lived in and around several Indian *pueblos* (towns formed of multistory apartmentlike buildings of adobe and mud) along the northern banks of the Rio Grande River in New Mexico. There were at least a dozen pueblos, and the buildings and the

people who lived in them are referred to as Tiguex (TEE wesh). Piedras Marcadas is one of the original Tiguex pueblos.

Skirmishes between the Tiguex and Coronado's forces were common, partly as a result of numerous demands made by the Spanish, including the eviction of the pueblos' residents. After the short, brutal "Tiguex War" in the winter of 1540-1541, all of the pueblos were abandoned.

Schmader's team discovered most of the artifacts at Piedras Marcadas using electrical resistivity, a remote-sensing technique involving the conduction of an electric current between metal probes pushed into the ground. Measurements of subsurface resistance to the current allow archaeologists to map features at various depths. Schmader's investigations led to the discovery of three large adobe-walled rooms, wrought iron nails of Spanish origin, belt buckles, lead buttons, and more than 1,000 additional metal artifacts linked to the Coronado Cibola expedition. The archaeologists were able to excavate no deeper than 7.6 centimeters (3 inches), because the native Puebloans identify Piedras Marcadas as an ancestral site, and they objected to large-scale excavations.

Among the important battle items recovered were 32 lead balls (used in a type of musket), 21 copper crossbow bolt heads, and the tip of a steel dagger. Some of the lead balls were mushroom-shaped from impacts, and many of the crossbow bolts had been broken out of their wood shafts. A chemical analysis of the lead balls revealed that they matched balls previously found at a Coronado expedition campsite in Texas.

Schmader proposed that Piedras Marcadas is the original site of the Moho pueblo, where Coronado staged his final violent assault on the native population. Other experts disagreed, arguing that Piedras Marcadas does not match the Spanish description of the Moho pueblo. Investigators planned to dig additional test pits to look for evidence of 30 individuals known to have been killed in the Moho pueblo.   ■ Thomas R. Hester

See also **ANTHROPOLOGY; FOSSIL STUDIES.**

CANNON FROM BLACKBEARD'S *QUEEN ANNE'S REVENGE*

Workers haul a cannon covered in sand, salt, and barnacles aboard a ship from ocean waters off the coast of North Carolina in October 2011. The cannon was retrieved from the wreckage of *Queen Anne's Revenge,* a ship captained by the British pirate Blackbeard, who terrorized the Carolina and Virginia coasts in 1717 and 1718. The ship sank after running aground on a sandbank about 3 kilometers (2 miles) off the Carolina coast in 1718. Since the wreckage of *Queen Anne's Revenge* was discovered in 1997, researchers with the North Carolina Department of Cultural Resources have retrieved several cannons and many other artifacts, including cannon shot, shackles, riggings, and wine glasses.

ASTRONOMY

Evidence that Jupiter wandered through the solar system early in its history can be found in the relatively small size of Mars and the absence of large bodies in the asteroid belt, according to a July 2011 report by an international team of planetary scientists led by Kevin J. Walsh of the Southwest Research Institute in San Antonio, Texas. The scientists described a computer simulation that modeled the movements of Jupiter and the other "gas giant" planets through the disk of gas and dust from which the planets of the solar system formed some 4.6 billion years ago. The simulation revealed the effects of these movements—called migrations—on the formation of the smaller planets and the Main Belt of asteroids (a region of rocky and metallic bodies between the orbits of Mars and Jupiter).

The small size of Mars, which has approximately 1/10 as much *mass* (amount of matter) as Earth, has long been a mystery to astronomers. Astrophysicists believe that in disks of gas and dust around new stars, the dust quickly collects into *planetesimals* (planetary building blocks) and then into bodies the size of the moon and Mars. Fol-

SEE ALSO THE SPECIAL REPORT **WHEN GALAXIES COLLIDE** PAGE 12

lowing this period of rapid growth, the pace of planetary development slows. Walsh's team analyzed the gravitational effects of Jupiter, which is presumed to have grown rapidly during an early developmental phase, when plenty of gas was available in the solar system's disk. Jupiter's gravity is believed to have tugged on moon-sized and Mars-sized bodies—dubbed "planetary embryos"—until their orbits became more elongated. The elongated paths of the planetary embryos crossed with one another, resulting in increased collisions and the rapid growth of the planets. According to this scenario, however, a Mars-sized body is never left behind at the end of planet formation. Rather, continued collisions of planetary embryos should cause Mars-sized planets to grow into Earth-sized planets.

Walsh and his colleagues investigated a suggestion that if the region where Mars formed was mostly cleared of planetary embryos, a Mars-sized body could be left be-

KEPLER DETECTS PLANETS ORBITING DOUBLE STARS

A large gaseous planet known as 34b is one of a number of extrasolar planets found orbiting double stars (right in an artist's illustration) by scientists using data collected by NASA's Kepler space telescope. Planet 34b's yellow, sunlike stars, which are about 4,900 light-years from Earth, were reported in January 2012. (A light-year is the distance traveled in one year by a pulse of light— 9.46 trillion kilometers [5.88 trillion miles]). Also that month, the same scientists reported finding another planet, known as 35b, orbiting a double-star system about 5,400 light-years away. In September 2011, other scientists detected a Saturn-sized gaseous planet, named Kepler 16b, in orbit around an orange star and a red star. That double-star system is some 200 light-years away.

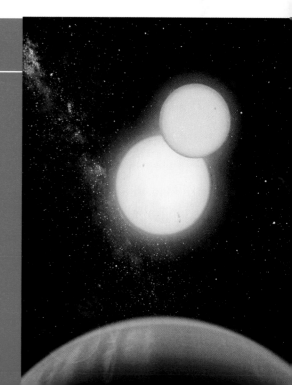

ASTRONOMY continued

hind. For that to have happened, however, Jupiter (the fifth planet from the sun) must have been closer to the present-day orbit of Mars (the fourth planet). The scientists also studied the locations of Jupiter-sized planets around other stars. Many of these large planets are currently so close to their parent stars that they must have migrated inward from a more distant region (where gas giants could have formed more easily). Walsh and his team examined migration as the way to bring Jupiter closer to the sun, to a location where its gravity would have cleared the region around Mars and the asteroid belt.

The researchers then examined how Jupiter could have returned to its more distant orbit. Based on their computer simulation, when two giant planets—such as Jupiter and Saturn—are present in a gaseous disk, both planets may migrate, and the gravitational pulling of the two giants on each other can lead to complicated additional movements. The computer model showed that if Saturn and Jupiter were in certain positions relative to each other, Jupiter would have orbited the sun three times for every two orbits of Saturn (an example of orbital resonance). The gravitational influences from such interactions could have pulled both planets outward after their inner migrations.

Further analysis showed that under some conditions, the smaller of the two gas giants (Saturn) would have migrated inward faster than the larger giant (Jupiter). But if Saturn formed after Jupiter, Jupiter would have had time to move inward to the region corresponding to present-day Mars. Saturn, developing later, would have swept inward at higher speed until it locked Jupiter into resonance—and pulled Jupiter outward.

This idea—labeled the Jupiter "grand tack maneuver" after the sailing term for moving into the wind—accounted for gravitational effects that would have caused both the smallness of Mars and the absence of large bodies in the asteroid belt. Because the idea implies certain ages for Jupiter and Saturn relative to the age of the solar system's original gaseous disk, future data from

space probes investigating Jupiter, Saturn, and their many moons may help confirm or refute the proposal.

Flattened Titan. The shape of Saturn's moon Titan is related to its atmospheric chemistry, according to a January 2012 report by planetary scientists Mathieu Choukroun and Christophe Sotin of NASA's Jet Propulsion Laboratory in Pasadena, California. Based on an analysis of data gathered by the NASA–European Space Agency Cassini spacecraft, the researchers described how Titan's shape is really that of a flattened sphere. The flattening is much more pronounced at the moon's north pole than at its south pole. This flattening is related to the types of *hydrocarbons* (molecules containing only carbon and hydrogen) produced high in the atmosphere.

Titan, Saturn's largest moon, is the only satellite in the solar system with a dense atmosphere. Composed mostly of nitrogen—like Earth's atmosphere—this atmosphere also consists of 5 percent methane, a hydrocarbon, near the surface. The amount of methane decreases with increasing altitude. Exposure to the sun's ultraviolet light at high altitudes results in the chemical conversion of the methane (made of one carbon atom and four hydrogen atoms) into ethane (two carbon atoms and six hydrogen atoms), acetylene (two carbon atoms and two hydrogen atoms), and other molecules (containing carbon, hydrogen, and nitrogen). These molecules grow in size and fall to Titan's surface, where both methane and ethane fill basins as liquids.

–In 2006, images from Cassini, in orbit around Saturn, revealed hundreds of *maria* (Latin for *seas*) that appeared to contain liquid, likely ethane and methane. All but a few of these basins are concentrated around Titan's north pole. The largest maria exceed the size of Lake Superior, the largest of the Great Lakes. Astronomers speculate that the maria are evidence of reservoirs of liquid ethane and methane within Titan's icy subsurface.

Choukroun and Sotin reasoned that because the hydrocarbon basins are concentrated around Titan's north pole, these basins may be associated with the flattening, or depression, of the northern part of the satellite. But the nature of the association was puzzling. They noted that if Titan's *crust* (the rigid layer comprising the immediate subsurface) is made mostly of water ice, as observations suggest, then the liquid hydrocarbons would not be able to "weigh it down." That is because the hydrocarbons are less dense than the ice. Thus, the scientists proposed than another effect of the hydrocarbon basins—the formation of so-called gas hydrates—is responsible for the flattening.

Gas hydrates are solids formed from a combination of water ice with one or more other substances, often hydrocarbons. In gas hydrates containing molecules of ethane and methane, tiny cagelike crystal structures are formed by water ice molecules trapping within them individual molecules of methane or ethane. Such gas hydrates are referred to as clathrate hydrates.

Choukroun and Sotin found, by investigating reports of previous laboratory experiments, that a gas hydrate composed of only water and methane is less dense than pure liquid water. By contrast, a gas hydrate composed of only water and ethane is more dense than liquid water. They then concluded that as methane is converted into ethane over time in Titan's upper atmosphere, the satellite's surface and subsurface will become progressively enriched in ethane and depleted in methane. As a consequence, ethane will substitute for methane in the gas hydrates, making the gas hydrates denser than liquid water.

This was an important conclusion because previous Cassini evidence strongly indicated that a layer of liquid water exists beneath the water ice crust of Titan. Choukroun and Sotin argued that the ethane-rich gas hydrates partially sink into this liquid water layer. But because the crust is partly rigid, the crust *subsides* (sags) rather than sinks completely, causing a depression at the surface where the ethane is most abundant. This region includes the hydrocarbon basins of the north polar area, accounting for the flattened shape at Titan's north pole. Further refinement of the under-

FLOWING SALT WATER ON MARS?

Long, wavy lines marking the slope of a crater on Mars suggest that salt water sometimes flows across the surface of Mars, according to findings published in August 2011 by planetary scientist Alfred McEwen of the University of Arizona in Tucson and colleagues. Photographs taken by a high-resolution camera on the Mars Reconnaissance Orbiter showed that the lines, seen on crater sides and certain other slopes, change throughout the year—lengthening in spring and fading in winter. The scientists proposed that the lengthening occurs as seasonally increasing temperatures cause ice in the ground to melt and flow downward. They noted that the water may flow as *brine* (water containing large amounts of salt). Brine can remain liquid at temperatures at which pure water would freeze.

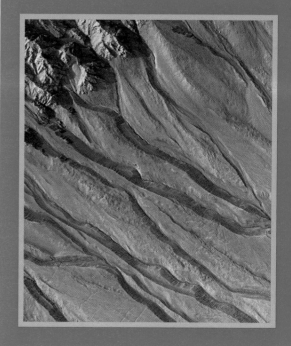

standing of Titan's shape and the composition of Titan's hydrocarbon basins were expected to come from additional observations by Cassini.

Dawn over Vesta. In July 2011, following a journey of almost four years, NASA's Dawn spacecraft went into orbit around the large asteroid Vesta. Photographs taken by cameras on the craft gave astronomers their first close-up view of an asteroid in the Main

ASTRONOMY continued

Belt. Vesta formed from remnants of the original material in the gas-and-dust disk out of which the planets of the solar system took shape. Studying the surface of Vesta provides scientists with a view of material that has remained relatively unchanged since the formation of the solar system.

Images from Dawn revealed that Vesta has a heavily cratered northern hemisphere and a smoother southern hemisphere. Other data from Dawn's instruments indicated that the asteroid shows many similarities to the inner rocky planets of Earth, Mars, Venus, and Mercury. For example, Vesta has ancient *basaltic* (volcanic) lava flows on its surface and possibly a large iron core. It also has such geologic features as troughs, ridges, cliffs, hills, and a large mountain.

The large mountain, located in a circular depression at Vesta's south pole, was an area of special interest to investigators. Several hundred kilometers wide and nearly three times as high as Earth's Mount Everest, the mountain rises about 21 kilometers (13 miles) above the average level of the surrounding area. Although astronomers are uncertain about the origin of this feature, they speculated that the mountain may have arisen from a combination of collisions between Vesta and other objects and internal processes within Vesta itself.

Milky Way planets. In January 2012, a team of astronomers led by researchers at the Paris Institute of Astrophysics in France reported that there are likely more planets than stars in the Milky Way, our galaxy. If that conclusion is correct, the Milky Way has more than 100 billion planets.

The team's observations were based on data resulting from the magnification of background objects that occurs when multiple celestial bodies are situated along a single line of sight as seen from Earth. This phenomenon, known as gravitational lensing, occurs because light rays do not travel in straight lines. Rather, like a running back in a football game swerving in and out of congested regions on the field, light is deflected as it travels past regions in the universe with large amounts of mass. For

ICEBERGS, LAKES, AND AN OCEAN ON EUROPA

Horizontal ridges and vertical cracks score the surface of an immense lake of liquid water that exists within the icy surface layer of Europa, a moon of Jupiter, in an artist's rendition. According to a November 2011 report, such lakes may explain the jumbled icebergs that have been observed in numerous places on Europa. Planetary scientist Britney Schmidt of the University of Texas at Austin and colleagues proposed that the icebergs form as water from the shallow lake wells upward and warms the icy surface. The warmth causes the ice to break into icebergs, which float on slushy *brine* (salty water) and flip over before freezing into place. These lakes, noted Schmidt, might also harbor some forms of life. A deep ocean is believed to exist below the lakes.

example, the image of a distant star appears magnified when another star, closer to Earth, lies directly in the path of the light rays coming from the distant star. More of the light from the distant star reaches Earth because the intervening star deflects light rays that would otherwise not have reached Earth. More light rays reach us, so the distant star appears bigger and brighter.

This magnification of the distant star lasts for several months, until the intervening star moves out of direct alignment with the distant light rays. While the star is magnified, there are brief times when a planet associated with the intervening star also lines up along the light path. This alignment causes the background star to appear brighter for a brief time, typically less than 24 hours. It is this characteristic brief brightening that alerts astronomers to the presence of a planet orbiting the closer star.

Jean-Philippe Beaulieu led a team of astronomers analyzing data from two surveys that monitored millions of stars for evidence of this temporary magnification. The first survey was the Optical Gravitational Lensing Experiment (OGLE), a long-term international project that measures the brightness of millions of stars during every clear night. When a possible planetary event was found with OGLE data, the astronomers followed up with data from a global network of telescopes known as the Probing Lensing Anomalies Network (PLANET). The PLANET data allowed them to carefully measure the star's brightness continuously over a month-long period.

Even the two monitoring systems together cannot always detect a planet orbiting a star. To resolve this uncertainty, Beaulieu and his team calculated how many planets would have been detected if every star system contained one planet. They found that such a conservative scenario would result in fewer planets than had actually been detected with the monitoring systems. Thus, the investigators concluded that there must be more planets than stars in our galaxy.

Gravitational lensing of galaxies. By studying how images of distant galaxies are magnified and distorted through gravitational lensing, astronomers can calculate how much intervening mass the galaxy light trav-

eled though on its journey to Earth. Such calculations are allowing astronomers to map the distribution of matter between the distant light sources and our solar system. In November 2011, two teams of astronomers—at Fermi National Accelerator Laboratory in Batavia, Illinois, and Lawrence Berkeley National Laboratory in California—produced the largest maps ever of the distribution of matter in the universe.

Both groups of astronomers used data from the Sloan Digital Sky Survey (SDSS), a project that has recorded images of millions of distant galaxies using cameras on the SLOAN telescope at Apache Point Observatory in New Mexico. The SDSS images covered roughly 250 square degrees (an area roughly 1,000 times as large as the size of the moon) of the sky. Individual photographs made with the SDSS cameras did not record many galaxies because not enough light was collected in a single exposure. Thus, the teams combined all the exposures to see the faint, distant galaxies. The multiple-exposure data allowed the scientists to find more than 10 million galaxies. In the SDSS images, the more distant galaxies appear slightly less circular and more elongated than nearby galaxies because of the distortion caused by gravitational lensing.

By analyzing the amount of distortion in the images of the distant galaxies, the scientists were able to arrive at the best measurements yet of the amount and distribution of matter in the universe—including dark matter. Dark matter is invisible matter thought to make up the majority of the matter in the cosmos. Unlike ordinary matter, dark matter does not give off, reflect, or absorb light rays. Thus, it can be detected only through observations of the effects of its gravitational pull on visible objects.

The results of the astronomers' analysis indicated that dark matter makes up approximately 25 percent of the total mass of the universe. Scientists planned additional surveys to scan larger portions of the sky to learn more about dark matter—as well as dark energy. Dark energy is a mysterious form of energy that apparently makes the universe expand more and more rapidly. Dark energy is believed to make up roughly 70 percent of the universe.

ASTRONOMY continued

Microwave background radiation. In July 2011, scientists working with the Atacama Cosmology Telescope (ACT) in Chile reported using gravitational lensing to explore the distribution of the cosmic microwave background (CMB) radiation. The CMB radiation consists of radiation left over from the earliest moments of the universe, soon after the big bang (the cosmic explosion that scientists believe gave birth to the universe some 14 billion years ago). The *photons* (elementary particles of electromagnetic radiation) that make up the CMB radiation have traveled freely through the universe since the big bang, providing scientists with a pristine window through which to observe the universe when it was very young.

The ACT team detected and measured the small deflections in CMB radiation resulting from gravitational lensing caused by intervening mass. These measurements enabled the astronomers to create maps of the CMB radiation's temperature and distribution in very high resolution. A satellite named the Wilkinson Microwave Anisotropy Probe had previously mapped how the radiation is spread across the sky, but the new map revealed even finer details of temperature fluctuations in the radiation. These fluctuations, in turn, allowed the astronomers to extract additional information about how mass was unevenly spread throughout the early universe. Furthermore, a statistical analysis of the data enabled the team to confirm the existence of dark energy.

This accomplishment opened a new field of study for astronomers interested in investigating the mass and energy of the early universe. Continued investigation with more powerful and sensitive telescopes was expected to help astronomers learn even more about mass and energy in the universe.

■ Jonathan I. Lunine and Scott Dodelson
See also **PHYSICS; SPACE TECHNOLOGY.**

EXOTIC SUPER-EARTH IS A WATERWORLD

The planet GJ 1214b (shown in an artist's illustration) is made up mostly of water, with an ocean on the surface and thick vapor in the atmosphere, according to an analysis published in February 2012 by scientists led by astronomer Zachary Berta of the Harvard-Smithsonian Center for Astrophysics in Cambridge, Massachusetts. GJ 1214b, a so-called "super-Earth," orbits a red dwarf star 40 light-years from Earth. The planet, which was discovered in 2009, has a diameter almost three times as large as that of Earth. Berta and his team reached their conclusion by using the Hubble Space Telescope to analyze the *spectra* (distribution of light wavelengths) of the planet. Different chemicals have different wavelengths. The team noted that high temperatures and high pressures on GJ 1214b suggest that the surface water exists as a superfluid, a type of liquid that flows without friction and that has other unusual properties.

ATMOSPHERIC SCIENCE

Extremes characterized weather in North America from early 2011 through mid-2012. Residents of various parts of the United States experienced record-breaking heat waves, extreme drought and unprecedented wildfires, fierce spring tornado outbreaks, and killer hurricanes with record flooding.

Extreme weather events took a deadly toll. According to the U.S. National Weather

SEE ALSO

THE SPECIAL REPORT
TWISTED—MORE TERRIBLE TORNADOES
PAGE 28

THE SPECIAL REPORT
MELTDOWN: CLIMATE CHANGE IN THE ARCTIC
PAGE 42

RAINDROPS KEEP FALLING

Impressions of ancient raindrops in a 2.7-billion-year-old fossil from South Africa have added to scientists' understanding of the atmosphere of ancient Earth. Reporting in *Nature* in March 2012, an international team of scientists said the fossilized raindrops led them to deduce that Earth's ancient atmosphere was about as dense as the atmosphere today but contained a much higher concentration of carbon dioxide, methane, and other heat-trapping greenhouse gases. Scientists know, from other evidence, that the ancient sun was dimmer than it is now. The weak sunlight should have made Earth an ice planet, but fossils indicate that liquid water was abundant. The splatter pattern of the fossilized raindrops indicate that Earth's ancient atmosphere was about as dense as it is now. The scientists concluded that the planet's unexpected warmth must have resulted from a high level of greenhouse gases.

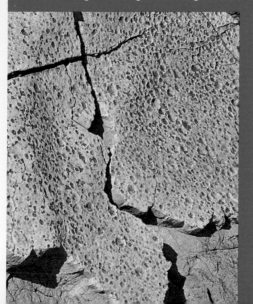

Service, a branch of the National Oceanic and Atmospheric Administration (NOAA), at least 550 people died in tornadoes in 2011, making it the deadliest year since 1936. In August 2011, Hurricane Irene took 45 lives in the United States.

Federal agencies subsequently reported that the United States in 2011 experienced a record 14 weather-related events that produced at least $1 billion in damages. Authorities estimated total U.S. losses of $55 billion from weather-related events in 2011.

On the burner. Drought and record heat caused hardships and serious damage to agriculture across Texas, Oklahoma, New Mexico, Arizona, southern Kansas, and western Louisiana. According to the National Weather Service, the city of San Angelo in west-central Texas set records for its hottest month ever in each of the three summer months of June, July, and August 2011. During the entire summer, the city experienced 21 days with maximums of at least 40.6 °C (105 °F). Many other Texas locales endured similar heat.

Texas was also the U.S. drought center, with more than 90 percent of that large state experiencing extreme or exceptional drought conditions through the summer and much of the fall. In much of west Texas and western Oklahoma, farmers and ranchers lost their winter wheat crops and had to sell off livestock for lack of forage. The U.S. Department of Agriculture estimated agricultural losses of nearly $10 billion in this region.

Some regions of the Southern Plains received much needed rainfall in the first quarter of 2012. However, west Texas, western Oklahoma, and southwestern Kansas remained in extreme drought well into 2012.

ATMOSPHERIC SCIENCE continued

The drought and heat in the southern tier of states also set the stage for another weather-related disaster—wildfires. From late spring 2011 into mid-autumn, wildfires of unprecedented ferocity and magnitude raged across parts of Texas, New Mexico, and Arizona. According to authorities in these states, the fires were responsible for the loss of at least five lives and damages of more than $1 billion.

The Bastrop Fire in the scrub woodland just east of Austin, Texas, was the most costly single fire in that state's history. It destroyed more than 1,500 homes. Throughout 2011, wildfires burned more than 1.2 million hectares (3 million acres) of Texas range and forest, inflicting more than $750 million in damage to property and agriculture. In Arizona, the Wallow Fire consumed more than 200,000 hectares (500,000 acres), making it the largest wildfire in that state's history, according to forestry officials.

Hurricane Irene, the ninth named storm of the 2011 hurricane season, became the first hurricane to strike the United States since Hurricane Ike in September 2008. Irene, born over tropical Atlantic waters off West Africa in mid-August 2011, swept through Puerto Rico and the Bahamas days later. On August 27, Hurricane Irene slashed across eastern North Carolina. It then skittered up the mid-Atlantic coastline, making landfall again on Long Island, just east of New York City, on August 28. From there, the storm pushed through Connecticut, Vermont, and New Hampshire.

Irene inflicted damage all along its track, but the greatest destruction came from the torrential rainfall and flooding associated with the storm as it moved into New England. Particularly hard hit was mountainous Vermont. There, rivers became raging torrents that washed away substantial sections of the state's rural highway system.

Along its entire path, Hurricane Irene claimed 56 lives, with 45 lives lost in the

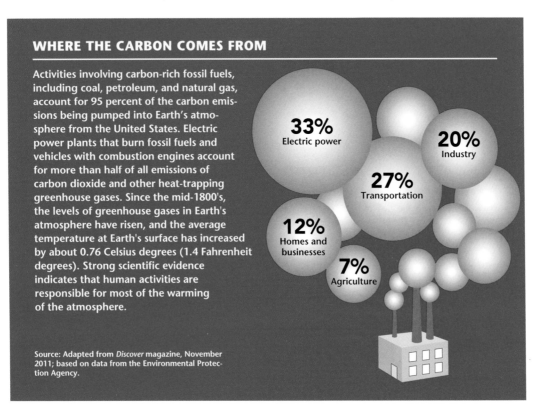

WHERE THE CARBON COMES FROM

Activities involving carbon-rich fossil fuels, including coal, petroleum, and natural gas, account for 95 percent of the carbon emissions being pumped into Earth's atmosphere from the United States. Electric power plants that burn fossil fuels and vehicles with combustion engines account for more than half of all emissions of carbon dioxide and other heat-trapping greenhouse gases. Since the mid-1800's, the levels of greenhouse gases in Earth's atmosphere have risen, and the average temperature at Earth's surface has increased by about 0.76 Celsius degrees (1.4 Fahrenheit degrees). Strong scientific evidence indicates that human activities are responsible for most of the warming of the atmosphere.

33% Electric power

20% Industry

27% Transportation

12% Homes and businesses

7% Agriculture

Source: Adapted from *Discover* magazine, November 2011; based on data from the Environmental Protection Agency.

United States alone. Authorities estimated U.S. damages at more than $7.3 billion.

The winter that wasn't. From December 2011 through March 2012, the eastern two-thirds of the United States experienced one of the warmest winters on record. According to the U.S. Weather Service, the lower 48 states experienced their fourth-warmest winter ever—surpassed only by the winters of 1991–1992; 1998–1999; and 1999–2000. The Weather Service reported that in the first quarter of 2012—January, February, and March—U.S. reporting stations set over 15,000 new records for local daily maximum temperatures. In fact, the lower 48 states experienced their warmest March ever in 2012.

Early and violent tornado season. Warmer-than-average temperatures in early 2012 created an environment favorable for the early onset of the spring tornado season. January was unusually active, with 97 tornadoes reported in the United States. The only January on record with more twisters was in 1999. The Weather Service reported 63 tornadoes in February 2012, also well above the long-term average. On February 29, a powerful twister swept through Harrisburg, Illinois, severely damaging the town and killing seven people.

March remained active, with more than 220 tornadoes reported in the United States, according to the Weather Service. That tally eclipsed the long-term average of 80 twisters for the month of March. On March 2 and 3, an outbreak of severe storms in the Ohio Valley and the Southeast spawned 65 tornadoes. Especially hard hit were areas of southeastern Indiana and eastern Kentucky. Tornadoes in these two states accounted for the majority of the 40 fatalities reported in the widespread outbreak. Authorities estimated $1.5 billion in damages inflicted by all of these early March tornadoes, making this the first weather event of 2012 to exceed $1 billion in damages and losses.

What's going on? A succession of extraordinary weather events in 2011 and early 2012 seemed to suggest a "new normal" of extreme weather across the Northern Hemisphere. In the United States, in particular, unprecedented snowstorms in early 2010

and 2011 gave way to unprecedented winter warmth in early 2012, punctuated by exceptionally numerous and violent outbreaks of tornadic storms.

Meteorologists look for explanations of weather events in *teleconnections*—influences exerted by distinctive regional weather patterns across long distances, even from one part of the globe to another. Scientists know that such large-scale patterns as the El Niño-Southern Oscillation (ENSO) and the North Atlantic Oscillation (NAO) collectively influence weather across much of the Northern Hemisphere. (An oscillation is a pattern that shifts back and forth between contrasting conditions. A phase is a particular condition within an oscillation.)

The ENSO involves oscillations between warmer-than-normal temperatures in the equatorial Eastern Central Pacific Ocean (El Niño phase) and cooler-than-normal temperatures in the same region (La Niña phase). The NAO involves oscillations of atmospheric pressure in various parts of the Arctic and certain regions of the temperate Northern Hemisphere. These oscillations greatly affect the position of storm tracks and the movement of Arctic air masses in the hemisphere.

Since late 2010, North America has been dominated by a La Niña—the cold phase of the ENSO in the equatorial Pacific. In the winter of 2010–2011, La Niña interacted with the NAO in such a way that water vapor from the tropics was steered into and over cold air positioned over the northeastern United States. This interaction caused massive snowstorms in the region.

For the remainder of 2011 and into 2012, with the NAO in a contrasting phase, La Niña and the NAO interacted quite differently. These teleconnections resulted in a persistent ridge of high pressure over the Southern Plains. This ridge of dry, dense air kept storm tracks far to the north, preventing much needed rainfall in the region. The same pattern blocked frigid Arctic air masses that, in average winters, sweep into the Great Plains of the United States and push southward and eastward. Without this inflow of Arctic air, the U.S. winter stayed mild. Meteorologists noted that the pattern itself was not unusual, but the duration of the La Niña phase of the ENSO was exceptional.

ATMOSPHERIC SCIENCE continued

OZONE HOLE RECOVERING—SLOWLY

The "ozone hole" above Antarctica, which reached its greatest extent in September 2006 (satellite image below), is healing, thanks to the 1987 Montreal Protocol, according to a December 2011 report by chemist Paul Newman of NASA's Goddard Flight Center. (Purple indicates the region of the greatest depletion.) The ozone hole is a region of the atmosphere over Antarctica where a layer of ozone, a form of oxygen, thins every spring. In the stratosphere, ozone prevents harmful ultraviolet light, which can damage skin and eyes, from reaching Earth's surface. Signatories to the Montreal Protocol, endorsed by most of the world's nations, agreed to phase out the production of chemicals called chlorofluorocarbons (CFC's), which were widely used in refrigerators and other products. Chemical reactions involving CFC's deplete the ozone that forms in the stratosphere. Effects of the banning of CFC's are slow to appear because CFC molecules can take years to rise from the ground to the stratosphere. Scientists predict that the Antarctic ozone layer will recover during the 2030's.

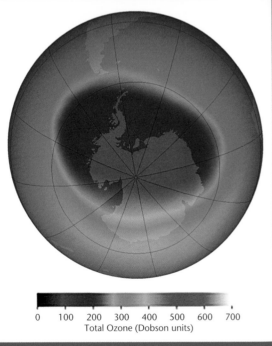

| 0 | 100 | 200 | 300 | 400 | 500 | 600 | 700 |
Total Ozone (Dobson units)

Source: National Aeronautics and Space Administration.

Signs of global warming? Scientists, as well as members of the general public, wonder whether the apparent "new normal" of extreme and atypical weather events is linked to global warming. Scientists point out that warmer air masses are capable of absorbing more water vapor than cooler masses. Large volumes of water vapor tend to make air masses unstable, setting the stage for such potentially extreme weather events as storms and torrential rains. For these reasons, scientists speculate, one feature of a warming climate is likely to be more frequent extreme weather.

Jennifer A. Francis, a climatologist at New Jersey's Rutgers University, has presented evidence that rapid warming in the Arctic and unprecedented summer melting of the polar icecap in recent decades is affecting the behavior of the polar jet stream. The jet stream is a high-altitude band of winds that serves as a steering mechanism for storms and other weather patterns.

Francis's research suggests that declining temperature contrasts between the Arctic and the middle latitudes is causing meanders in the jet stream to move from west to east more slowly than before. As a result, specific weather patterns tend to linger longer in a locale. If such weather patterns as heat waves, torrential rains, or blizzards stall, extreme weather events become extraordinary or even catastrophic.

Other climatologists, using different computer-based models, arrive at different conclusions. NOAA climatologist Martin P. Hoerling, for example, has reported that his own computer analyses have failed to confirm a widespread effect on weather events outside the Arctic from unprecedented shrinkage of the polar icecap.

Meanwhile, scientists continue to study large-scale weather patterns and their global teleconnections. Linking these patterns to specific weather events has, so far, proved to be an elusive goal. Is a succession of extreme weather events such as those experienced in 2011–2012 an indicator of global warming? At present, science cannot provide a clear answer to this question.

■ John T. Snow

■ BIOLOGY

The gorilla became the last of the great apes to have its *genome* (total genetic material of a species) decoded, reported scientists at the Wellcome Trust Sanger Institute in the United Kingdom in March 2012. The decoding, or sequencing, of a genome involves determining the order of all the chemical units called bases that make up the DNA of chromosomes, the structures that carry genes. The sequencing of the gorilla genome made it possible to compare the genome of gorillas with those of the other great apes (chimpanzees and orangutans) and with that of human beings.

The DNA analyzed in the gorilla genome project was obtained from a female western lowland gorilla, named Kamilah, at the San Diego Zoo in California. The scientists also sampled DNA from other gorillas to explore genetic differences between different kinds of gorillas.

The research team examined more than 11,000 genes from humans, chimpanzees, and gorillas to look for differences in the makeup of the genes. The analysis revealed that gorillas are more closely related to human beings than previously believed. Although chimpanzees are our closest animal relative, 15 percent of the human genome resembles the gorilla genome more closely than it does the comparable sections of the chimpanzee genome.

"The gorilla genome is important because it sheds light on the time when our ancestors diverged from our closest evolutionary cousins," said biologist Aylwyn Scally of the Sanger Institute. Based on the genetic analysis, the scientists concluded that the gorilla *lineage* (line of descent) diverged from that of humans and chimpanzees approximately 10 million years ago. The split between eastern lowland

ELEPHANTS ON TIPTOE

An elephant's foot contains a small bony growth that is actually a sixth "toe," reported a team of investigators led by evolutionary biologist John Hutchinson of the Royal Veterinary College in the United Kingdom in December 2011. First discovered in 1706, the structure had been viewed by many biologists as a piece of cartilage with an unknown function. Hutchinson and his team conducted a detailed examination of the structure with *computed tomography* (advanced X-ray imaging), electron microscopy, and dissection. They determined that the structure (circled in red below) is a bone, not cartilage. Furthermore, they proposed that the function of the bone is to help support the immense weight of these massive mammals. In essence, elephants walk on tiptoe.

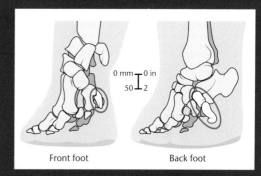

Front foot   Back foot

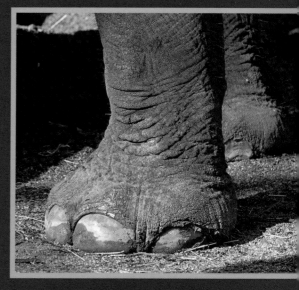

BIOLOGY continued

and western lowland gorillas occurred within the last 1 million years. The researchers also found that in gorillas, chimpanzees, and humans, genes related to sensory perception, hearing, and brain development have shown many accelerated changes—though these changes appeared to be most pronounced in gorillas and humans.

Chimpanzee cops. Chimpanzees and human beings share many traits, including using "police" to keep the peace, reported researchers at the University of Zurich in Switzerland in March 2012. The scientists studied a *troop* (group) of chimpanzees at the Walter Zoo in Gossau, Switzerland. They found that certain members of the troop, both male and female, broke up quarrels without taking sides. Such impartial intervention in conflicts is rare among animals. Policing by chimpanzees may indicate how morality and ethics in human behavior originated, the researchers proposed.

Double-duty stripes. The stripe patterns that help camouflage zebras among the tall grasses of their surroundings, protecting them from prowling lions, also hide them from bloodsucking horse flies, scientists reported in February 2012. The stripes interfere with the way that the flies detect polarized light, which is reflected from the hides of animals and that serves as an attractant to the flies. Polarized light consists of light waves that vibrate in simple, regular patterns oriented in the same direction, rather than the many different directions of normal light. After being attracted to the hides by the light, the flies bite the animals to feed on their blood, potentially spreading diseases in the process.

Polarized light reflects the best from black hides, which is why horse flies are more attracted to dark horses than to white horses. The scientists, from Eotvos University in Hungary and Lund University in Swe-

DIVING BELL SERVES AS "GILL" FOR UNDERWATER SPIDER

A diving bell spider (*Argyroneta aquatica*) manipulates a bubble of air suspended in an underwater web. The spider, which lives in the Eider River in Germany, obtains oxygen from the bubble, which draws in more oxygen from the water as the spider uses it. In this way, the bubble functions somewhat like the gill of a fish. This process was described in June 2011 by biologists Roger Seymour of the University of Adelaide in Australia and Stefan Hetz of Humboldt University in Germany. The scientists used a tiny probe to measure the amount of oxygen in the diving bell as the spider used it. They concluded that the spider can spend much of its time close to the bubble, living off its oxygen supply and avoiding venturing into the open water. However, the spider occasionally must swim to the surface to obtain additional oxygen, which it carries in a "trap" between its legs and abdomen. The spider then swims back to the bell to replenish its oxygen supply.

den, reasoned that a zebra-stripe pattern should attract more flies than a solid white hide and fewer flies than solid black hide. However, their experiments showed that the striped pattern attracted the fewest flies. Furthermore, the patterns with the narrowest stripes attracted the fewest flies of all.

The scientists concluded that the contrast between the high amounts of polarized light reflected from the black stripes and the low amounts of polarized light reflected from the white stripes in a zebra's hide confuses the vision of the flies. This confusion makes it difficult for the flies to target the source of the light. The researchers proposed that zebras evolved a coat pattern in which the stripes are narrow enough to attract only relatively few parasitic flies , thereby protecting the zebras against the diseases carried by the flies.

Lightning-fast muscles. The muscles that bats use to emit calls are "superfast," scientists reported in September 2011. Bats' calls reflect off objects as echoes that enable the bats to navigate and find prey in the dark, a process called echolocation. The scientists found that a bat's vocal muscles can *twitch* (contract and relax) 20 times as quickly as the fastest human muscles. Such speedy muscles were previously known only from the sound organs of rattlesnakes and some fish and birds. At top speed, the bat muscles can twitch in less than one-hundredth of a second, said the researchers, who were from the University of Southern Denmark and the University of Pennsylvania in Philadelphia.

Superfast muscles are needed for echolocation because bats obtain only a brief snapshot of their environment from each call and echo. These snapshots force bats to make many calls in rapid succession to keep track of a moving object. To catch a flying insect that can change course in a flash, bats need instantaneous updates on the insect's position. Just before a bat strikes, it pinpoints the insect's location by producing what is known as a "terminal buzz," consisting of about 190 calls per second. This process demands that the superfast muscles twitch as rapidly as possible.

Poison-using rats. The African crested rat is the first mammal known to defend itself using poison from a plant, according to

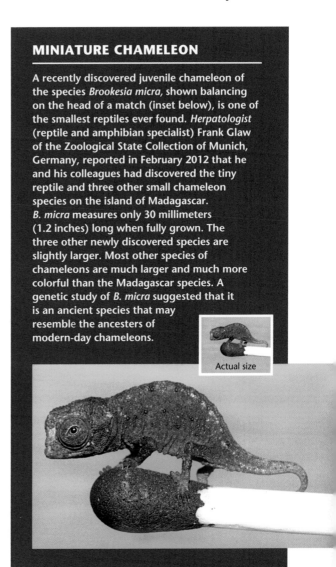

MINIATURE CHAMELEON

A recently discovered juvenile chameleon of the species *Brookesia micra,* shown balancing on the head of a match (inset below), is one of the smallest reptiles ever found. *Herpatologist* (reptile and amphibian specialist) Frank Glaw of the Zoological State Collection of Munich, Germany, reported in February 2012 that he and his colleagues had discovered the tiny reptile and three other small chameleon species on the island of Madagascar. *B. micra* measures only 30 millimeters (1.2 inches) long when fully grown. The three other newly discovered species are slightly larger. Most other species of chameleons are much larger and much more colorful than the Madagascar species. A genetic study of *B. micra* suggested that it is an ancient species that may resemble the ancestors of modern-day chameleons.

Actual size

research reported in August 2011 by scientists at the National Museums of Kenya, the University of Oxford in the United Kingdom, and the Wildlife Conservation Society of New York City. The rat chews up poison-containing bark from trees in the genus *Acokanthera* and applies a mixture of the chewed-up bark and saliva to spongy hairs on its flanks. The scientists found, by examining the hairs of the rat with an electron microscope, that tiny holes in the hairs absorb the poisonous mixture. Any predators that attack the rat risk getting a mouthful of poison-filled hair.

Researchers had suspected that the

BIOLOGY continued

crested rat might be poisonous, in part because its flanks are boldly colored in contrasting black and white. The rat flashes these flanks when threatened. Vivid colors often serve as a warning to predators that potential prey is poisonous or otherwise unpleasant. In addition, dogs have been known to die after mouthing crested rats.

The researchers proved that the rats use the tree's poison by providing a wild-caught rat with branches and roots from the tree. They then observed the rat as it chewed up the bark and applied the poisonous mixture to its fur. The scientists have not discovered why the poison does not affect the rat.

New city frog. Not all new species of animals are discovered in remote wildernesses. Scientists announced in March 2012 the discovery of a previously unknown species of leopard frog living in New York City and its suburbs, with the center of its range near Yankee Stadium in the Bronx.

The frog joins the more than 12 species of leopard frog already known to inhabit North America.

Unlike other leopard frogs, whose calls typically resemble repetitive chuckles or snores, the newly found species emits a single cluck, reported a team of biologists including ecologist Jeremy Feinberg of Rutgers University in New Jersey. The newly discovered leopard frog resembles most other species of leopard frog, with large dark brown spots surrounded by light borders. Only when they examined the frog's DNA did the researchers learn that it was a distinct species. The discovery of the frog demonstrated that wildlife conservation remains important in urban areas, the scientists noted.

Zombees. A parasitic fly that turns honeybees into "zombies" may play a role in colony collapse disorder (CCD), according to a report published in January 2012. CCD has wiped out at least 30 percent of honey-

COMMUNICATING BY BEAK

Ravens communicate with one another by gesturing with their beaks and wings the way people gesture using their hands, according to research published in November 2011 by biologist Simone Pika of the Max Planck Institute for Ornithology in Germany. Pika reported that his observations of such gestures as displaying or offering an object to other ravens (right) constitute the first evidence of the use of gestures by any animal besides human beings and other *primates* (monkeys, apes, and humans). Pika found that ravens typically show or offer a piece of moss, a stone, or a twig to a bird of the opposite sex as a way to attract the bird's interest. This gesture may lead to such interactions as touching or clasping bills or manipulating the item together. Through such interaction, said Pika, a raven can gauge the interest of a potential mate or strengthen an already existing bond.

bee colonies in the United States since it was discovered in 2006.

After the fly *Apocephalus borealis* lays eggs in the abdomens of honeybees, the bees stagger around in circles, "something like a zombie," said biologist Andrew Core of San Francisco State University in California. The infected bees abandon their hives during the night, "in what is literally a flight of the living dead," and eventually perish. The larval flies then emerge from the bodies of the dead bees.

The scientists discovered the parasitic flies affecting honeybee colonies in 24 of 31 sites in the San Francisco Bay area, as well as in commercial hives elsewhere in California and in South Dakota. They also found that some of the bees and flies were infected with a virus that causes deformed wings and with the fungus *Nosema ceranae*, both of which had previously been implicated in CCD. The scientists said that additional research was needed to clarify the role of the parasitic flies in contributing to CCD. For example, it was not clear to what extent the flies harm the bees by spreading the deformed wing virus and *N. ceranae* fungus.

Leafy loudspeakers. Dish-shaped leaves that work like loudspeakers help a rain forest vine attract nectar-feeding bat pollinators to its flowers, researchers reported in July 2011. While feeding on the nectar, the bats transfer pollen between the flowers of the vine, a species known as *Marcgravia evenia*, which grows in Cuba. The leaves lure the bats to the flowers by reflecting echoes of the high-pitched squeaks that the bats use to sense their surroundings (in the orientation process of echolocation). Observations revealed that the bats were able to find the flowers of *M. evenia* twice as fast as they could find the flowers of other plants in the rain forest.

The team of researchers, from the United Kingdom and Germany, noted than many plants use showy flowers or odors to attract pollinators. However, *M. evenia* is the first plant known to use the enhancement of sound to attract pollinators.

Plant biological clock. The biological clock that attunes plants to the cycle of day and night also enables them to prepare defenses against daytime raids by leaf-munching insects, reported biologists at Rice University in Houston in February 2012. Scientists have long known that some functions of plants are based on an internal clock linked to changing light conditions. For example, some plants track the westward movement of the sun with their leaves during the day. They then reset their leaves at night, moving them back toward the east in anticipation of sunrise.

The scientists studied a plant related to cabbage named *Arabidopsis thaliana* and a leaf-eating caterpillar called the cabbage looper. The researchers found that with the coming of daylight, when cabbage loopers feed most, the plant increased its production and concentration of a chemical called jasmonate. This chemical, which is found in many plants, interferes with insect digestion. The insects are then prompted to leave the plant alone.

The scientists confirmed the defensive importance of jasmonate by artificially changing light cycles in their laboratory, throwing off the plant's biological clock. Under these altered conditions, the plant's jasmonate production dropped, leaving it vulnerable to cabbage looper attack.

Batman bacteria. Bacteria can slingshot themselves across gooey surfaces using tiny hooks, according to research reported in July 2011 by scientists at the University of California at Los Angeles (UCLA). The hooks act like "Batman's grappling hooks," said UCLA bioengineer Gerard Wong, who led the research. To slingshot, the microbe grabs hold of the surface and stretches each hook like a taut rubber band. The hooks then snap loose, catapulting the bacterium forward. By slingshotting in this way, the bacterium can move 20 times as fast as its usual pace. The scientists made these observations with high-powered microscopes and high-speed cameras.

Pseudomonas aeruginosa, the bacterium studied by Wong's team, is partly responsible for deadly lung infections associated with cystic fibrosis, a disease in which certain glands in the body secrete large amounts of abnormally thick mucus. Wong said that research on the movements of the bacterium may help scientists develop better treatments for patients with these infections. ■ Edward R. Ricciuti

See also **ECOLOGY; FOSSIL STUDIES.**

BOOKS ABOUT SCIENCE

Here are 11 important new science books suitable for the general reader. They have been selected from books published in 2011 and 2012.

Astronomy. *How We See the Sky: A Naked-Eye Tour of Day & Night* by astronomer Thomas Hockey introduces readers to the basics of astronomy. With the help of pictures and diagrams, Hockey describes how and when to look at the night sky without the aid of a telescope. Readers will learn about lunar and solar motion, why there are seasons and eclipses, and the harmful effects of *light pollution* (artificial lighting that interferes with people's view of the night sky). Hockey also describes how several ancient sites, including Stonehenge and the Great Pyramid at Giza, were constructed with astronomical alignments in mind. (University of Chicago Press, 239 pp. $20.00)

Biology. *Feathers: The Evolution of a Natural Miracle* by conservation biologist Thor Hanson is a natural history of remarkable growths that can be found today only on birds. Feathers have an incredible number of functions. Birds use feathers for flight, insulation, and communication. Humans also use feathers—for fly fishing, padding, and decoration. Until modern times, the standard writing tool was the quill of a feather.

What are feathers and how did they evolve? To answer these questions, Hanson guides readers through time and across the world with wit and enthusiasm. Readers will come away from this engaging book with a better understanding of feathers and an appreciation of their many uses. (Basic Books, 336 pp. $25.99)

First Life: Discovering the Connections between Stars, Cells, and How Life Began by David Deamer, professor of Biomolecular Engineering at the University of California, Santa Cruz, stakes out a persuasive position in the long-standing debate over the origin of life on Earth. Deamer discusses the roles stardust in the ancient cosmos and volcanoes on the early Earth may have played in the evolution of simple organisms more than 3 ½ billion years ago. He also introduces readers to astrobiology. This new scientific discipline combines elements of astronomy, biology, geology, and other sciences for the study not only of life on Earth but also elsewhere in the universe. (University of California Press, 271 pp. $28.95)

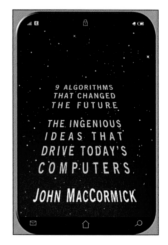

Computer science. *Nine Algorithms that Changed the Future: The Ingenious Ideas that Drive Today's Computers* by computer science professor John MacCormick explains in layman's terms the ideas behind nine mathematical processes that underpin many of our computer-related activities. We use these algorithms for such everyday actions as searching the Internet (Google's PageRank algorithm); banking and shopping online over a secure network (encryption algorithms); and downloading music and sending photos to friends (data compression algorithms). MacCormick's book will leave readers with an appreciation for some of the ideas that drive today's computers. (Princeton University Press, 219 pp. $27.95)

The history of science. *Boltzmann's Tomb: Travels in Search of Science* by geochemist Bill Green explains how Nicolaus Copernicus, Isaac Newton, Albert Einstein, and other important scientists have shaped the history of science over the last 500 years. The title of the book comes from the tombstone of Austrian physicist Ludwig Boltzmann (1844-1906), on which is engraved a formula the scientist conceived to explain why heat energy flows from warmer to cooler regions. Throughout the book, Green reveals his own evolution as a scientist, from his boyhood days in Pittsburgh, Pennsylvania, reading *Popular Mechanics* magazine to his career as a research scientist in Antarctica. (Bellevue Literary Press, 208 pp. $25.00)

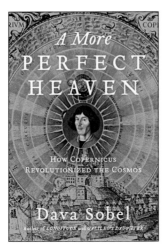

A More Perfect Heaven: How Copernicus Revolutionized the Cosmos by popular science writer Dava Sobel examines the life of Nicolaus Copernicus and the evolution of his theory of a *heliocentric* (sun-centered) universe. One of the key questions Sobel investigates is why Copernicus waited until shortly before his death in 1543 to publish his book *On the Revolutions of the Heavenly Spheres*. To explore this question, the author fashions

a two-act play dramatizing Copernicus's relationship with Georg Joachim Rheticus, the young Austrian mathematician who traveled to Poland in 1539 to learn more about Copernicus's ideas. Within months of showing up unannounced at Copernicus's door, Rheticus had persuaded Copernicus to publish his ideas. Because virtually no evidence of their relationship survives, no one knows what Rheticus said to Copernicus. However, Sobel provides an imaginative and entertaining account of conversations they might have had. (Walker & Company, 273 pp. $25.00)

Mathematics. *Cosmic Numbers: The Numbers that Define our Universe* by California State University mathematics professor James D. Stein is a collection of essays on *constants* (fundamental numbers) that make the universe intelligible. Stein explains such constants as the speed of light; *absolute zero* (the temperature at which atoms and molecules have the least amount of heat possible); Boltzmann's constant, which explains why heat flows from hotter to colder substances; and the Chandrasekhar limit, which determines if an aging star will explode into a supernova. Without numerical constants, much of what we know about the universe and how it works would have eluded us. Stein does an excellent job of explaining where these numbers came from, who discovered them, and what they tell us about the universe we live in. (Basic Books, 228 pp. $25.99)

The Man of Numbers: Fibonacci's Arithmetic Revolution by mathematician Keith Devlin tells the story of the Italian mathematician Leonardo of Pisa (1170?-?), better known

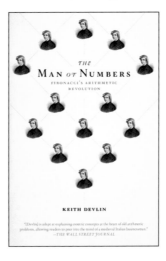

BOOKS ABOUT SCIENCE continued

today as Fibonacci. As a young man, Leonardo traveled to North Africa where he learned the Hindu-Arabic numeral system (the numerals 0, 1, 2, 3, 4, 5, 6, 7, 8, and 9). Soon after returning to Pisa in 1202, he published *Liber Abbaci* (Book of Calculation), a 600-page work that explained how to use the Hindu-Arabic numeral system to buy and sell goods, convert currencies, and solve other practical problems. Leonardo's book revolutionized commerce and banking, and it laid the foundation for modern mathematics. (Walker & Company, 183 pp. $25.00)

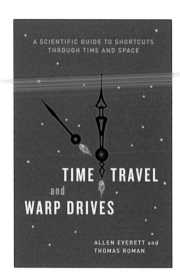

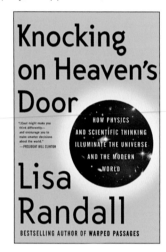

Physics. *Knocking on Heaven's Door: How Physics and Scientific Thinking Illuminate the Universe and the Modern World* by Harvard theoretical physicist Lisa Randall provides an overview of the latest ideas in theoretical physics, focusing on experimental research at the Large Hadron Collider (LHC) along the border of France and Switzerland. The LHC is an enormous underground machine that sends subatomic particles around a ring measuring nearly 27 kilometers (17 miles) in circumference at nearly the speed of light. Scientists believe that experiments at the LHC will reveal fundamental particles of nature and provide clues to the origin of the universe. (Ecco, 442 pp. $16.99)

Time Travel and Warp Drives: A Scientific Guide to Shortcuts through Time and Space by physics professors Allen Everett and Thomas Roman surveys what modern physics understands about time travel. Using no more than high school algebra, Everett and Roman explain the principles of Albert Einstein's theories of special and general relativity that make time travel theoretically possible. The authors also explain why time travel for human beings will remain in the realm of science fiction for at least the foreseeable future. The book includes several illustrations and diagrams that explain Einstein's ideas about the nature of time and space. (University of Chicago Press, 268 pp. $30.00)

Psychology. *The Happiness of Pursuit: What Neuroscience Can Teach Us About the Good Life* by Shimon Edelman, a psychology professor at Cornell University, examines relationships between the brain, the human body, and the mind—and how these interacting entities affect human self-perception and happiness. Edelman walks readers through the brain's basic computational skills: perception, memory, motivation, thought, and action. Because of the way our brains are wired, Edelman argues, happiness lies not in the attainment of end goals but in the continuing pursuit of new knowledge and experiences. He summarizes his advice for pursuing happiness with the following saying: "When fishing for happiness, catch and release." (Basic Books, 237 pp. $25.99)   ■ Jon Wills

BOOKS ABOUT SCIENCE FOR YOUNGER READERS

The following books about science are suitable for younger readers. They have been chosen from books published in 2011 and 2012.

Astronomy. *A Black Hole Is Not a Hole* by science writer and educator Carolyn Cinami DeCristofano, with illustrations by space artist Michael W. Carroll, explains what astronomers know about black holes. Although these mysterious celestial objects cannot be seen, scientists have learned about some of their properties by studying the effects black holes have on space, light, and matter. DeCristofano's text provides clear and simple descriptions of the life cycles of stars, the formation of black holes, and recent discoveries of black holes in various galaxies throughout the universe.

Carroll's dramatic illustrations and easy-to-understand diagrams and charts convey the awe and grandeur of space and of a phenomenon that scientists do not yet fully understand. A timeline, glossary, and pronunciation guide help young readers understand "what in the universe" a black hole is. (Charlesbridge, 80 pp. illus., grades 5-7, $18.95)

Biography. *Life in the Ocean: The Story of Oceanographer Sylvia Earle* by children's author and illustrator Claire A. Nivola introduces readers to pioneering underwater explorer and environmentalist Sylvia Earle. From the first time that she encountered the ocean at the age of 12, Earle was fascinated by this vast, little-known world. In 1970, she led an all-female expedition that lived and conducted marine research in a small cylinder called Tektite II, which was operating at a depth of 15 meters (49 feet) beneath the sea in the U.S. Virgin Islands. She set or tied several women's diving records; co-founded a company to advance marine engineering; and led efforts to clean up environmental damage caused by

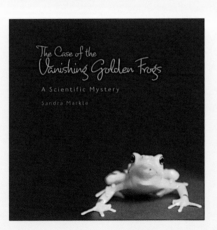

the Persian Gulf War of 1991 and the tanker *Exxon Valdez* oil spill in Alaska. Later, Earle served as chief scientist for the National Oceanic and Atmospheric Administration (NOAA) and as explorer-in-residence at the National Georgraphic Society.

Nivola's detailed, panoramic watercolors evoke Earle's life-long sense of wonder for "the blue heart of the planet." An author's note encourages readers to help preserve the world's endangered oceans. (Farrar, Strauss and Giroux, 32 pp. illus., grades K-4, $17.99)

Biology. *Biomimicry* by science writer Dora Lee, with illustrations by Margot Thompson, examines how new technologies often mirror natural processes. Each double-page spread highlights how a particular feature of nature has been adapted by scientists and engineers to solve human problems. Inventions inspired by nature include Velcro fastenings, sharkskin swimsuits, Japanese bullet trains, camouflage, and motors. Benefits of imitating nature are greater ecological balance and less waste. For example, today's scientists and engineers are using nature as a model to develop technologies that produce solar and other forms of renewable energy. This book's clear writing and colorful illustrations make it an excellent choice for readers interested in understanding how scientists are using nature to improve our world. (Kids Can Press, 40 pp. illus., grades 5-7, $18.95)

The Case of the Vanishing Golden Frogs: A Scientific Mystery by award-winning children's author Sandra Markle investigates why vast populations of Panamanian golden frogs began dying off in the mid-1990's. In 1992, biologist Karen Lips visited a high mountain forest in Panama with a large population of golden frogs. When she returned to the same forest in 1996, she could only find dead golden frogs. What happened? After looking at

BOOKS ABOUT SCIENCE FOR YOUNGER READERS continued

the evidence, Lips concluded that the frog deaths could not be attributed to habitat destruction, global warming, or pollution. After communicating with other scientists around the world, she discovered the real killer was a fungus that invades and damages a frog's skin.

Since 2008, few golden frogs have been found living in the wild. Scientists have discovered a chemical that can be used to combat the frog-killing fungus. However, this chemical can only be used in specially created environments that are built for the rescue of golden frogs. This book will help children understand the reasoning that scientists use to solve problems. It includes colorful photographs, a reading list, and a glossary. (Millbrook Press, 48 pp. illus., grades 5-7, $21.95)

The Polar Bear Scientists by children's author Peter Lourie follows a scientific research team as they study polar bears in icy waters off Alaska's Arctic North Slope. Lourie, who has also written books on scientists who study whales and manatees, provides readers with an up-close look at the work involved in the study of polar bears. Color photographs show scientists tracking and capturing bears; weighing them; drawing blood and conducting other medical tests; and tattooing the bears for future identification. In addition to providing information about polar bear populations, the data will aid in future conservation efforts.

Polar bears are threatened by global warming, the author explains. Most scientists predict that polar bear populations will decline sharply over the next several decades as rising temperatures reduce the amount of sea ice covering the Arctic Ocean. Polar bears live on and hunt largely from sea ice.

In addition to its engaging text and illustrations, *The Polar Bear Scientists* includes several maps, a glossary, a list of polar bear facts, and a list of suggested books and websites. (Houghton Mifflin Books for Children, 80 pp. illus., grades 5-8, $18.99)

Geology. *What's So Hot About Volcanoes?* by Northern Arizona University geology professor Wendell A. Duffield, with illustrations by Bronze Black, introduces readers to the science of volcanoes. Duffield, a volcanologist with more than 40 years of experience, explains how volcanoes form, why they erupt, and how scientists try to predict future volcanic activity. The book discusses the benefits of volcanic activity, which include the generation of geothermal and electric energy; the production of rock that can be used for the construction of roads, buildings, and other structures; and nutrient-rich volcanic ash that enriches soil. The book includes several useful maps, diagrams, and photographs. It also includes a glossary and a state-by-state list of places to explore volcanoes and volcanic fields in the United States. (Mountain Press Publishing Company, 89 pp. illus., grades 6-9, $16.00)

Fossil studies. *How the Dinosaur Got to the Museum* by illustrator and cartoonist Jessie Hartland takes readers behind the scenes as a dinosaur called *Diplodocus* is unearthed in Utah and then transported to a dinosaur exhibit at the Smithsonian Museum in Washington, D.C. *Diplodocus* was an extremely long, slender, plant-eating dinosaur that lived about 150 million years ago.

On each colorful, double-page spread, readers meet people who made the dinosaur exhibit possible. Among them are the dinosaur hunter who discovered the bones in 1923; the Smithsonian paleontologist who traveled to Utah to certify that the bones were authentic; and the museum director who opened the exhibit. The book also includes background information on *Diplodocus*. (Blue Apple Books, 32 pp. illus., grades K-4, $17.99)   ■ Jon Wills

CHEMISTRY

Two new chemical elements officially joined the periodic table in June 2011. These elements have atomic numbers 114 and 116. The atomic number is equal to the number of *protons* (positively charged particles) in an atom's *nucleus* (central part).

In December 2011, a committee composed of members from the International Union of Pure and Applied Chemistry and the International Union of Pure and Applied Physics assigned names to the new elements: flerovium (chemical symbol Fl) for element 114, and livermorium (chemical symbol Lv) for element 116. The names were chosen in honor of Russian physicist Georgy N. Flerov, founder of the Joint Institute for Nuclear Research (JINR) in Russia; and the Lawrence Livermore National Laboratory (LLNL) in California. Both institutions collaborated in research that led to the discovery of the new elements.

Flerovium and livermorium belong to the class of superheavy elements—those with atomic numbers higher than uranium, which has an atomic number of 92. Most superheavy elements are radioactive and *decay* (break down) in a short time, sometimes in less than a second. After the new elements were formed, half of the element 114 atoms decayed into lighter atoms in less than 3 seconds, and half of the element 116 atoms decayed in $^{60}/_{1,000}$ of a second.

The JINR and LLNL teams created element 116 by smashing calcium *ions* (electrically charged atoms)—each with 20 protons—into stationary targets of curium atoms—each with 96 protons. They performed the atom smashing in a particle accelerator, a machine that boosts atoms or subatomic particles to high speeds until they collide and fuse to form new atomic nuclei. The resulting element 116 decayed almost immediately to form element 114. The researchers also produced element 114 independently by replacing curium with a target of plutonium, which has 94 protons.

For decades, scientists have been intrigued by theoretical predictions that some undiscovered superheavy elements may belong to an "island of stability"—a region of the periodic table where superheavy elements would be stable enough to be investigated for chemical properties and possible applications. Additional research was needed to determine if the new elements could be investigated for such purposes.

New phase of hydrogen. A new *phase* (physical form) of hydrogen, the simplest and lightest element in the periodic table, was announced in March 2012 by researchers in the United Kingdom and United States. By squeezing atoms of hydrogen under immense pressures—several million times the weight of the atmosphere at sea level—the group reported that the atoms arranged themselves into a never-before observed solid phase made of six-membered rings. If confirmed by subsequent experiments, this new phase, created by a team headed by physicist Eugene Gregoryanz of the University of Edinburgh in Scotland, would join three other known phases of solid hydrogen.

The new phase was also expected to help scientists better understand how hydrogen behaves under tremendous pressures, bringing them a step closer to preparing metallic hydrogen, a form of hydrogen that would readily conduct electric current. Metallic hydrogen might be stable enough for use in practical applications, such as superconducting wires that would transmit electric current with no loss of power.

At room temperatures and ordinary pressures, hydrogen is a colorless, odorless gas, with molecules made of two atoms that are bonded together. When cooled to very low temperatures—near absolute zero (-273.15 °C [-459.67 °F])—and subjected to great pressures, hydrogen molecules form a liquid. With further cooling, they turn into a solid. One of the three previously known phases of solid hydrogen is a densely packed structure with freely rotating molecules. Another phase has a more ordered arrangement of molecules. The third phase has molecules with weakly bonded atoms that are free to move independently.

CHEMISTRY continued

For their research, Gregoryanz, along with scientists at the Carnegie Institution for Science's Geophysical Laboratory in Washington, D.C., used a diamond anvil cell, a laboratory device in which two halves of a diamond are forced together to exert ultra-high pressures on any item between them. The scientists compressed samples of hydrogen at room temperature under forces up to 3.1 million times as high as the pressure of air at sea level. Because diamonds are transparent, the researchers were able to study how the light-absorption properties of the hydrogen changed as the pressure was increased. They used an analytical tool called a Raman spectroscope, which produces a wavy pattern on a chart, showing how light is absorbed and scattered by samples. As the investigators increased the pressure on the hydrogen, some peaks on the chart were typical of the known solid phases of hydrogen. Other peaks appeared to represent a phase that had never been seen.

Gregoryanz and his team concluded that the unusual peaks were generated by a novel phase of hydrogen—one composed of six-membered rings of hydrogen atoms arranged into honeycomb-like sheets that are mixed with unbound hydrogen atoms. The six-membered rings resembled the honeycomb arrangement of carbon atoms in graphene, a form of carbon with potential uses in electronics and advanced energy production. However, the new hydrogen phase did not possess the conducting properties of a metal. Nevertheless, Gregoryanz and his colleagues believed that purer versions of their hydrogen phase, prepared under even higher pressures, may be electrically conductive.

Plastic removes carbon dioxide. The development of a low-cost plastic material that captures large amounts of carbon dioxide (CO_2) from the open air was reported in November 2011 by researchers led by Nobel Prize-winning chemist George A. Olah. Rising amounts of CO_2 in the atmosphere, generated mainly by the burning of *fossil fuels* (coal, oil, natural gas), have been blamed for global warming because of the ability of this greenhouse gas to "trap" radiated heat near Earth's surface.

According to the scientists in Olah's group at the University of Southern California in Los Angeles, the new plastic material could lead to a simple and economical way to remove roughly half of *anthropogenic* (human-caused) CO_2 emissions in the open atmosphere. Previous materials that had been tested for open-air CO_2 removal had limitations. For example, some of these materials did not function properly if the air contained traces of humidity. Other materials had to be heated to temperatures in excess of 800 °C (1,472 °F) to restore their gas-absorbing ability after they were saturated with CO_2. Still other materials were made of rare, expensive compounds.

Olah and his colleagues investigated a common plastic called polyethyleneimine (PEI), a *polymer* (long chain of atoms) made of linked carbon and nitrogen atoms. PEI readily absorbs CO_2, which forms temporary chemical bonds with the nitrogen atoms in the polymer. However, these bonds form only at the polymer's surface.

To increase the polymer's surface area—and its absorbing ability—the researchers dissolved PEI in a solvent and poured it over fumed silica, a powdery, porous compound of silicon and oxygen that contains numerous microscopic holes. After they evaporated the solvent, the resulting PEI-coated fumed silica had a much greater surface area than PEI alone, vastly increasing its CO_2-absorbing ability. The scientists found that the PEI-coated fumed silica captured 19 percent more CO_2 from the air than aminosilica, a material that was the previous record-holder for CO_2 absorption.

The scientists were encouraged by tests showing that their system worked at high humidities and that restoring the system's gas-absorbing ability after saturation required heating to a modest 85 °C (185 °F). In addition, the material was made of inexpensive, commercially available ingredients. The scientists said that the PEI-coated fumed silica might be suitable for use in devices that sop up excess CO_2 in the atmosphere and so reduce the rate of global warming. The new material may also have applications in *scrubbing* (removing pollutants) from the air inside submarines and spacecraft and in purifying the air used to make advanced batteries.

Electric power and wastewater. A novel technology to generate electric power from wastewater could also reduce the energy costs of cleaning up wastewater from homes, farms, and food processors, according to a March 2012 report by scientists at Pennsylvania State University in University Park. The new system, described by environmental engineer Bruce Logan and colleagues, combines two renewable sources of electric energy (sources that cannot be used up) based on battery-like devices.

The researchers started with an experimental technology called microbial fuel cells (MFC). In this system, selected strains of bacteria in one compartment of a water-filled chamber consume biological matter in municipal wastewater and release *electrons* (negatively charged particles) and *hydrogen ions* (positively charged hydrogen atoms). The released electrons flow over an external circuit into an electrode called a cathode, located in an adjacent compartment, resulting in a small electric current. Meanwhile, the hydrogen ions move from the first to the second compartment though a plastic membrane. As the electrons emerge from the cathode, they complete the circuit.

To improve the electrical output of their MFC device, the researchers combined it with a technology called reverse electrodialysis (RED). In RED, solutions of seawater—containing salt (sodium chloride)—and freshwater are pumped into alternating chambers separated by membranes. Some of these membranes allow only positively charged sodium ions through; others allow only negatively charged chloride ions through. As this process continues, an electric current is generated.

The Penn State group's hybrid system, which they called a microbial reverse-electrodialysis cell (MRC), placed the RED assembly between the electrodes of the MFC device. Linking the two systems boosted the efficiency of the MFC device, especially when the scientists replaced sodium chloride in their RED assembly with a salt called ammonium bicarbonate. Logan estimated that the MRC process could generate three-quarters of the electric energy that is consumed by U.S. towns and cities to break down wastewater. Other possible uses for the system, Logan said, might be water sanitation in developing countries, where electric power plants are scarce. ■ Gordon Graff

FIRE RETARDANT GOES NANO

Cotton fabric coated with a new ultrathin flame retardant (A) reveals little damage (B) after being exposed to an open flame for 10 seconds, as shown in highly enlarged images made by an electron microscope. The fire retardant, reported in August 2011, was developed by materials scientists led by Jaime Grunlan of Texas A&M University in College Station. The coating, which is about 1/1,000 inch thick, consists of 20 alternating layers of the chemical compounds polysodium phosphate and polyallylamine. Images of coated cotton fibers made at an even higher magnitude (C) show the protective foam bubbles (D) that form from the retardant at high temperatures. Grunlan also reported that the coating is less *toxic* (poisonous) than other flame retardants.

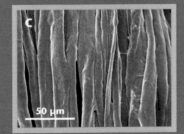
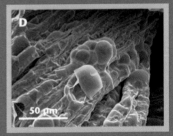

■ CLIMATE CHANGE

The United States National Climatic Data Center (NCDC) reported in early 2012 that 2011 was the 11th warmest year on record. Global surface temperatures were 0.51 Celsius degree (0.92 Fahrenheit degree) above average temperatures in the mid-1900's. It was the 35th consecutive year that global temperatures were above average, according to the NCDC. The warmest years on record were 2010 and 2005. All of the 10 warmest years recorded since 1880 have occurred since 1998.

Independent analysis by NASA's Goddard Institute for Space Studies (GISS) closely matched the NCDC findings. GISS concurred that temperatures in 2011 were 0.51°C (0.92°F) above average.

Nearly all climate scientists agree that the global warming trend is caused by a long-term increase in the atmospheric concentration of greenhouse gases. These gases trap additional heat in the atmosphere. Chief among these gases is carbon dioxide (CO_2). The atmospheric concentration of CO_2 is rising mainly because of such human activities as transportation and manufacturing.

The year 2011 was also remarkable for being warm despite a strong La Niña effect. La Niña is one phase of a cyclical variation in surface temperatures in the Pacific Ocean. Years when La Niña occurs are usually cooler than other years. Global temperatures in 2011 were indeed cooler than temperatures in 2010, a year of record warmth. However, temperatures in 2011 were the highest ever observed for a year with La Niña, according to the NCDC.

Heat absorption by oceans. Much of the variation in global temperatures from year to year depends upon the amount of heat absorbed by the oceans, researchers reported in September 2011 in the journal *Nature Climate Change*. The researchers, led by scientists with the U.S. National Center for Atmospheric Research (NCAR), analyzed temperature at various ocean depths and correlated the data with computer simulations of global climate.

They concluded that the oceans can mask global warming for up to a decade, by trap-

SEE ALSO THE SPECIAL REPORT MELTDOWN: CLIMATE CHANGE IN THE ARCTIC PAGE 42

ping heat in deep ocean currents 300 meters (1,000 feet) or more beneath the surface. However, this effect only delays warming of the surface, because the oceans eventually return heat to the atmosphere. The trapped heat helps to explain why mounting levels of CO_2 in the atmosphere do not produce record surface temperatures every year. In some years, the heat is stored deep in the oceans, and the surface is cooler; in other years, the oceans release heat, contributing to record temperatures.

The oceans have warmed significantly since the 1870's, scientists with the Scripps Institution of Oceanography at the University of California in San Diego reported. Their study was published in April 2012 in the journal *Nature Climate Science*. The researchers analyzed measurements of ocean temperatures collected by the H.M.S. *Challenger* between 1872 and 1876. The *Challenger* expedition, which was funded by the British Parliament, tracked more than 109,000 kilometers (68,000 miles) of oceans worldwide, collecting a wide variety of data about the oceans and sea life.

The Scripps scientists compared the *Challenger* data with modern data collected by a global array of robotic sensors called Argo. They confirmed that the surfaces of the oceans have warmed by 0.59 degree Celsius (1.1 degrees Fahrenheit) since the 1870's. The researchers noted that their project marks the first time scientists have correlated and compared *Challenger* data—the earliest significant oceanographic record in existence—with data obtained by Argo, which was deployed in 2000.

On thin ice. The Arctic Ocean sea ice shrank to the second-smallest area ever recorded by September 2011, just missing the record low set in 2007, according to scientists at the National Snow and Ice Data Center (NSIDC) in Colorado. However, scientists with the University of Bremen in

Germany reported that the 2011 minimum surpassed the 2007 record. Scientists with the NSIDC attributed the discrepancy to the different methods used by the U.S. and German scientists to analyze radar data from climate satellites.

The Arctic sea ice attained its maximum winter extent in March 2012, according to the NSIDC. It was the ninth-smallest maximum ever recorded. However, the sea ice did cover a larger area than any winter maximum since 2008. NSIDC scientists noted, however, that much of the new sea ice is thin and fragile. Older ice, on the other hand, is thicker and less vulnerable to melting. In 1979, ice older than four years made up about 25 percent of the winter sea ice cover. Now, it makes up only about 2 percent of the ice cover, according to NSIDC.

In a study published in the *Journal of Climate* in February 2012, NASA scientists confirmed that the oldest, thickest Arctic sea ice is quickly disappearing. Scientists use the term *multi-year ice* to identify older sea ice— specifically, ice that has survived at least two summer melt seasons.

The researchers studied 32 years of microwave data from NASA satellites. The satellites emit microwaves that echo back from the Arctic ice pack. Satellite instruments analyze the signature of the returning microwaves to determine ice thickness. The scientists found that the area covered by multi-year sea ice has shrunk by about 17 percent per decade over the last 30 years. They also determined that the loss of multi-year ice has accelerated since 2000. The scientists noted that the record melt of Arctic sea ice in 2007 was especially damaging to multi-year ice.

Global emissions of CO_2 in 2010 grew by 5.9 percent over CO_2 output in 2009, according to a report by the Global Carbon Project (GCP), an international collaboration of climate scientists. The report appeared in the Dec. 4, 2011, online issue of *Nature Climate Change*. As in previous years, the largest contributor to carbon emissions was the burning of coal. China and the United States retained their rankings as the biggest and the second-biggest producer of atmospheric carbon, respectively.

GLOBAL LOSS OF ICE

Glaciers in places other than Greenland and Antarctica— the sites of the world's major icecaps—experienced significant ice loss from melting from 2003 to 2010, as this map shows. This finding was reported by an international team of scientists in the Feb. 9, 2012, issue of *Nature*. An equivalent volume of melted water would cover the entire United States up to a depth of 18 inches (46 centimeters). Scientists had possessed fairly accurate data about ice loss from the great icecaps for some time but lacked good data about ice masses in other locations. A satellite system called GRACE (Gravity Recovery and Climate Experiment), which maps tiny variations in the gravity—and, therefore, the surface—over time enabled the scientists to make their calculations.

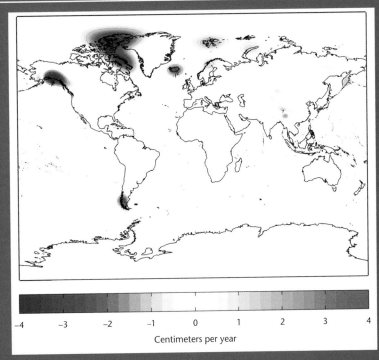

Centimeters per year

SOURCE: NASA/JPL-Caltech/University of Colorado.

CLIMATE CHANGE continued

The statistic for 2010, on the heels of a 1.4-percent drop in carbon output during recession-ridden 2009, represented the largest percentage of increase since 2003, according to the GCP. In absolute terms, the 2010 increase was the largest year-on-year surge in CO_2 emissions ever recorded. For the first time, total global emissions reached 10 billion metric tons of carbon.

Scientists estimate that about half of the CO_2 contributed by human activity remains in the atmosphere; most of the rest is absorbed by the oceans. In 2010, CO_2 concentration in the atmosphere reached 389.6 parts per million (ppm), according to GCP. Scientists estimate that CO_2 concentration 250 years ago was about 280 ppm.

Extreme weather. The year 2011 was the second wettest on record, according to the NCDC. Only 2010 had more precipitation. Climate scientists warn that global warming will change patterns of precipitation and increase overall precipitation. This is because heat promotes evaporation and warmer air holds more moisture than cooler air, the scientists explain.

Australian scientists reporting in the April 27, 2012, issue of the journal *Science* found that such changes in precipitation may be more extreme than scientists had anticipated. To analyze changes in the water cycle—the cycle that involves the transfer of water from the oceans to land and back again—the researchers used measurements of ocean *salinity* (salt content). Salinity increases as water evaporates and decreases as rain falls.

The scientists found that rising surface temperatures have accelerated the global cycle of evaporation and rainfall by about 4 percent since 1950. That rate is twice the rate predicted by climate models. As Earth's surface continues to warm, the global water cycle will intensify further, the scientists projected. Areas that already receive large amounts of precipitation will become even wetter, while some dry areas will become drier, they predicted.

A special report from the United Nations Intergovernmental Panel on Climate Change (IPCC) also found that global warming is contributing to extreme weather events. The report, issued in November 2011, stated that global warming has likely already led to more numerous heat waves and droughts as well as more frequent coastal flooding and heavier precipitation. The authors of the report predicted that extreme weather will become even more common as the world continues to warm. ■ Brian Johnson

GLOBAL WARMING LINKED TO VOLCANOES AND EARTHQUAKES

Scientists from the University of Iceland and the California Institute of Technology in 2012 described correlations between seasonal changes intensified by global warming, on the one hand, and the frequency of volcanoes and earthquakes, on the other. The Icelandic scientists noted that accelerated summer melting in Iceland's glaciers—such as in the meltwater pond shown at right—influences the timing of volcanic eruptions. As glaciers melt in summer and most of the water drains away, the weight exerted on volcanoes under the glaciers shifts. This change can trigger volcanic eruptions. The scientists noted that recent eruptions of the volcano Katla have all occurred between the months of May and November. The Caltech scientists noted a similar effect in the Himalaya region of India. There, summer monsoonal rains send torrents down the mountains into India's northern plains, where the added weight can trigger earthquakes. Climate scientists predict that monsoons will intensify as the Earth warms.

COMPUTERS AND ELECTRONICS

In 2012, a consumer could buy a mobile phone with about the same computing power as a large desktop computer from 2002. The 2012 phone contained more computing power than NASA had at its disposal during the 1969 moon landing mission, according to NASA sources. As electronic devices continued to shrink at an exponential rate in the second decade of the 2000's, researchers explored the possibilities—and limits—of computing at the smallest physical scales.

Perhaps no other modern industry has undergone such rapid development as the computer and electronics industry. In a trend known as Moore's Law, manufacturers have managed to double the number of components on a computer chip about every 18 months—by continually shrinking the components. The "law" is named after Gordon Moore, an American researcher who first observed the trend in 1965.

Moore's Law underpins the incredible transformation of computers from cavern-sized machines into television-sized desktops, notebook-sized laptops, and pocket-sized smartphones. It also underpins the revolution in electronics screen quality and thinness—as many of those same shrinking components are used in liquid crystal displays (LCD's) and other screen technologies.

However, manufacturers can only shrink computer components so far. The smallest such components widely used today—electronic switches called transistors—consist of as few as 100 atoms. If Moore's Law holds, those components would need to shrink to the size of a single atom.

To attain such tiny components, researchers have turned to nanotechnology, the scientific study of objects at an extremely small scale. Using nanotechnology, physicists in 2011 and 2012 successfully developed two important atom-scale computing components, though neither is yet practical for general use. Researchers also made advances in quantum computing, a

SEE ALSO CONSUMER SCIENCE **HEADS IN THE CLOUD** PAGE 97

still-experimental branch of computer science that could upend the size limits imposed on Moore's Law.

Twelve-atom memory storage. In January 2012, researchers from IBM revealed an experimental method of storing a single bit of data using just 12 iron atoms. The term *bit* is short for binary digit—that is, a 1 or a 0. Bits, strung together, form codes for larger pieces of information—such as words, pictures, sounds, videos, and computer programs. Hard drives in modern computers typically require a million atoms to store just a single bit of data.

To store data, a device must be able to maintain, and switch between, two physically ordered states. One ordered state stands for "1"; the alternate state stands for "0." In addition, the two states must be able to hold their order over a long period of time—otherwise, the data they represent will be lost. IBM's 12-iron-atom storage device, like many modern computer hard drives, uses magnetic properties to store data. Magnetic materials—like iron—readily form regions of stable, long-lasting magnetic alignment. Also, each region can rapidly shift its magnetic alignment between two orientations, representing 1 or 0.

The IBM researchers succeeded in shrinking the size of a magnetically ordered region to just 12 atoms, arranged in two 6-atom rows. The bit value—either '1' or '0'—is expressed by a particular configuration formed by the magnetic orientation pattern of all 12 atoms. One unique configuration represents bit 1; the opposite configuration represents bit 0.

Researchers used a device called a scanning tunneling microscope (STM) to detect the atoms' magnetic alignment or to manipulate the alignment. An STM's tip exerts an electric force so precise that it can "poke" individual atoms. Poking the atoms with a

COMPUTERS AND ELECTRONICS continued

small force enables the STM to read the magnetic configuration and, thus, the bit value. Poking with a larger force causes the whole group of atoms to flip their magnetic alignment—thus changing from a composite value representing "1" to the reverse value representing "0"—or vice versa.

LIVING CELLS AND ELECTRONICS COMPONENTS MEET

Bright red *tendrils* (stringlike extensions) of mouse nerve cells thread their way into extremely tiny semiconductor tubes in an experiment conducted by researchers at the University of Wisconsin, Madison, and publicized in 2011. The researchers noted that the nerve cell tendrils seemed to seek out the tubes and readily followed their contours. The scientists speculated that such cellular behavior could be harnessed to create interfaces between electronic elements and living nerve tissue. Such interfaces might someday support seamless linkages between prosthetic devices and the nervous systems of users of such devices, for example.

IBM's researchers also found that shrinking a magnetic storage region any smaller than 12 atoms would very likely be physically impossible, because such a device would be rendered unstable by quantum mechanical effects. According to the laws of quantum mechanics, the tiniest objects—such as individual atoms and subatomic particles—have the properties of waves. Because of this characteristic, the particles are difficult or impossible to pin down and control at any given instant. A magnetic bit of less than 12 atoms could not occupy a stable state long enough to practically store data, the researchers theorized.

The IBM scientists noted that their experimental 12-atom bit was not practical for mass-market applications, because the storage medium had to be kept at a temperature a few degrees above absolute zero (–273.15 °C [–459.67 °F]) to maintain stability. However, they speculated that, with further research, a storage bit fashioned from a small number of atoms could be stabilized at higher temperatures.

Single-atom transistor. In February,

a team of Australian and American physicists created the world's smallest working transistor from a single atom of phosphorus. A transistor does not store a bit of information, as does a magnetic region of a hard drive. Instead, a transistor's job is to help process digital information. Thus, it is not important for a transistor to be able to maintain a bit state for more than a moment. For this reason, it is practical to design a transistor that is smaller than a usable storage bit.

Transistors are used in virtually every kind of electronic equipment. In computers, a transistor is essentially a switch: It turns a flow of electric current on or off. A transistor's "on" and "off" states simulate the 1's and 0's that represent digital information.

A modern computer chip the size of a fingernail may contain billions of transistors. In market-available products, the very smallest transistors are at least 100 atoms large.

The researchers created the single-atom transistor by etching it into a crystal of silicon—a process similar to that used in manufacturing today's commercially available transistors. Virtually all electronic devices use a silicon crystal base because of silicon's properties as a semiconductor. (A semiconductor conducts electric current better than an insulator, such as wood, but not as well as a conductor, such as copper.)

However, etching a single-atom transistor involved challenges unique to the atomic scale. Researchers had to precisely place the single phosphorus atom using an STM.

The researchers also had to contend with the outsize effect of heat on atom-sized components. Room-temperature air, which barely affects larger devices, contains enough energy to easily jiggle an individual atom out of its place. Thus, the researchers had to keep the single-atom transistor at temperatures at least as cold as −200 °C (−328 °F). Given these limitations, the one-atom transistor is likely to be applicable mainly to specialized computers in research facilities, experts said.

Into the quantum realm. In February, researchers at IBM revealed important technical advances in quantum computing that could bring this highly theoretical field closer to practical application. A quantum computer would not merely involve fabricating ever tinier devices. Quantum computing could change the equation behind Moore's Law and lead to vastly more powerful computing than is possible with classical (traditional) computers.

In a classical computer, a transistor either conducts electric current or does not. A magnetic memory storage bit either flips one way or the alternate way. Other components of classical computers behave in the same way. Modern computing is largely based on such "either/or" states. According to Moore's Law, the ability to expand computing power depends on shrinking these components more and more.

With quantum mechanical phenomena, reality works differently. A quantum computer uses such fundamental particles as electrons as its components. An electron, like certain other fundamental particles, possesses a quality called spin, which can take on an "up" state or a "down" state.

These two states might be expected to function as bits—1's and 0's—just as in a classical computer. But as inhabitants of the quantum scale, electrons have wavelike properties that confound an "either/or" distinction between two states. At any given moment, one of these fundamental particles can exist in a *superposition* of its two spin states—that is, in both states at once.

The nature of superposition is central to quantum computers. The quantum-scale building blocks of such a computer are designated *qubits*. Under certain conditions, a qubit exhibits superposition instead of a classical transistor's either/or (that is, 1/0) states. In other words, in a qubit, the states exist simultaneously.

Superposition in a quantum computer radically expands computing power. Consider a 20-bit classical computer. According to the rules of the binary arithmetic used in digital computers, this 20-bit device is capable of encoding 2^{20} (2 multiplied by itself and its products 20 times) states—that is, about 1 million distinct states. Changing from any one of these 1 million states to another requires the computer circuitry to flip some or all of 20 switches from "on" to "off," or vice versa. But a 20-qubit quantum

COMPUTERS AND ELECTRONICS continued

computer could encode the 1 million distinct states simultaneously, without any physical intervention. (Computer scientists note that a quantum computer of this size is, at present, entirely theoretical. However, the principle holds true at any size.)

One can imagine these 1 million possible states (derived from 20 bits or qubits) as a huge room with 1 million doors. The classical computer has to open each door one by one, which takes a great deal of time. The quantum computer, thanks to superposition, can open all the doors at once.

Suppose that one of these 1 million doors holds "treasure"—such as the solution to a complex mathematical problem. Because of superposition, the quantum computer can open all the doors to find the treasure in a fraction of the time it would take the classical computer. Computer scientists believe that quantum computers could quickly perform certain tasks that would take even the most powerful classical computer billions of years to process.

The challenges of building even a single qubit, however, are enormous. No one has ever built a truly practical quantum computer. Beyond the precision required to manipulate such tiny objects, engineers also confront an inherent problem in the way fundamental particles behave. The mere act of sampling or measuring such a particle causes it to reverse its spin. Quantum engineers say that a qubit's superposition "collapses" into one spin state or the other in response to interference. When this happens, the particle ceases functioning as a qubit.

Extracting useful information from quantum computations has thus proven extremely difficult. Even if a quantum computer quickly finds which door out of a million holds treasure, engineers have not perfected a way of moving that information out of the qubits.

A chief goal of quantum computing research is to find ways to manipulate qubits and yet have them remain in superposition long enough to perform meaningful calculations. On February 28, IBM announced that a team of company scientists was able to build a functional, 2-qubit quantum computer that maintained superposition for about 10 microseconds (millionths of a second). That brief period was nevertheless thousands of times longer than previous experimental quantum computers have been able to achieve. The researchers thought it might be just long enough for the quantum computer to practically process data.

Voice recognition comes of age. In October 2011, Apple Inc. released the iPhone 4S—the first device of its kind to feature a built-in "personal assistant" computer program. Named Siri, the assistant program could—with some exceptions—understand human speech, answer simple questions, and perform such commands as scheduling an event on a calendar or calling a friend.

Siri heralded remarkable advances in computer-human interaction and artificial intelligence, although it was not the first such program. Nuance Communication—which developed the voice recognition software that helps power Siri—previously marketed a popular line of speech recognition software called Dragon. Google Inc. offers voice recognition alongside its widely used search engine and other services. Microsoft's Kinect videogame device enables people to control games, browse menus, and select online media with spoken commands. Electronics companies are also working to develop televisions with voice-operated commands that could eventually render TV remotes obsolete.

Many aspects of modern voice recognition software rely on Internet connectivity. The "brains" of Siri, for example, are mostly stored on Apple's server computers, far from a consumer's iPhone. In order to function effectively, the phone's Siri program must have an active Internet connection to Apple's servers. Those servers—not the phone's own processor—parse the phone-user's voice, search websites for answers to questions, and translate voice commands into actions. The servers then send results back to the phone, which

SCAN ME!

With her smartphone, a shopper scans a Quick Response (QR) code on a handbag she is considering purchasing in a shop. The QR code, an expanded type of bar code that looks like geometric squiggles in a square, guides the user to a website with information about the product. In 2011 and 2012, QR codes were finding their way into many areas of commerce and communications. Movie posters, ads for television shows, and a wide array of retail products have begun to carry QR codes. One popular application was the Skanz bracelet, which holds a QR code that accesses web-based information about the wearer. Other people can wave a cell phone over the bracelet's QR code and access the relevant data on a website. Industry analysts say that the distinctive graphics are likely to become commonplace.

reads them in a computerized voice or displays them.

High-resolution displays gained further prominence in 2012 with the release of Apple's third-generation iPad. The tablet computer featured a "retina" display—a very-high-resolution screen tightly packed with more than twice as many pixels per square unit as most other commercially available display screens. (A pixel is a tiny light-producing dot.)

The new iPad's 24.6-centimeter (9.7-inch) screen formed a retina display from a grid of 2,048 by 1,536 pixels. Apple's iPhone 4, released in June 2010, also featured a retina display, with an 8.9-centimeter (3.5-inch) screen made of 960 by 640 pixels. By contrast, a high-definition television (HDTV) typically has 1,920 by 1,080 pixels set in a much larger screen. Thus, the new iPad, with a to-

tal display capacity of 3,145,728 pixels, outstrips a (larger) high-definition TV screen, with its display capacity of 2,073,600 pixels.

Apple's screens use LCD technology. Liquid crystals are molecules that respond to electrical signals by either blocking or not blocking a beam of light. The light comes from a thin light-emitting diode (LED) behind the liquid crystals. Light passes through the crystals and then travels through filters that produce the colors. Apple's new iPad, like the iPhone 4, simply doubled the number of liquid crystals from previous versions of the device. However, the new iPad's extra LCD pixels require more electrical signals—and thus more battery power—to work. To compensate, Apple engineers designed the new iPad with a larger battery and a slightly heavier weight than the 2010 iPad.

■ Daniel Kenis

Escape from the Digital Dark Ages

Digital data are the dominant forms of information in our 21st century. Such data—electronic representations encoded on various electronic or magnetic devices—serve purposes ranging from entertainment to scientific research. But the ease and accessibility of the digital era masks a startling vulnerability. Many technology specialists fear that rapid digitization will plunge humanity into a "Digital Dark Age" as the ever-changing formats used to create, store, and retrieve digital data fade from use and digital files become unreadable. To solve this problem, scientists and archivists seek to understand the nature of digital data and develop ways to keep it alive for future generations.

Throughout history, each new form of *media* (the means of information storage and communication) tends to be less enduring than the ones that came before. Some of the oldest existing writing etched on stone and clay has survived thousands of years. Less permanent but more practical media such as *papyrus* (scrolls made from fibers of the papyrus plant) and *parchment* (sheets made from animal skins) are still around hundreds or thousands of years later.

Paper became the world's dominant medium after the invention of mass printing methods, first by the Chinese and later, by Europeans. Even today, books printed on acid-free paper and stored in an air-conditioned library can last 500 years. During the 1800's and 1900's, important new media appeared—photographs and motion pictures on film.

With the widespread use of computers in the last quarter of the 20th century, earlier forms of media rapidly became eclipsed by digital technology. For example, word-processed documents displaced typewriter-written copy; e-mail messages displaced handwritten letters; and digital photography displaced film.

Digital data have obvious advantages over earlier forms of media. Information can be easily created and shared. Digital storage devices, such as hard drives, are increasingly smaller, faster, and more efficient. Also, digital information is extremely easy to copy, and copies are generally error-free. Increasingly, data are being created in digital-only formats. For example, the avalanche of information on the World Wide Web (the Internet) is digital. Most photographs and video are now captured and stored digitally.

However, digital data are more transient than most people realize. Digital formats become obsolete at a rapid pace as they are replaced by newer formats that work better. A *digital format* encompasses useful digital information—such as a song or a document—plus embedded digital coding that instructs electronics hardware how to access and use it.

The *software* (computer programs) and *hardware* (computers and other electronic devices) used to create, store, and access digital data evolve so rapidly that they become obsolete in a few years. Most software and hardware are designed to operate only until the next inevitable upgrade appears. Given this relentless pace of change, digital information tends not to stay readable for very long.

Not many people worry about how long their digital data—fast, cheap, and easy to change—will last. Such a casual attitude suits most people's needs, but it could have drastic implications for posterity. For example, many photographs taken on film by past generations have long survived. But will today's digital

Punch Cards

Punch cards served as the chief means for inputting programs and data into computers in the early days of computing. The medium consisted of a stiff paper card punched with small rectangular holes whose patterns represented data. Technicians called keypunchers prepared the punch cards on a typewriterlike machine called a keypunch, according to instructions submitted by programmers. The cards were then fed into a mainframe computer through a device called a card reader.

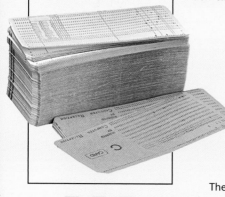

photographs be accessible to future generations, or will they disappear when the programs used to create or display them have become obsolete?

On a larger scale, how will we retain data critical to scientific advances if the documentation that describes them is destined soon to become indecipherable? Inevitably, such advances build upon previous scientific knowledge. Will humanity be able to overcome such long-term problems as disease, pollution, or climate change if scientific research is trapped in unreadable formats?

For those concerned with the preservation of digital data, there are two main issues: storage and readability. Digital data must be recorded onto a physical medium, such as a CD or a DVD. These media are typically not reliable enough to preserve data indefinitely. Experts note, for example, that fragile CD's and DVD's are subject to warping or scratching that can render them unreadable.

Even if the physical medium remains viable, the data are useless without the software to read them and the hardware to display them. More mature computer users recall the 5¼-inch floppy discs of the 1970's and 1980's. These storage media are now indecipherable, because the drives to read them are long obsolete.

One method used by librarians and archivists to keep digital information accessible is *migration,* the movement of data to new formats. Because digital formats age rapidly, migration is a constant process. According to Peter Layman, former librarian at the University of California, Berkeley, upgrades to digital formats are necessary about every 18 months. Keeping up with such rapid change can become expensive and time-consuming.

Data that have become outmoded can sometimes be resurrected through an *emulator*—software or hardware that mimics an old format. One example of emulation is the rescue of the British Broadcasting Corporation's Domesday project, a 1986 computer-based video survey of everyday life. The Domesday project was recorded on LaserDiscs that became unreadable within 15 years when the technology became obsolete. In 2003, the University of Leeds (United Kingdom) and the University of Michigan (Ann Arbor, Michigan) completed a three-year joint project that recovered the Domesday data by using an emulator of the hardware that originally read the material.

Emulation is now a common method for reviving old software. However, emulators themselves must eventually be emulated in order to stay compatible with constantly changing hardware.

Efforts to preserve and resurrect digital data often confront another challenge: encryption. Encryption is a digital process that transforms data into an unreadable form to protect it from unwarranted use. A special digital key—that is, a specific string of computer code—is required to decrypt the data. Unlocking encrypted data is typically dependent on having access to the key and specific software.

A further complication is that some data connect to other types of data. For example, a website may connect to picture files. For this reason, many digital archivists advocate for "metadata," that is, a tag or layer of digital information that tells about the digital artifact and how it functions.

Many data conservationists endorse open source formatting. Open source describes the practice of publicizing computer code in the form of a widely used programming language. Computer code in this form is not dependent on

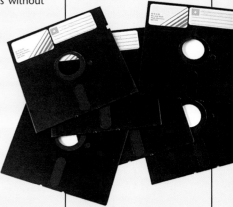

Floppy Discs

Floppy discs became the storage medium of choice with the advent of the personal computer in the late 1970's. The medium consisted of a thin disc of magnetized plastic inside a paper or plastic sleeve. Users inserted the floppy disc into a disc drive. The drive "read" the magnetic code through a slot in the sleeve as the disc spun around. The earliest commercial floppy discs contained one-tenth of a megabyte or less of data. A contemporary DVD can hold about 200,000 times as much data.

CONTINUED

any particular software or hardware for decipherability. Therefore, it is widely accessible.

However, digital data are often subject to proprietary encoding, a restrictive formatting scheme used by commercial copyright holders to protect licensed software from piracy. Because this restrictive coding cannot be deciphered by "outsiders," it poses risks for the long-term durability of digital information.

For example, many commercial DVD's use a protection scheme known as digital rights management (DRM). DRM discourages the piracy of movies and other intellectual property—but it also prevents libraries from migrating the content to a new media format. If the company that uses the proprietary encoding goes out of business, the data may be lost.

Companies in the digital market are starting to recognize open source formatting as a safe alternative to being locked into a specific platform. For example, in April 2012 the United States software giant Microsoft announced that it was creating a division solely devoted to

Avoiding Digital

A stainless steel and glass ball holding a disk called the Rosetta Disk may provide a way to preserve information for perhaps thousands of years without the use of digital technology. The disk is being developed by the Long Now Foundation, an organization that focuses on projects for the very long-term. The disk holds 13,000 pages microetched with information on more than 1,500 languages. Each page is only 0.5 millimeter (0.019 inch) across, about the width of five human hairs. Individual pages are visible when magnified 100 times.

making source code available for its new products.

Open source formatting is a step in the right direction, experts note, but it does nothing for the huge backlog of data waiting to be migrated. There is little financial incentive to preserve digital data, so the task is often left to libraries, universities, or government agencies. Some governments have attempted to address the problem. With a $100-million grant from the U.S. Congress, the Library of Congress in 2010 launched the National Digital Stewardship Alliance to conserve the nation's digital resources. Other nations are taking similar steps.

In the end, there may be no digital substitute for physical methods of data preservation. For example, the Long Now Foundation, an organization devoted to long-term cultural growth, took special pains to preserve documentation for its Rosetta Project. This project is an ongoing, multiformat archive of documentation for more than 1,500 human languages, some of which are extinct or nearly so. Archivists with the program designed a 7.62-centimeter (3-inch) nickel-alloy disk that has been microetched with more than 13,000 pages of language translations viewable through a microscope. The first version of the disk, which the foundation says could last for 2,000 years, was issued in 2008.

The viability of various techniques of digital preservation will be tested by time. Whether or not the Digital Dark Age descends will ultimately depend on public awareness of the problem and support from governments, universities, and other institutions to preserve our digital heritage. Unless we continue to develop strategies to keep digital data alive, our cultural memory may disappear with it.

■ Scott Witmer

CONSERVATION

Life in the world's oceans is nearing a condition similar to a mass extinction, according to a June 2011 report by the International Programme on the State of the Ocean (IPSO), an international team of marine scientists. A mass extinction is an event during which a large number of species die out in a relatively short time. Only five mass extinction events are known to have occurred in Earth's history, the most recent being 65 million years ago when the dinosaurs died out.

The scientists highlighted a number of critical dangers to the health of today's oceans. Overfishing has led to the collapse of populations of a number of fish species. The loss of almost all members of a species can cause rippling effects throughout an ecosystem. (An ecosystem includes all the living and nonliving things in an area and the relationships among them.)

The scientists cited increasing concentrations of carbon dioxide in the atmosphere, caused by emissions from the burning of fossil fuels and other human activities, as a serious threat to ocean health. Atmospheric carbon dioxide reacts with ocean surfaces and causes ocean water to become more acidic. Ocean acidification interferes with shell- and bone-building processes in many sea animals.

The scientists cited global warming, also related to carbon build-up in the atmosphere, as another threat. Global warming raises sea temperatures, encouraging the growth of algae and bacteria that feed on dead algae. Nitrogen-rich runoff from agricultural pollution further favors such organisms, resulting in the rapid growth of their populations. Such teeming populations use up the oxygen dissolved in the water, creating a condition called hypoxia. In hypoxic waters, many sea animals die off.

All five known mass extinctions in Earth's history were characterized by acidic, oxygen-starved oceans. The scientists contributing to the IPSO report warned that entire ocean ecosystems, including whole coral reefs, could die off within a generation.

Deep-sea fisheries unsustainable. In September 2011, an international team of marine scientists recommended an end to commercial deep-sea fishing. Their report, entitled "Sustainability of Deep-Sea Fisheries," was funded by the Lenfest Ocean Program, a Washington, D.C.-based foundation that supports scientific ocean research.

According to the analysis, the deep ocean is "the world's worst place to catch fish." Food experts estimate that less than 1 percent of the world's seafood comes from deep-sea fishing. But the practice causes serious, long-term harm to fish species and their ecosystems, the scientists asserted.

Deep-sea fish grow more slowly than fish that live near the surface. Their cold, dark environment harbors less food than warmer, lighter regions of the oceans. The long life-

RHINO TRANSPORTATION

A black rhinoceros is carefully airlifted by helicopter in the first leg of a journey from its home in South Africa's KwaZulu-Natal Province to a new home in that nation's Limpopo Province. The operation was part of the Black Rhino Range Expansion Project, a multiyear effort by the WWF (World Wildlife Fund) and Ezemvelo KZN Wildlife, a South African organization, to extend the habitat of the black rhino. Before being airlifted, the animal was injected with a tranquilizer and blindfolded. Experts say the operation does not harm the animal. Although the black rhino remains threatened, its numbers have grown over the past two decades to an estimated 4,000 animals.

CONSERVATION continued

spans of deep-sea fish make them especially vulnerable to overfishing, because replacing depleted stocks may require decades.

The scientists cited the collapse of orange roughy populations as a cautionary tale. Orange roughy require 30 years to reach adulthood and can live more than 100 years. The fish were rarely eaten before the 1980's, when orange roughy fisheries began expanding. Harvesting of the fish spiked during the 1980's and 1990's. By the early 2000's, the species had become scarce, and many orange roughy fisheries had collapsed.

FORESTS FACE DOUBLE THREAT

A wooded mountainside in Montana displays the damage caused by two threats to forests in western North America: infestation by tree-killing mountain pine beetles (lower left); and forest fires (upper right). Both phenomena are being fueled by climate change, as summers in the region become hotter and drier and winters grow warmer. In 2012, researchers with the University of Colorado at Boulder reported that mountain pine beetles are now producing two generations of young per year—as opposed to the once-annual reproduction cycle observed previously. Dry summers are also weakening the trees' resistance to beetle attacks. Unusually warm winters have enabled more beetles to survive from year to year.

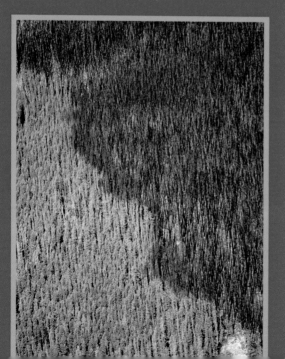

Deep sea fisheries that harvest grenadiers and blue ling face similar risks of collapse, according to the report authors.

Overfishing hotspots. In February 2012, researchers from the University of British Columbia released a conservation risk index that ranked seacoast areas by the level of threat from overfishing. Topping the list were coastal areas along northeastern Canada, western Mexico, Peru, New Zealand, southern and southeastern Africa, and Antarctica.

Researchers devised the index using such criteria as a region's economic growth and fishery stock populations. They recommended that governments and international agencies use the index to prioritize their marine conservation efforts and resources.

New park. In April, the government of the state of Western Australia announced plans to create Camden Sound Marine Park, a 7,000-square-kilometer (2,700-square-mile) marine (seacoast) park in the state's remote north. New zoning laws to protect land and waters in the park area would go into effect in mid-2012, officials said.

The new park's focus is conservation along the region's Kimberley Coast. A remote and highly productive marine environment, the Kimberley Coast is the most important calving area for humpback whales in the Southern Hemisphere. The coastal region, rich in areas of sea grass, coral reefs, tidal flats, and mangrove forests, serves as a habitat for many animal species, including dolphins, crocodiles, and dugongs.

The park's design includes several distinct zones. A "special purpose" zone was set aside to protect the estimated 22,000 humpback whales that live in the area during calving season. A "wilderness fishing" zone was designated to accommodate recreational fishers—with the caveat that they must release or eat their catch before leaving the zone. In addition, two "sanctuary" zones were to be created around the Champagny Islands and Montgomery Reef.

According to the conservation plan, 23 percent of the park is to be closed to all commercial fishing, and 48 percent, to commercial trawl fishing. In this method of fishing, a boat drags a weighted, funnel-shaped net along the ocean bottom. The practice damages the sea floor and often pulls in undersized or protected fish.

Satellite-guided conservation. In November 2011, German and British researchers published a study on endangered reptiles and amphibians on the Comoros, an *archipelago* (island chain) in the western Indian Ocean. The researchers analyzed satellite imagery to determine how much natural rain forest remained on the islands. They discovered that only about 9 percent of the island area is covered by such forests. The research team also conducted traditional field studies to assess which species were best able to adapt to such new environments as farms and plantations. These analyses enabled scientists to identify species most threatened by the loss of rain forest habitat.

Shark sanctuaries. In June 2011, the government of Honduras outlawed shark fishing in its waters. Those waters cover 240,000 square kilometers (93,000 square miles) along the country's Pacific and Caribbean coasts. In July, the government of the Bahamas enacted a similar ban, putting 630,000 square kilometers (243,000 square miles) off limits to shark fishers.

Sharks are vulnerable to fishing because their fins fetch a high price at market. In many countries, shark fin soup is considered a delicacy. Fishing crews sometimes simply cut off a shark's fin and dump the shark back into the ocean.

Sharks are long-lived fish, with some species requiring decades to reach maturity. Thus, shark populations require much time to recover from overfishing. Up to one-third of the world's sharks and shark relatives are threatened, according to the International Union for the Conservation of Nature, a Switzerland-based international nonprofit environmental group.

Tracking conservation successes. In August 2011, researchers at the National University of Singapore (NUS) released a report detailing conservation success stories. The report divided conservation efforts into three types: microscale, mesoscale, and macroscale. Microscale efforts involve the protection of specific species or habitats through such means as establishing protected areas or banning hunting. The report not-

RARE, COLORFUL TOAD

A Borneo rainbow toad *(Ansonia Latidisca)* makes its first public appearance in nearly 90 years, in a photo taken by members of a scientific expedition to the mountainous rain forest of Borneo in June 2011. European explorers had discovered the reclusive amphibian and produced black-and-white illustrations of it in 1924. The 2011 expedition, led by Indraneil Das of Sarawak Malaysia University in Malaysia's Sarawak state, was part of the "Global Search for Lost Amphibians," an international conservation program sponsored by the Washington, D.C.-based environmental group, Conservation International. *A. latidisca* is documented as endangered on the "Red List," a global inventory of species under threat published by the International Union for Conservation of Nature.

ed that such efforts had achieved some successes. For example, Brazil's expansion of protected areas in the Amazon rain forest helped contribute to a 37-percent decline in deforestation between 2002 and 2009.

Mesoscale conservation involves larger-scale efforts that cross national boundaries in a certain geographical region. For example, contiguous national parks in several countries of sub-Saharan Africa have helped protect the population of mountain gorillas. The parks are parts of the Democratic Republic of Congo, Uganda, and Rwanda. In this region, the population of mountain gorillas has nearly doubled in the past 30 years.

Macroscale conservation involves global systems of trade and regulation. As an example of macroscale conservation, the researchers cited pressure that such

CONSERVATION continued

multinational corporations as Nike and Wal-mart brought to bear on Amazon-region beef producers. The companies demanded that the Amazon producers submit proof that their beef is not raised at the expense of forest land. In response, Brazil established regulations to track cattle with genetic testing and ear tags. Conservationists estimate that Brazil has lost one-fifth of its forest—mostly in the Amazon region—since 1980. Conservationists blame most of the loss on the expansion of cattle ranching.

The NUS authors stressed the need to track conservation projects over the long term to better assess their effectiveness. They also urged conservation researchers to publish and report their data and results, so that other scientists can learn from the successes and failures.

Grimmer assessment. Scientists around the world remain grim about prospects of species loss. Such was the finding of a survey published in November 2011 in the journal *Conservation Biology*. The survey of 583 international scientists, conducted by environmental scientist Murray Rudd of the United Kingdom's University of York, revealed that a large majority of scientists agree that

serious loss of biodiversity is occurring on the planet. Most of the survey respondents identified tropical coral communities as the ecosystems most imminently threatened.

The survey sought to identify not only conservation challenges but also values and priorities that the scientists could embrace to solve conservation problems with necessarily limited resources. For example, the survey asked scientists whether conservationists should use conservation triage.

This controversial practice is inspired by medical triage, in which medical professionals responding to people injured in a disaster focus their efforts on seriously injured individuals thought to have a good chance at survival. People likely to die are simply made comfortable. Similarly, conservation triage means allowing certain endangered species to die off without any intervention if the species' chances for survival seem slim. Making this difficult choice allows scientists to focus their efforts on helping species that appear to have a good chance of coming back from the brink. More than half of the scientists in the survey agreed that conservationists should have conservation triage in their toolkit.   ■ Daniel Kenis

WATER—A PRECIOUS RESOURCE

Earth's water supply is represented by three bubbles on North America, in a diagram created by a team led by Howard Perlman of the United States Geological Service. The largest sphere represents the total water on the planet, including salt and fresh; liquid, gaseous (vapor), and solid (ice). This sphere also includes the water in people and other living things. In reality, this bubble would be 1,385 kilometers (860 miles) in diameter. If the bubble were to burst, the water would cover the lower 48 states of the United States to a depth of about 172 kilometers (107 miles). The next-largest sphere represents all the liquid freshwater on the planet, including groundwater and surface water. It would be 273 kilometers (170 miles) in diameter. The smallest sphere (arrow) represents liquid freshwater on Earth's surface only; its diameter would be 56 kilometers (35 miles). About 1.1 billion people, or 18 per cent of the world's population, lack access to safe drinking water.

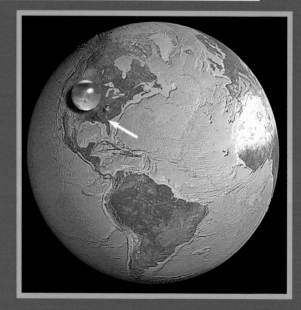

DEATHS OF SCIENTISTS

Notable people of science who died between June 1, 2011, and May 31, 2012, are listed below. Those listed were Americans unless otherwise indicated.

Avery, Mary Ellen (1927–Dec. 4, 2011), medical researcher who proved that a common breathing problem in newborn infants—especially premature infants—is caused by a lack of *surfactant* (a mix of fat and protein) that coats the air sacs and allows the lungs to expand. The surfactant typically develops before birth but may be absent or deficient in babies born prematurely. Avery's work led to much-improved outcomes for premature infants.

Baruj Benacerraf

Benacerraf, Baruj (1920–Aug. 2, 2011), Venezuelan-born American immunologist who shared the 1980 Nobel Prize in physiology or medicine with France's Jean Dausset and American scientist George Snell. Benacerraf discovered that a group of genes, called immune response genes, explains why some people have stronger immune responses than others. His research also shed light on organ rejection by transplant recipients and the variability of risk for such autoimmune diseases as lupus and multiple sclerosis.

Burke, John F. (1922–Nov. 2, 2011), surgeon responsible for the development of the first practical synthetic human skin. The invention has saved or substantially improved the lives of innumerable severely burned patients. Burke and chemist Ioannis

V. Yannas constructed the artificial skin using plastics, shark cartilage, and cow tissues. The skin consists of a protective synthetic top layer and a bottom layer incorporating the animal tissues. This deeper layer acts as a kind of scaffold on which healthy human skin cells can grow.

Chertok, Boris (1912–Dec. 14, 2011), Russian engineer who designed many of the navigational systems used on Soviet spacecraft. Chertok's systems were on board Sputnik 1 in 1957 and Yuri Gagarin's capsule in 1961. These milestones marked, respectively, the first satellite in orbit and the first human in space. Chertok also helped design navigation systems for first-generation Soviet intercontinental ballistic missiles.

Cowan, George (1920–April 20, 2012), chemist who played a key role in the development of nuclear weapons. Cowan participated in the Manhattan Project of the 1940's, which led to the development of the atomic bomb. He was also a leading contributor to the development of the hydrogen bomb by the United States in the early 1950's.

Renato Dulbecco

Dulbecco, Renato (1914–Feb. 19, 2012), Italian-born virologist who shared the 1975 Nobel Prize in physiology or medicine with American scientists Howard M. Temin and David Baltimore. Dulbecco was awarded a share of the prize for research that established a link between genetic mutations and cancer. In 1986, Dulbecco proposed cata-

DEATHS OF SCIENTISTS continued

loguing all human genes. The proposal is now seen as a precursor of the Human Genome Project, an international program that completed a human gene map in 2003.

Li-Zhi Fang

Fang, Li-Zhi (1936–April 6, 2012), Chinese physicist and dissident whose advocacy helped spur the 1989 Tiananmen Square prodemocracy movement. As a physicist, Fang broke with convention by writing essays against political interference in science and introducing the big bang theory, long considered taboo by the Chinese scientific establishment. These activities resulted in his being jailed and stripped of his job and credentials. Eventually, Fang immigrated to the United States and joined the faculty at the University of Arizona in Tucson.

Wilson Greatbatch

Greatbatch, Wilson (1919–Sept. 27, 2011), inventor of the first reliable, implantable pacemaker. Greatbatch made his breakthrough when he installed the wrong resistor in a heart-rhythm recording device. This error resulted in a small device that produced electrical impulses similar to those of a human heartbeat. Greatbatch went on to develop a practical pacemaker, which was first successfully implanted into human patients in 1960. Today, more than one-half million pacemakers are implanted worldwide every year, according to the American Heart Association.

Hauptman, Herbert A. (1917–Oct. 23, 2011), mathematician who shared the 1985 Nobel Prize in chemistry with American chemist Jerome Karle. Hauptman and Karle were honored for developing new methods of determining a molecule's structure. Their discovery, initially published in the 1950's, was eventually used to study the structure of such biological molecules as hormones, antibiotics, and *analgesics* (pain medications).

Bernadine P. Healy

Healy, Bernadine P. (1944–Aug. 6, 2011), cardiologist who became the first woman to lead the National Institutes of Health. Healy mandated the inclusion of women in clinical trials and started the Women's Health Initiative, a study dedicated to the prevention and treatment of such diseases as cancer and heart disease in women.

Jobs, Steve (1955–Oct. 5, 2011), technology leader and cofounder of Apple Inc. Jobs, Steve Wozniak, and Ronald Wayne founded the company in 1976, but Wayne left the partnership within weeks. As Apple grew, Jobs put his personal stamp of a strong aesthetic coupled with cutting-edge

Steve Jobs

technology on the company's products. Apple products have strongly influenced mass-market computing, from 1977's Apple II computer to such products of the 2000's as the iPod, the iPhone, and the iPad. The iPod transformed the music industry, and the iPhone revolutionized telephone technology. Analysts predict that mass-marketing of the iPad could lead to dramatic changes in publishing, movie distribution, and other industries.

Khorana, H. Gobind (1922–Nov. 9, 2011), Indian-born American biochemist who shared the 1968 Nobel Prize in physiology or medicine. Khorana, along with Americans Robert W. Holley and Marshall W. Nirenberg, was awarded the prize for discoveries illuminating the complex process by which cells decode genetic instructions in DNA to produce proteins. Proteins are, in effect, the workhorses of cells.

Irving Millman

Millman, Irving (1923–April 17, 2012), microbiologist who worked with 1976 Nobel Prize winner Baruch S. Blumberg to develop a test and vaccine for hepatitis B. Millman's vaccine has saved millions of lives worldwide. Millman also developed a blood test for hepatitis B, which vastly increased the safety of blood transfusions.

Mössbauer, Rudolf L. (1929–Sept. 14, 2011), German physicist who shared the 1961 Nobel Prize in physics with American physicist Robert Hofstadter. Mössbauer was awarded the prize for his discovery of a new type of *spectroscopy* (the study of radiation given off by a material). His discovery, called the Mössbauer effect, is a method of producing gamma rays with a predictable wavelength. This enables physicists to use gamma radiation to make precise measurements at the subatomic level. Mössbauer's work was used to confirm some predictions made by Einstein's relativity theory.

Old, Lloyd J. (1933–Nov. 28, 2011), physician who made critical discoveries in the field of cancer *immunotherapy* (the use of cells from a cancer patient to help his or her immune system kill the cancer cells). Old began his work in the late 1950's, when such therapies were considered fringe science. Today, however, immunotherapy is a standard treatment option for many kinds of cancer. Old, along with American physician Edward A. Boyse, discovered cell surface *markers* (a type of protein occurring on the surface of all cells). The immune system uses cell surface markers, which uniquely identify cell types, to initiate an immune response. This discovery also led to techniques for diagnosing, and vaccinating against, cancer.

Ramsey, Norman F. (1915–Nov. 4, 2011), physicist who received the 1989 Nobel Prize in physics for his work on the development of the atomic clock. Ramsey first developed a technique for measuring frequencies of electromagnetic radiation and determining which frequencies atoms and molecules could easily absorb. This technique, called the Ramsey Method, allows scientists to analyze atomic and molecular structures more accurately. It has also led to magnetic resonance imaging (MRI) technology and extremely accurate atomic clocks. Physicists used one of Ramsey's clocks, the hydrogen maser, to confirm some of Einstein's predictions about the effects of gravity on time.

DEATHS OF SCIENTISTS continued

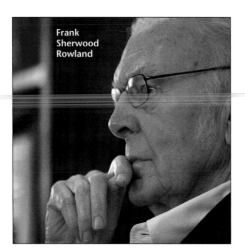

Frank
Sherwood
Rowland

Rowland, Frank Sherwood (1927–March 10, 2012), chemist who shared the 1995 Nobel Prize in chemistry with Mario Molina and Paul Crutzen. They were honored for their discovery of the dangers posed by atmospheric chlorofluorocarbons (CFC's). (A chlorofluorocarbon is a human-made molecule consisting of chlorine, fluorine, and carbon atoms.) The scientists' research showed that CFC's in the stratosphere were absorbing ozone molecules, thus depleting the ozone layer that prevents harmful ultraviolet rays from reaching the Earth's surface. These findings were initially dismissed, but the discovery of a hole in the ozone layer over Antarctica in 1985 supported the conclusion and helped bring about a ban on CFC's.

Segal, Hanna (1918–July 5, 2011), Polish-born British psychoanalyst whose writings introduced the concept of play therapy to a wide professional audience. In play therapy, therapists use toys to help children express their ideas and feelings. Segal refined and expanded upon the work of the groundbreaking psychoanalyst Melanie Klein (1882–1960), publishing *Introduction to the Work of Melanie Klein* in 1964. Her book strongly influenced child psychologists and therapists in the 1960's and afterward.

Steinman, Ralph (1943–Sept. 30, 2011), Canadian cell biologist who shared the 2011 Nobel Prize in physiology or medicine with American immunologist Bruce A. Beutler and French biologist Jules A. Hoffmann. Steinman was awarded the prize for his discovery of *dendritic cells* (a type of white blood cell that engulfs and breaks up invading microbes). His research led him to develop a pioneering immunotherapy treatment, which he used in an attempt to treat his own pancreatic cancer. Steinman died just three days before his Nobel Prize was announced. The prizes cannot be awarded posthumously if the recipient has died before the announcement is made. However, the Nobel Assembly made an exception in his case.

Vale, Wylie W., Jr. (1941–Jan. 3, 2012), *endocrinologist* (scientist who studies the workings of glands and the hormones they produce) renowned for his isolation of the hormone corticotrophin releasing factor (CRF)—the hormone "switch" responsible for the body's fight-or-flight response. Vale, a researcher with the Salk Institute in San Diego for more than 40 years, contributed substantially to the identification of hormones involved in human growth, temperature regulation, and reproduction.

Voss, Janice (1956–Feb. 6, 2012), astronaut who examined the effects of space flight on different phenomena. One of only six women to make five trips into space, Voss spent a total of 49 days circling Earth and logged nearly 30.6 million kilometers (19.0 million miles). She conducted experiments in fluid physics, medicine, botany, and other fields of science.

Waltz, David L. (1943–March 22, 2012), computer scientist whose research laid the groundwork for the development of today's Internet search engines. Waltz developed memory reasoning, a method of information retrieval in which a computer recognizes characters, words, images, or voices by making comparisons with previously stored data. Memory reasoning enables a search engine to filter large amounts of data and give accurate results. Other research by Waltz led to breakthroughs in three-dimensional rendering, with important implications for computer vision and artificial intelligence.

■ Annie Brodsky

DRUGS

The United States Food and Drug Administration (FDA) approved 30 new drugs in 2011 and 8 more as of March 31, 2012. In 2011, the agency approved 93 first-time *generic medications* (less expensive copies of brand-name drugs whose patents have expired). The FDA approved 6 additional generics as of February 28, 2012. In 2011, generics accounted for nearly 80 percent of U.S. drug sales, according to IMS, a Danbury, Connecticut-based pharmaceuticals market research company.

Drug shortages in late 2011 and early 2012 posed threats to public health and prompted action by the administration of President Barack Obama and the FDA. Among the more than 200 reported shortages were critical deficits in supplies of the anticancer drugs Doxil (doxorubicin hydrochloride liposome) and methotrexate. Doxil is used in the treatment of recurrent ovarian cancer and bone cancer. Methotrexate treats acute lymphocytic leukemia (ALL), a common form of childhood leukemia, and certain other cancers.

On Oct. 31, 2011, President Obama issued a presidential executive order concerning drug shortages. The order instructed the FDA to take steps to solicit prompt reporting of potential shortages by drug manufacturers and to expedite the review of replacement drugs for domestic drugs in short supply. In February 2012, the FDA approved the temporary importation of replacement drugs for Doxil and methotrexate from pharmaceutical factories in India and Australia, respectively.

FDA officials reported that the agency had taken steps soon after the president's executive order to prevent over 100 drug shortages. Analysts of the pharmaceutical industry predicted future drug shortages and highlighted the need for a more comprehensive response by the federal government. In early 2012, members of Congress introduced legislation to expand the FDA's authority to enforce prompt reporting of shortages by drug companies. A bill neared final approval in mid-2012.

SEE ALSO

THE SPECIAL REPORT
KNOCKING HEADS: THE DANGERS OF CONCUSSION
PAGE 70

Cystic fibrosis. In January, the FDA approved ivacaftor (sold under the brand name Kalydeco), the first drug that treats the underlying cause of cystic fibrosis (CF). Ivacaftor combats a specific genetic mutation, identified as G551D, that leads to cystic fibrosis. The drug does not treat forms of CF caused by other genetic mutations.

Cystic fibrosis is a disease in which the body produces abnormally thick, sticky mucus, which interferes with lung function and the functioning of some other organs. Life expectancy for people born with CF is typically less than 40 years. An estimated 30,000 Americans have cystic fibrosis.

Although ivacaftor treats only 4 percent of patients with cystic fibrosis, medical researchers regard it as an important first step in combating the disease. It is the first treatment to target the defective protein that causes CF; other available therapies only treat the symptoms of the disease.

Vertex Pharmaceuticals, the company that developed ivacaftor, received a contribution of $75 million from the Cystic Fibrosis Foundation (CFF), a nonprofit, patient advocacy organization, to fund research and development of CF medications. Industry analysts cited the Vertex/CFF partnership as an example of "venture philanthropy." In this emerging model of drug development, experts note, nonprofit advocacy organizations provide incentives to drug companies to develop treatments for rare diseases in which the organizations have a particular interest.

Diabetes. In January, the FDA approved Bydureon, the first weekly self-injectable treatment for diabetes. Diabetes is a disease that disrupts the body's ability to use glucose, a sugar that is dissolved in blood, as an energy source. Treatments for diabetes help the body use glucose and keep glucose levels in the blood from rising to levels capable of damaging body tissues.

DRUGS continued

Bydureon is a re-engineered form of Byetta, a drug approved in 2005 by the FDA and marketed by Amylin Pharmaceuticals. Byetta must be taken twice daily, but patients inject Bydureon once per week. The main ingredient in both drugs is exenatide, a hormone derived from the saliva of the Gila monster, a lizard native to desert regions in the southwestern United States and Mexico. Experts in the treatment of diabetes noted that the ability to administer medication on a weekly, rather than a daily or twice-daily, basis, could lead to better outcomes for patients, some of whom have difficulty taking their diabetic medications consistently.

Cancer therapy. In August 2011, the FDA approved brentuximab vedotin (sold under the brand name Adcetris), the first new drug treatment for Hodgkin's disease in 35 years. Hodgkin's disease is a form of cancer that affects certain cells of the lymphatic system, the network of vessels that returns fluids to the bloodstream and helps fight disease. According to the Centers for Disease Control (CDC), 10,000 individuals are diagnosed with Hodgkin's disease annually in the United States. Adcetris is also designed to treat a rarer, related form of cancer called anaplastic large cell lymphoma (ALCL).

Reproductive health. In October, an advisory committee to the CDC recommended that boys ages 11 and 12 be vaccinated against the sexually transmitted human papillomavirus (HPV), which is known to cause cancers of the male and female reproductive tracts and rectum and some cancers of the mouth and throat. In 2006, the FDA had approved Gardasil, the first vaccine for protection against HPV. That same year, the CDC recommended vaccination for girls ages 11 and 12.

In December 2011, U.S. Secretary of Health and Human Services (HHS) Kathleen Sebelius overruled a decision by the FDA to approve over-the-counter status for the "morning-after pill" for girls under 17 years of age. The action marked the first time in which the HHS secretary has intervened to reverse a decision taken by the FDA.

The so-called "morning-after pill" is a medication taken by a female as an emergency *contraceptive* (medication or device to prevent pregnancy) after—instead of before—sexual intercourse. Since 2009, the drug has been available without a prescription to females age 17 or older but to younger girls only with a doctor's prescription. ■ Rebecca J. Fiala

CARTOON CHARACTER IS NO LAUGHING MATTER

Blood drains from the carton figure Tranman in an image from a 2011 YouTube video because the drug tranexamic acid is not available to prevent him from bleeding to death. Tranman, a *claymation figure* (cartoon character made of clay and filmed in a stop-action sequence), was created by Hywel Roberts, a British college student majoring in animation. Hywel's uncle, epidemiologist Ian Roberts of the London School of Hygiene and Tropical Medicine, coordinated a 2010 trial of the drug that compared trauma outcomes in 40 hospitals worldwide. Test results showed that injecting hemorrhaging accident victims with tranexamic acid improved their chances of survival by 30 percent. The two Robertses collaborated to publicize the lifesaving drug in a format they thought likely to reach paramedics and trauma personnel globally.

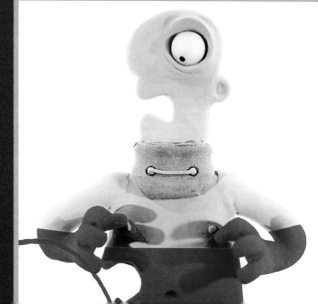

ECOLOGY

The ecological effects caused by the loss of *apex predators* (large animals at the top of a food chain) was the subject of a wide-ranging report published by an international team of scientists in July 2012. The report, in the journal *Science*, examined data from studies involving land, freshwater, and ocean ecosystems. (An ecosystem includes all the living and nonliving things in an area and the relationships among them.) In many areas, hunting, destruction of habitat, and other human actions have killed off apex predator populations. The scientists documented how the loss of an ecosystem's top predator often ripples through the rest of the system in extreme and surprising ways.

Apex predators, which typically roam large areas in search of prey, keep prey populations in check. For example, sea otters prey on kelp-munching sea urchins. In the absence of sea otters, exploding populations of sea urchins may ravage kelp forests.

In parts of Africa, the decline of lions and leopards—both apex predators—has affected olive baboon populations. With fewer predators to cull their numbers, growing numbers of baboons are more likely to come in contact with humans. The increased contact spreads intestinal parasites among both baboons and humans.

In another example, gray wolves disappeared from Yellowstone National Park in the 1970's. Subsequently, the park elk population increased, and those animals overgrazed aspen and willow trees. Since Congress authorized the reintroduction of wolves to the park in 1995, both the wolf population and vegetation have recovered.

The scientists noted in their report that populations of apex predators are relatively small and vulnerable to human activity. They expressed hope that conservationists might focus efforts on preserving apex predators.

Oil spill ecology. A study by scientists at the University of California at Santa Barbara (UCSB) offered new insights into the ecological effects of oil spills. The researchers focused on the Gulf of Mexico oil spill of 2010, caused by the explosion of BP's *Deepwater Horizon* drilling rig and the subsequent hemorrhaging of oil from the wellhead at the bottom of the gulf. The study, entitled "A Tale of Two Spills," appeared in the May 2012 issue of the journal *Bioscience*. The title alludes to the scientists' specification of a new model of oil dispersal in seawater.

Traditional models of oil dispersal predict that in a marine oil spill—a spill in an ocean, gulf, or bay—most of the oil will float to the surface, because oil is less dense than water. The new study explains how a large proportion of the oil from the *Deepwater Horizon* explosion remained below the surface because the oil gushed from the wellhead at extremely high pressures. The scientists' model shows how such high pressure could emulsify oil—that is, break it into tiny droplets that mix readily with water and do not float to the surface.

Emergency responders, however, dumped huge amounts of *dispersants* (chemicals designed to break up oil) onto the surface of the gulf. Their primary goal was to stop the oil from reaching nearby coasts.

The new model suggests that the response may have been misguided. With so much of the oil staying below the surface, the UCSB scientists questioned whether the risks of using so many dispersants, which are toxic to many organisms, outweighed the benefits. They also suggested that further study is needed to assess the impacts of oil spills on organisms and habitats in the ocean depths.

Vine sends out bat signals. A species of flowering vine in a Cuban rain forest attracts pollinating bats in an unusual way. The vine, *Marcgravia evenia*, has evolved the ability to manipulate sound waves. Biologists from Germany's University of Ulm reported this finding in July 2011 in the journal *Science*.

A variety of animals pollinate flowers, carrying pollen from one plant to another. Pollinators include bees, hummingbirds, butterflies, moths, and bats. The pollen fertilizes flowers and enables a plant to reproduce. Most flowers attract pollinators by means of color or smell. But *M. evenia* takes a differ-

ECOLOGY continued

COUGARS AND COTTONWOODS

The importance of a thriving population of apex predators—and their absence—on an ecosystem is illustrated in photos of contrasting areas of Utah. In one of the areas (below), the low, brushy vegetation is lush and includes cottonwood seedlings. This area still has a viable population of cougars, an apex predator that preys on deer. The vegetation benefits from the cougars' check on the population of deer, which browse on tender young shoots and are particularly destructive to young seedlings. Another area (bottom) has a very different vegetation pattern. In this area, human activity has driven cougars away, and deer populations have exploded. The browsing deer have not only destroyed cottonwood seedlings but also stripped away most of the low vegetation, exposing the streambank to erosion.

ent approach. The plant has dish-shaped leaves that create distinctive echoes. The bats, which navigate largely by sound, are attracted by these echoes.

Bats can easily home in on the echoing leaves. When they do, they are rewarded with nectar from the vine's flowers. The vine is rewarded by having its pollen dispersed.

The University of Ulm study is the first to describe a plant with *acoustic* (sound) properties that attract bat pollinators. The researchers said that they intended to search for other plant species that summon bat pollinators through sound.

Nativist bias in ecology? An argument against a perceived bias against nonnative species in ecological studies was the focus of a joint letter published in June 2011 by a group of leading ecologists. The letter appeared in the journal *Nature*.

Often called "invasive species," nonnative species are widely vilified for harming ecosystems. In some cases, an introduced species has reduced populations of natives by outcompeting them for food—or by eating them. However, not all invasive species wreak such havoc.

The ecologists argued that scientists unfairly make value judgments that favor native species over nonnative ones. Nonnative species should not be maligned simply for adapting well to new environments, they asserted. The scientists also argued that the harm caused by nonnative species is sometimes exaggerated. For example, nonnative tamarisk trees introduced into the Southwest spread rapidly. Some ecologists have argued that the trees damage ecosystems by consuming large amounts of water. But the scientists writing in *Nature* noted that the trees also provide nesting space for endangered birds and help control erosion.

The scientists pointed out that human-caused environmental changes, including climate change and destruction of natural habitat, have displaced many native species. Such shifts in animals' natural ranges, according to the authors, may render the distinction between "native" and "introduced" less meaningful. ■ Daniel Kenis

New Top Predator?
Pythons in the Everglades

Burmese python—the very name evokes visions of the steamy jungles of southeast Asia that are this giant snake's native habitat. So what are these fearsome reptiles doing in the swamps of southern Florida? The answer is that they have become one of the region's most troubling invasive species. (Invasive species are animals, plants, and other living things that spread rapidly in new environments where there are few or no natural controls on their growth.) In fact, Burmese pythons have been so successful in Florida that they may soon overtake alligators as the area's top predator.

As a group, pythons include some of the largest snakes in the world. They are native to Africa, southeast Asia, Australia, India, and the Pacific Islands. There, they live in tropical rain forests or in areas with low, dense vegetation. They kill their prey—usually lizards and small mammals—by coiling themselves around the animal and squeezing until the creature stops breathing. Then they swallow their catch whole and spend days digesting it. Pythons reproduce by laying as many as 100 eggs in a nest, though clutch sizes of 29 to 50 eggs are more common. The female incubates the eggs until they hatch, in about two to three months. The average life span of a python in the wild is 20 to 25 years.

There are several kinds of pythons. The reticulated python and the African rock python can grow as long as 9 meters (30 feet). The Indian python grows to about 6 meters (20 feet) long, and the green tree python reaches about 2 meters (7 feet). The smallest of the group, the pygmy python, reaches only about 60 centimeters (2 feet) in length. Scientists believe the Burmese python is either a subspecies of the Indian python or a closely related species.

According to the United States Fish and Wildlife Service, approximately 17,000 of the snakes were imported into the United States for the *exotic* (nonnative) pet trade from 1970 to 1995; about 99,000 more were brought in from 1996 to 2006. A Department of the Interior report issued in 2010 places the estimate much higher—at more than 300,000 Indian pythons imported into the United States over the past 30 years. The snakes were then sold through pet stores or reptile trade shows to snake fanciers.

Burmese pythons are appealing to some people because of their beautifully

Snakes in the grass

South Florida Water Management District employees hold a Burmese python they shot and killed in the Everglades. At 4.9 meters (16 feet 2 inches) in length and weighing 54 kilograms (120 pounds), the snake was one of the largest of this invasive species found living in the south Florida wetland. Ecologists believe that the snakes either escaped into the wild during hurricanes or were deliberately released by pet owners no longer able to care for them. Scientists estimated that by early 2012, there were 30,000 Burmese pythons in the Everglades, feeding on native species that have no natural defenses against them.

patterned skin—large reddish blotches outlined in cream or gold against a tan, yellowish brown, or gray background. The snakes also have a reputation for being generally docile. However, Burmese pythons grow quickly, from 50-centimeter (20-inch) hatchlings to 2.4-meter (8-foot) predators in a year. Adults may reach 7 meters (23 feet) in length and 90 kilograms (200 pounds) in weight. In addition, the snakes have been known to turn on their handlers. Owners are often unprepared to maintain the large constrictors, and if they are unable to find new homes for them, they sometimes release the snakes into the wild.

If a Burmese python was released into the wild in Michigan, it probably would not survive, according to one scientific *model* (computer simulation). Snakes, like other reptiles, are cold-blooded—that is, their body temperature varies with the air temperature around them. Most snakes are active and able to hunt for prey only when their body temperature measures between 20 and 35 °C (68 and 95 °F). They are not able to move when their temperature falls below about 4 °C (39 °F). Scientists with the National Wildlife Research Center reported in 2010 that even as far south as Gainesville, Florida, pythons did not survive an unseasonably cold Florida winter. (Another scientific model, however, predicts that the snakes could survive at least as far north as Delaware.)

Unfortunately, the Everglades of southern Florida seem to provide an ideal habitat for Burmese pythons. The area's warm temperatures, permanent sources of water, and vast undisturbed landscape—which provides excellent camouflage—have allowed the species to not only survive, but also thrive. The first Burmese python was spotted in the wild in Florida in 1979. The first nest was discovered in 2006, within the 6,000-square-kilometer (2,300-square-mile) boundaries of Everglades National Park. By early 2012, scientists estimated that about 30,000 Burmese pythons were living in the Everglades. They believe that virtually all of the snakes were born there.

So why are scientists and government officials concerned about pythons in the Everglades? Few people live there. However, as an invasive species, pythons are not as constrained in Florida as they are in their native habitat by such factors as a limited food supply or territory or by predators that may prey on them. Instead, they compete with such native predators as the Florida panther for food. And they reduce the numbers of native wildlife populations. Scientists in February 2012 reported the drastic changes that the snakes are effecting on the Everglades ecosystem. A team of 11 researchers led by ecologist Michael Dorcas of Davidson College in North Carolina found that as the number of pythons has increased, populations of large- and medium-sized mammals in the area have plummeted.

From 2003 to 2011, the study's researchers surveyed native mammal populations. Over a period of 313 nights, they counting live and dead animals along a road that runs to the southern tip of the park. They then compared their tallies to population surveys done in 1996 and 1997. In areas of the Everglades where pythons have lived the longest, populations of raccoons had fallen by 99.3 percent. The number of opossums had dropped by 98.9 percent. The number of white-tailed deer was reduced by 94 percent. Bobcat populations had fallen by 88.5 percent. The researchers were unable to find any rabbits or foxes. Populations of na-

Born in the U.S.A.

A researcher subdues a female python found incubating a nest in the Everglades. Burmese python nests usually contain from 29 to 50 eggs, though as many as 100 eggs have been found in a single nest. According to scientists, the presence of nests indicates that this invasive species is not only surviving, but also thriving in its new habitat.

tive animals remained unchanged in areas not yet invaded by pythons. The United States Association of Reptile Keepers disputed the findings of the study, claiming that mercury pollution in the Everglades has played a major role in the disappearance of the mammals.

In March 2012, researchers with the Smithsonian Museum of Natural History reported a similar concern. The pythons are consuming not just the Everglades' mammals, but also birds and their eggs. The researchers examined the stomach contents of 300 captured snakes. They found the remains of 25 species of birds, including great blue herons, egrets, and storks. They also found egg shell fragments. Unlike other snakes, the pythons aren't simply sucking out the contents of an occasional bird egg—the reptiles are hunting for nests and swallowing the eggs whole. Conservationists are concerned about the effect such predation will have on the breeding cycle of Florida's native birds.

Conservationists' worries extend beyond the Everglades. In 2007, a single male python was found in the Florida Keys, at Key Largo Hammock Botanical State Park. The python's swimming ability is well known. Apparently, the reptile, which normally lives in fresh-water habitats, can survive in salt water—at least for a certain period.

A number of governmental and academic institutions have banded together to try to limit the spread of Burmese pythons. (Eliminating the secretive and hard-to-hunt snakes from the Everglades completely, the experts agree, would be impossible; however, there may still be hope of eradicating the small numbers of them from the Florida Keys.) University of Florida researchers are capturing pythons, implanting them with radio transmitters, and tracking them to find groups of snakes during breeding season. The snakes are then captured and euthanized. Radio tracking also allows the researchers to learn what kinds of habitats the snakes prefer and to study their diet.

Dogs, which have proved so adept at finding people lost in the wilderness or trapped in rubble after an earthquake, have also been recruited to locate snakes. Researchers at Auburn University have trained black Labrador retrievers to track pythons by their scent. The dogs alert their handlers to the presence of the snake by sitting down 5 meters (16 feet) away, to avoid a confrontation.

In January 2012, the U.S. Fish and Wildlife Service banned the importation of Burmese pythons, African rock pythons, and the yellow anaconda into the United States. The agency also banned the transportation of these snakes across state lines. While officials hope that these and other measures will stop the damage that pythons are inflicting on the Everglades ecosystem, the move may also have another consequence—saving the Burmese python. Ironically, the snake is in danger of becoming extinct in its native habitat, where it is hunted for its meat and skin.

■ Kristina Vaicikonis

Survival of the fittest

An American alligator struggles with a python. The alligator had long been the top predator in the Everglades. However, since their introduction into the area, Burmese pythons have not only decimated the mammal population—the alligator's main prey—but also sometimes made a meal of the alligator.

Vanishing Mammals

A dramatic decline in the number of live and dead mammals observed in Everglades National Park from 2003 to 2011 compared with 1996 to 1997 has been linked to an increase in the number of Burmese pythons in the park. The decline was documented by researchers led by biologist Michael E. Dorcas of Davidson College in Davidson, North Carolina.

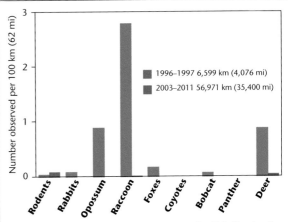

Number observed per 100 km (62 mi)

1996–1997 6,599 km (4,076 mi)
2003–2011 56,971 km (35,400 mi)

Rodents, Rabbits, Opossum, Raccoon, Foxes, Coyotes, Bobcat, Panther, Deer

Source: Dorcas, et al. "Severe Mammal Declines Coincide with Proliferation of Invasive Burmese Pythons in Everglades National Park." *PNAS* Feb. 14, 2012, pp. 2177–2684.

ENERGY

Researchers in 2011 and 2012 reported progress in the development of artificial forms of photosynthesis, the process by which plants, algae, and cyanobacteria (sometimes called blue-green algae) use the energy of sunlight to produce their own food from carbon dioxide and water. These organisms split water molecules into hydrogen and oxygen atoms. Scientists were seeking to develop photosynthesis-like processes to obtain hydrogen for use as a fuel or to generate an electric current.

In December 2011, researchers at three institutions in the United States and Europe—including Argonne National Laboratory in Lemont, Illinois—reported improvements in the performance of photoelectrochemical cells (PEC's), devices that have previously been used to split water molecules. The scientists developed highly efficient PEC electrodes by combining iron oxide (iron combined with oxygen) with phycocyanin, a protein extracted from cyanobacteria. The addition of this photosynthetic protein made the electrodes twice as efficient at splitting water molecules as electrodes made of only iron oxide.

In February 2012, researchers at the University of Tennessee at Knoxville and two other institutions announced the development of a solar cell that uses molecular structures extracted from cyanobacteria to generate electric energy. The cell consists of small tubes made of zinc oxide that are coated with molecules, called photosystem-I (PSI), from the bacteria. When sunlight strikes the tubes, the PSI releases *electrons* (negatively charged particles), which "jump" onto the zinc oxide. This electron movement produces an electric current. The researchers noted that though their artificial photosynthesis system is simple and inexpensive, it requires further refinement.

Quantum dots. Traditional solar cells convert sunlight into an electric current, but their *efficiency* (the amount of sunlight converted into electricity) remains low and their cost remains high. Quantum dot solar cells are an emerging technology with the poten-

tial to make solar energy an efficient and low-cost energy alternative. Progress in the development of this technology was announced in September 2011 by researchers at the University of Toronto in Canada, King Abdullah University of Science and Technology in Saudi Arabia, and Pennsylvania State University in University Park.

In a traditional solar cell, a semiconductor material, usually silicon, captures *photons* (wavelike particles) of light. A semiconductor is a material with conducting properties midway between a conductor and an insulator. When a photon strikes an electron in a layer of the semiconductor, the electron absorbs the photon's energy and jumps to a higher layer. The movement of electrons creates an electric current.

Most of the photons striking a solar cell are not captured because their energy levels (frequencies) are too high, and they escape without being converted into electric current. Quantum dot technology offers a way to capture those high-energy photons. A quantum dot is a tiny bit of semiconductor on the scale of a *nanometer* (billionth of a meter). The quantum dots are dispersed within a substance called a colloid, which wraps around each quantum dot. The resulting assembly is known as a colloid quantum dot (CQD) solar cell. In previous research, colloids in CQD solar cells had been made of relatively bulky *organic* (carbon-based) compounds. The bulkiness prevented the quantum dots from packing closely together, as is necessary for maximum efficiency.

In the research reported in September 2011, scientists used inorganic molecules smaller than a nanometer to wrap the quantum dots. This made it possible to create densely packed assemblies of the dots, allowing electrons to move quickly and efficiently through the solar cells. The scientists noted that the tight dot assembly could absorb and use the high-energy photons that conventional solar cells cannot convert into an electric current.

Although this breakthrough represented

the most efficient CQD solar cells to date, the cells were less efficient than conventional solar cells, which can convert as much as 20 percent of the sunlight striking them into electric energy. However, the researchers believed that with further development, their CQD solar cells might achieve efficiencies of more than 40 percent. Moreover, the quantum dots could be quickly sprayed onto films of plastic, making the technique an inexpensive way to create solar cells.

Hydrogen storage. Improved ways of storing hydrogen in fuel cells were reported in 2011. A fuel cell uses stored hydrogen with oxygen from the air to produce electric power from chemical reactions. In a vehicle, the electric current powers a motor that propels the vehicle. The hydrogen and oxygen are then combined to produce water as a waste product of the process. A fuel-cell vehicle produces none of the pollutants resulting from the burning of gasoline.

The storage of hydrogen in fuel-cell vehicles has been problematic because the hydrogen is under high pressure, risking an explosion in a collision. A solution to that problem would involve storing the hydrogen in a stable liquid or solid compound that gives up the hydrogen as needed. One solid compound under investigation is ammonia borane, which contains hydrogen, nitrogen, and boron atoms. However, researchers have encountered difficulty in getting ammonia borane to release its hydrogen.

In August 2011, scientists at the University of Southern California in Los Angeles announced the development of a *catalyst* (a substance that causes a chemical reaction while itself remaining unchanged) containing the element ruthenium that extracted a record amount of hydrogen from ammonia borane. The researchers said that their system was lightweight and efficient enough to be used in vehicles with fuel cells.

In November 2011, scientists at the University of Oregon in Eugene reported the development of a stable liquid compound for storing hydrogen in fuel cells. The compound contained amines, organic compounds derived from ammonia, and it released hydrogen in an efficient and controllable manner. The researchers noted that a liquid compound could be distributed through the same channels already being used for gasoline in vehicles, pipelines, and filling stations. ■ David L. Dreier

CARBON SEQUESTRATION IN ILLINOIS

The first large-scale carbon sequestration project associated with a biofuel facility in the United States began full operation in November 2011 in Illinois. Sequestration is a process for preventing carbon dioxide (CO_2) from entering the atmosphere. In the project, gaseous CO_2 emissions are collected from a refinery, owned by Decatur-based Archer Daniels Midland Company, that produces corn-based ethanol fuel. The gas is then converted to a liquid under high pressure. The liquid is then injected deep underground beneath a sandstone formation, where it is trapped. According to the project's operators—the Midwest Geological Sequestration Consortium (led by the Illinois State Geological Survey)—approximately 1 metric ton (1.1 tons) of liquid CO_2 was being trapped each day. Strong scientific evidence indicates that rising atmospheric concentrations of carbon dioxide produced by human activities are a primary cause of global warming.

ENGINEERING

A small bridge built in 2011 carried big potential for helping Americans cross over to a new era of recycled plastics. Every year, millions of tons of plastic products are discarded in landfills in the United States. This plastic waste not only contributes substantially to filling available landfill space, but some of it also poses potential hazards to ecosystems through the leakage of *toxic* (poisonous) chemical compounds. Recycling and reusing plastic products could help solve this problem. According to the United States Environmental Protection Agency, however, of 31 million tons of plastic waste generated in 2010, only 8 percent of this waste was recovered for recycling. The recycling of plastic materials remains challenging, partly because many plastics lose their structural strength as recycled products.

In December 2011, the American public saw a major advance in the use of recycled plastics when the construction of a bridge made from a distinctive formulation of recycled plastic was completed in the small town of York, Maine. The recycled plastic was developed by Thomas Nosker, professor of engineering at Rutgers, The State University of New Jersey, in New Brunswick, and engineers at Axion International of New Providence, New Jersey. To make the vehicle-ready bridge, which spans Rogers Brook and is 8 meters (26 feet) long by 4.6 meters (15 feet) wide, the engineers created a composite material from shredded plastics and fiberglass. The key to their design was a combination of two types of *polymers* (large molecules formed by the chemical linking of many smaller molecules into long chains)—polystyrene and high-density polyethylene—derived from recycled laundry detergent bottles, juice bottles, and automobile bumpers. For this development, Nosker was honored in the April 2011 issue of *Inventors Digest* as one of the top mechanical engineers in the United States.

The York bridge was the first plastic bridge used in a public highway application in the United States. A similar bridge, designed with the recycled plastic composite

SEE ALSO THE SPECIAL REPORT **SKY-HIGH TECH** PAGE 56

material developed by Nosker's team, was completed over the River Tweed in Peeblesshire, Scotland, also in December 2011. These bridges were the latest in a series of structures that the engineering team had built. In 2009, the team demonstrated that a military training bridge built from the plastic composite material at Fort Bragg in North Carolina could withstand the weight of a 63.5-metric-ton (70-ton) M1 Abrams tank. That bridge was the first recycled plastic structure shown to be capable of holding such massive weight without breaking.

Besides making bridges, Nosker and his colleagues had used their composite material to construct railroad ties and boardwalks. They planned to build other public projects, including additional bridges and highway sound barriers, with the material.

Other engineers praised the work of Nosker and his team. Referring to the Peeblesshire bridge, engineering professor Robert Lark of Cardiff University in Wales said, "This initiative has the potential to deliver durable, low maintenance alternatives to traditional structures manufactured from recycled waste, the benefits of which should be far reaching both economically, socially and environmentally."

Microbe-produced fuel. The development of genetically engineered microorganisms that produce a substance with the potential of being used as an alternative to diesel fuel was reported in September 2011 by researchers at the U.S. Department of Energy's Joint BioEnergy Institute (JBEI) in Emeryville, California. Diesel fuel is a type of gasoline processed from *crude oil* (liquid petroleum). Because of the finite amount of available crude oil and its sometimes harmful impact on the environment, scientists are investigating advanced *biofuels* (energy resources derived from plant materials, animal wastes, and microbes). Biofuels offer the advantages of less impact on the environment

SAN FRANCISCO-OAKLAND BAY BRIDGE REENGINEERED
TO WITHSTAND MAJOR EARTHQUAKES

In October 2011, the final of 28 sections was fitted into place in the new east span of the San Francisco-Oakland Bay Bridge, which connects the two California cities across San Francisco Bay. The Bay Bridge, which originally opened in 1936, was damaged in a powerful earthquake in 1989, when a large part of the upper of its two decks collapsed. The redesign of the east span, which began in 2006, was meant to make the bridge capable of withstanding such powerful quakes. The old east span (on the left in both photos) was replaced by the new span (on the right), which, at a length of

about 400 meters (1,312 feet), constituted the world's longest single-tower, self-anchored suspension bridge. The suspension tower, 160 meters (525 feet) high, was constructed of four pieces connected by beams that could move separately and act as shock absorbers during an earthquake. A single steel cable, about 1.6 kilometers (1 mile) long, was anchored to the east (Oakland) side of the bridge and extended down the suspension tower to loop around the bridge decks and their foundations on an island in the bay. This system helps to sustain the tension of the cable and allows the roadway to safely sway during a quake. The new span of the bridge was scheduled to open in 2013.

ENGINEERING continued

and unlimited supply, as well as continued use of existing methods of fuel storage and distribution.

Engineer Taek Soon Lee of the JBEI led a team of biologists and engineers in the investigation of bacteria and yeast that were genetically altered to secrete large amounts of a chemical compound called farnesyl diphosphate. The researchers then treated this compound with *enzymes* (substances that promote chemical reactions) to transform it into a compound called bisabolane, which has a chemical structure similar to a type of diesel fuel called D2. Laboratory tests confirmed that the *biosynthetic* (artificially produced from biological processes) bisabolane had fuel properties almost identical to those of D2 diesel fuel. However, Lee noted that the bisabolane would have certain advantages over D2 because it has a much lower freezing point and *cloud point* (the temperature at which a fuel gets a cloudy appearance and a tendency to clog fuel filters and injectors in vehicles).

The researchers showed how their microbial technique could be used to produce many gallons of bisabolane. They planned to test the bisabolane in diesel engines to demonstrate that it is both effective and economically viable as a fuel alternative.

Printing bonelike material. Imagine using a computer's inkjet printer to print tissue for repairing an injury in your body. That is basically what a team of materials engineers led by Susmita Bose of Washington State University in Pullman reported in November 2011. The team published experimental results on the use of a special printer to print a three-dimensional (3-D) material with a bonelike structure, which could serve as a scaffold on which to grow new bone customized for the particular needs of patients.

The engineers adapted a commercially available industrial printer used in metal manufacturing. The printer normally works by depositing inkjet spray onto a plastic surface over a bed of powder in several layers of 20 microns each—approximately half the width of a human hair. The researchers loaded the printer with a material consisting of

tricalcium phosphate with added silica and zinc oxide—similar to the makeup of bone. The engineers programmed the printer to produce a particular 3-D scaffoldlike configuration for repair of bone tissue. The printer sprayed the bonelike material onto a surface into the exact shape and size programmed into the printer's computer.

Next, the researchers "seeded" bone cells onto the printed bonelike scaffold. The successful growth of the bone cells on the printed structure indicated the possibility of using such structures as implants in the human body. In the future, according to the researchers, doctors may be able to print customized bone replacement tissue based on findings from a patient's computed tomography scans, which would show images of the precise shape and size of tissue needed to repair that patient's bone injury. Such a development would be important, because each individual who has a bone injury has distinct and precise needs that are otherwise difficult to meet.

Bose noted that she and her colleagues had finished testing the printed bone tissue only *in vitro* (in laboratory culture), though they had begun testing it in rabbits and rats. The preliminary results of these tests, she said, were promising. She hoped her team's research would lead to clinical tests in human patients.

Nanoparticles in medical imaging. In August 2011, researchers at Yale University in New Haven, Connecticut, reported that they developed a novel nanoparticle that allows magnetic resonance imaging (MRI) to show the growth of bioengineered tissue in living animals. Nanoparticles are particles slightly larger than atoms and molecules that are created through techniques of nanotechnology. Bioengineering is the application of engineering principles to the study and production of biological tissues. The research team was led by medical scientist Christophor K. Breuer and biomedical engineer Tarek M. Fahmy.

The investigators created blood vessels by growing blood cells called macrophages on scaffoldlike vascular structures in laboratory culture. The cells were "labeled" with specially designed iron oxide nanoparticles designed to be visible in MRI images, which show structures inside a body as a result of applying a magnetic field and radio waves. The blood vessels were then surgically implanted in mice. Using a series of MRI images, the scientists were able to monitor the growth of the implanted nanoparticle-labeled blood vessels in the mice.

The achievement marked the first successful use of MRI for studying cellular-level processes in implanted bioengineered tissue. The scientists noted that a similar technique could be applied to human patients who receive bioengineered tissue. Scientists had previously shown that engineered tissue can grow inside a human body, but they had no ability to monitor the tissue growth or to control the extent or timing of the growth. The new advance gave scientists the ability to observe and fine-tune the changes that happen in an individual's body as bioengineered tissue grows.

Physician Gerald Weissmann, editor-in-chief of the Journal of the Federation of American Societies for Experimental Biology (in which the study was published), wrote, "As we progress toward an era of personalized medicine—where patients' own tissues and cells will be re-engineered into replacement organs and treatments—we will need noninvasive [nonsurgical] ways to monitor what happens inside the body in real time. This technique fulfills another promise of nanobiology."

DNA data in biometrics standards. In November 2011, the National Institute of Standards and Technology (NIST) published revised standards for the exchange of biometrics information throughout the United States and with other countries. Biometrics consists of scientific and engineering methods for identifying individuals based on unique physical or behavioral characteristics, such as fingerprints, face shape, and iris patterns. The new standards were the first international standards for the exchange of DNA data, and, thus, were expected to improve the use of such data by forensic scientists in the investigation of crimes and the identification of victims in plane crashes and other disasters.

The revised biometrics standards were to be used by several U.S. agencies, including the Department of Defense, the Federal Bureau of Investigation, and the Department of Homeland Security, as well as corresponding agencies in other countries. NIST scientists planned to incorporate additional biometrics information, such as data on voice and dental characteristics, in future standards.　　■ Irene Y. Tsai

See also **MEDICAL RESEARCH; SPACE TECHNOLOGY.**

GOOGLE'S "SELF-DRIVING" CAR

A prototype "self-driving" automobile—modified from a Toyota Prius by engineers working for Google Inc. of Mountain View, California—cruises down a street in Nevada. In May 2012, the government of Nevada licensed the car for legal use on public roads in the state, though it was approved only for test drives, not for sale to the public. The license was the first ever granted for a so-called "autonomous vehicle" in the United States. The robotic car uses a sensor system, including computers, video cameras, and radar, to monitor traffic, pedestrians, and other objects in the road. Although a human driver remains necessary, the sensor system assists the driver in avoiding obstacles and maintaining control of the vehicle. For example, the car can automatically maintain a safe distance from a car in front of it. Future technology was expected to allow the car to read traffic signs and truly drive itself.

ENVIRONMENTAL POLLUTION

In 2011 and 2012, scientists published research linking air pollution to a range of physical and mental health problems. Pollution in air includes gases as well as tiny airborne particles called particulates. The particulates can invade and inflame body tissues. Sources of airborne particulates include power plants, factories, and vehicle exhaust.

In July 2011, researchers at Ohio State University published a study linking learning and memory deficits in mice to long-term exposure to air pollution. The researchers exposed mice for 10 months to a mixture of air designed to simulate urban air pollution. They then conducted behavioral tests on these mice and on mice that had not been so exposed (the control group). The tests revealed that mice in the control group learned simple tasks better and more quickly than the pollution-exposed mice.

The researchers then examined the brains of the exposed mice. In the hippocampus—a region associated with learning and memory—they detected stunted dendrites. Dendrites are branching extensions of nerve cells that help transmit signals. In the hippocampus tissue, the researchers also detected chemical messengers associated with inflammation. They theorized that the inflammation was a response to particulates breathed in by the mice.

A study reported in February 2012 by researchers from Rush University Medical Center in Chicago found that long-term exposure to airborne particulates can cause a decline in human *cognitive* (thinking and reasoning) ability. The study focused on more than 19,000 U.S. women, aged 70 or older, over a period of 4 years. Women who had been exposed to higher levels of air pollution experienced faster decline of their cognitive abilities than women not so exposed. The difference in mental aging was about two years, the researchers estimated.

Air pollution and strokes. A study conducted by researchers at Beth Israel Deaconess Medical Center in Boston found a heightened risk of stroke associated with

DUSTY SUMMER IN PHOENIX

A haboob envelops parts of the Phoenix metropolitan area on Aug. 18, 2011. The haboob, a swirling dust storm, was the third such event in Phoenix during the summer of 2011. Previous haboobs moved into Phoenix on July 5 and 18. A haboob sometimes forms in arid areas when a thunderstorm is weakening. Winds flow outward from the dying storm, picking up dust and debris and eventually form a front of dust-choked air as high as 3,000 meters (10,000 feet) and as wide as 80 kilometers (50 miles). The dust storm poses a serious threat to people with respiratory problems and can cause eye damage. Health officials advise people to stay indoors or to use appropriate protective covering. The swirling dust may also interrupt air travel and cause electrical outages.

short-term exposure to relatively modest levels of air pollution. Strokes are sudden losses of brain function caused by blood clots. The study appeared in the February 14 issue of *Archives of Internal Medicine.*

Researchers examined medical data associated with stroke victims in the Boston area and correlated their disease severity and progression with levels of air pollution before onset of symptoms. The researchers said that an increased risk of stroke was apparent after mere hours of exposure to air pollution levels deemed "moderate" by the Environmental Protection Agency (EPA).

Good news about air quality. A team of scientists in 2011 measured a significant drop in levels of airborne sulfur dioxide near coal-fired power plants in the eastern United States, as compared with levels detected in 2005. Sulfur dioxide forms when sulfur combines with oxygen in the air. It can form acid rain and harm the respiratory systems of people and animals. The scientists, affiliated with Environment Canada, a department of Canada's federal government, and NASA, used the NASA satellite-based Ozone Monitoring Instrument (OMI) to monitor sulfur dioxide levels during the period of study.

The scientists credited the EPA with the improvement. In 2005, the EPA issued a ruling that required U.S. coal-fired power plants to install sulfur-filtering technology. Compliance by power plants resulted in a nearly 50-percent drop in sulfur emissions.

Fracking and tainted water. In December 2011, the EPA released a draft report that linked hydraulic fracturing in Wyoming to contamination of groundwater in one locale. Hydraulic fracturing, often called fracking, is a method of extracting natural gas from deep underground.

Fracking cracks open a natural gas reservoir by injecting highly pressurized fluids. The fracturing fluids carry chemicals and sand particles that help break through the reservoir rock and enable gas to flow through it.

The gas and associated petroleum products lie below reservoirs of groundwater that feed aboveground wells. Deep fracking operations are supposed to bypass the shallow water supply, and the drilling holes are supposed to be sealed tightly with cement. However, in 2008, residents in Pavillion,

Wyoming, which lies near fracking operations, complained to the EPA about bad smells and tastes in their well water.

The EPA installed two deep wells that monitored the presence of chemicals in the water supply. In the wells, EPA scientists detected petroleum compounds associated with nearby fracking operations and chemicals used in fracking fluids.

Wyoming state officials and representatives of Encana, the energy company that is extracting the gas, protested the EPA's December 2011 draft report. In March 2012, EPA officials agreed to retest the Pavillion water supply in collaboration with Wyoming officials.

Meanwhile, the EPA continued working on a nationwide review of fracking safety. The agency last issued a generalized study of fracking in 2004, but environmental groups and other critics alleged that the report was flawed.

Microplastic ocean pollution. In September 2011, an international team of researchers published a study implicating wastewater from washing machines as a major source of microplastic pollution in the ocean. Microplastics are simply tiny bits of plastic material. One common form of microplastic are such *synthetic* (artificial) fibers as polyester in clothing and other textiles.

The researchers washed a load of clothing in a washing machine and then measured the synthetic fibers left behind. They found that a single piece of clothing containing synthetic fibers can shed more than 1,000 such fibers into the machine's wastewater. This water gets flushed into sewer systems and eventually reaches coastal waters via currents and tides in streams.

The scientists sampled 18 shorelines around the world for microplastic pollution. They found large concentrations of the material at all locations. Because microplastic pieces are so small, organisms easily ingest them. Plastic materials may cause health problems in the bodies of living things and readily make their way up the food chain.

City lights and animal navigation. A study released in October by researchers at the Free University of Berlin and the Leibniz Institute of Freshwater Ecology and Inland Fisheries, Berlin, found that light pollution

ENVIRONMENTAL POLLUTION continued

can interfere with the ability of *nocturnal* animals (those active at night) to navigate. Light pollution, caused by streetlamps and other outdoor light sources, creates an artificial skyglow at night. The researchers found that this skyglow blots out a pattern of polarized moonlight, invisible to human eyes, that certain night creatures use as an essential navigation aid. (In polarized light, the light waves vibrate in regular, rather than random, patterns.)

The researchers found that the polarized moonlight works as a "celestial compass" for certain species of beetles, moths, crickets, and spiders. Interference with this "compass" could disrupt food webs and destabilize entire ecosystems, the researchers theorized.

Fungi versus lead pollution. In January 2012, biologists from the University of Dundee in Scotland reported that fungi can help change harmful lead pollution into a stable and relatively harmless mineral called pyromorphite. Lead, a heavy metal used in many products and industrial processes, can cause severe health problems. In young children, it is known to cause developmental problems and learning difficulties.

The scientists coated one lead sample with fungus; they left an identical lead sample unexposed to fungus to use as a control in the experiment. After a month, the researchers discovered evidence of pyromorphite formation on the fungus-coated lead. But the uncoated lead showed evidence only of less-stable lead compounds formed by normal corrosion. A stable compound, such as pyromorphite, is less likely to release lead into the environment than an unstable compound, and is, therefore, much safer.

The scientists speculated that the fungus might be used to help clean up lead-polluted sites. More research would be needed, they added, to develop a useful industrial application. ■ Daniel Kenis

POT GROWERS IN NATIONAL FORESTS

Scattered trash and stripped ground mar a patch in a national forest in California where criminals had been raising marijuana before detection by law enforcement officials. The site is one of hundreds of such sites that official suspect have been cleared in national forests across the United States. In December 2011, David Ferrell, Director of Law Enforcement and Investigations with the U.S. Forest Service, testified before a Senate committee about the infiltration of illegal marijuana growers onto federal lands. According to Ferrell, many of the pot-growing operations are run by drug-trafficking organizations with deep financial resources and sophisticated methods. Some of the plots are patrolled by armed guards and ringed by landmines. Ferrell also testified that in operations thus far discovered, large amounts of toxic pesticides have been found as well as elaborate irrigation systems. The growers bring in hoses or pipes and pumps to draw water from nearby lakes or streams. Their operations harm pristine forest environments and take a toll on wildlife. The Forest Service estimates an average cost of $10,000 to $15,000 per acre to clean up lands fouled by the illegal marijuana-growing operations.

FOSSIL STUDIES

Fossils of advanced compound eyes—each with thousands of lenses—belonging to some of the first arthropods were reported from Early Cambrian Period deposits, about 515 million years old, by two teams of scientists in 2011. Arthropods, animals with *exoskeletons* (outer skeletons) and jointed legs, include such creatures as crabs, lobsters, shrimp, spiders, and insects. Two teams of paleontologists discovered the fossils in shale deposits at Emu Bay in South Australia.

In June 2011, paleontologist Michael Lee of the South Australian Museum in Adelaide and five colleagues described fossils of compound eyes that each had more than 3,000 tiny lenses. The fossil eyes, which likely belonged to a shrimp-like arthropod, were the oldest known evidence for complex eyes—by more than 85 million years—and some of the best preserved. The size and arrangement of the lenses suggested to the scientists that these marine animals were actively swimming predators adapted to low light levels in the sea. The fossils provided evidence that complex eyesight evolved rapidly after the Cambrian Explosion, a dramatic increase in the variety of animal species that occurred roughly 540 million years ago.

In December 2011, Lee, along with John Paterson of the University of New England in Australia and other paleontologists, described the Early Cambrian eyes of a marine predator known as *Anomalocaris*. This bizarre arthropod grew to a length of about 1 meter (3 feet). It had a pair of long segmented appendages near its mouth, which had slicing, spiny jaws that resembled a pineapple ring. The two eyes of *Anomalocaris* were each about 2.5 centimeters (1 inch) across and borne on short stalks. The well-preserved fossils revealed that each compound eye was made of more than 16,000 *hexagonal* (six-sided) lenses.

According to Lee and Paterson, *Anomalocaris* likely had highly sensitive vision, with eyes that rivaled the most sophisticated eyes of modern-day arthropods. This discovery, together with the discovery announced in June, showed that complex, compound eyes developed in arthropods or arthropod ancestors more than half a billion years ago.

Dinosaur "fleas." The discovery of fossils of large flea-like insects more than 2 centimeters (0.8 inch) long that may have fed on the blood of dinosaurs and *pterosaurs* (flying reptiles) was reported in February 2012 by paleontologists led by Huang Diying of Nanjing Institute of Geology and Palaeontology in China. The fossils were found in deposits dating from 165 mil-

WORLD'S FIRST SUPERPREDATOR

Anomalocaris—a large *carnivorous crustacean* (meat-eating shellfish) with huge eyes on stalks, sharp claws at the front of its head, and a razor-sharp mouth—hunts for prey, in a prehistoric sea, in an artist's illustration. The discovery of the crustacean, which topped the food chain 515 million years ago, was reported in December 2011 by a team of paleontologists led by John Paterson of the University of New England in Australia. The fossils were found on Kangaroo Island in South Australia. *Anomalocaris*, which measured about 1 meter (3 feet) long, was much larger than other animals of that time. Each eye was about 2.5 centimeters (1 inch) in diameter and contained more than 16,000 lenses, giving the predatory crustacean exceptionally sharp and clear vision.

FOSSIL STUDIES continued

lion to 125 million years ago—the Mid-Jurassic Period to the Early Cretaceous Period—at two sites in China.

The insects had stout biting and sucking mouthparts, indicating they were adapted to piercing the tough hides of dinosaurs and other reptiles. The structure of these mouthparts suggested to the researchers that the parasitic insects may have evolved from non-parasitic, siphon-bearing scorpion flies, a group of flies that plays a role in pollinating plants today.

Archaeopteryx debate continues. A number of studies reported in 2011 shed light on *Archaeopteryx* and the origin of birds. *Archaeopteryx* was a feathered animal that lived about 150 million years ago, near the end of the Jurassic Period. Since the discovery of the first *Archaeopteryx* fossils in the 1860's, this animal has been widely accepted as the oldest bird. Since about 2000, however, increasing numbers of well-preserved fossils of feathered dinosaurs have been recovered from deposits dating to the Late Jurassic Period. These findings have complicated scientists' understanding of the origins of birds, as well as the distinction between birds and dinosaurs.

In July 2011, paleontologists Xing Xu, Hailu You, Kai Du, and Fenglu Han of the Institute of Vertebrate Palaeontology and Palaeoanthropology in Beijing, China, described a small feathered dinosaur, named *Xiaotingia zhengi*, from Late Jurassic deposits in China. In an analysis that provoked widespread disussion, the scientists concluded that the animal was similar to *Archaeopteryx* and that neither *Xiaotingia* nor *Archaeopteryx* was a bird. Rather, according to the researchers, both creatures belonged to an evolutionary side branch of feathered dinosaurs that led to birds. Other scientists, while agreeing with Xing Xu, proposed that *Archaeopteryx* may have belonged to yet another group of feathered dinosaurs that were closely related to *Velociraptor*, a meat-eating dinosaur.

A report arguing for the continued status of *Archaeopteryx* as the first bird was published in October 2011 by a group led by

DINO DEATHS IN A NEST

The fossilized bones of 15 baby dinosaurs of the species *Protoceratops andrewsi* cover the floor of a 70-million-year-old nest discovered in what is now Mongolia. The find was reported in November 2011 by paleontologist David Fastovsky of the University of Rhode Island. The dinosaurs were from 10 to 15 centimeters (4 to 6 inches) long and less than 1 year old when the nest was buried, possibly by windblown sand dunes in a desert-like environment. Because the young dinosaurs apparently spent a long time together in the nest, Fastovsky proposed that *P. andrewsi*, a sheep-sized *herbivore* (plant-eater) related to *Triceratops*, may have cared for its young, as do many modern-day birds. By contrast, most modern-day reptiles abandon their eggs after laying them.

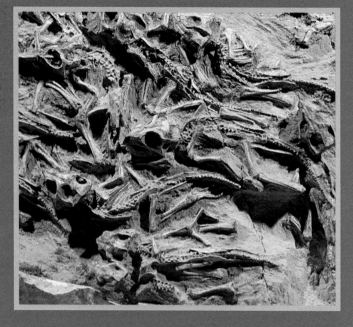

Michael Lee of the South Australian Museum. Lee and his colleagues reanalyzed data on the body structure of *Archaeopteryx and* compared this structural information with data on the body structure of a variety of small, feathered dinosaurs using sophisticated statistical techniques. The team concluded that the *Archaeopteryx* fossils represent animals more closely related to birds than to the feathered dinosaurs that other researchers had proposed.

In other *Archaeopteryx* research, reported in December 2011, paleobiologist Ryan Carney of Brown University in Providence, Rhode Island, and four associates described their analysis of pigment-bearing structures called melanosomes, obtained from a fossilized feather of *Archaeopteryx*. A comparison of the shapes of these prehistoric melanosomes with those of melanosomes from modern-day birds suggested that the feathers of *Archaeopteryx* were black, like those of a crow. The paleontologists also determined that the feather was nearly identical in structure to the flight feathers of many modern birds.

Feathered tyrannosaur. The discovery of a large dinosaur with feathers was reported in April 2012 by a team led by Xing Xu of the Institute of Vertebrate Paleontology and Paleoanthropology in China. The team described three well-preserved fossil specimens, discovered in Liaoning Province, of a predatory dinosaur from a group called tyrannosaurids, or tyrannosaurs. The dinosaur, dubbed *Yutyrannus huali*, lived about 60 million years before the well-known *Tyrannosaurus rex*. The fossils were uncovered in sediments dating from the Early Cretaceous Period, 125 million years ago.

The specimens included one adult, estimated to have been about 10 meters (33 feet) long and to have weighed 1.4 metric tons (1.5 tons), and two juveniles, which each weighed about half a ton. The specimens showed *filamentous* (thread-like) feathers along the tail, making these tyrannosaurs the largest animals known to have possessed feathers. They weighed about 40 times as much as the next largest-known feathered dinosaur.

The existence of such large animals with feathers surprised researchers. Animals with massive bulk can easily retain body heat and, thus, do not require the insulation provided by feathers—unless they live in cold climates. The Chinese paleontologists speculated that *Yutyrannus* lived during a cool interval in the Cretaceous Period, during which average temperatures may have been about 10 °C (50 °F). Other scientists noted that if the dinosaurs had not needed insulation against the cold, the feathers may have functioned as camouflage or in mating displays.

Aquatic animals and live births. Fossil discoveries reported in March 2012 by a team led by paleontologist Graciela Piñeiro of the Facultad de Ciencias in Uruguay provided evidence of possible live births in very ancient reptiles. The evidence included two fossil *embryos* (immature animals in early stages of development) of the aquatic reptile *Mesosaurus*, dating from the Early Permian Period, about 280 million years ago. *Mesosaurus* grew to nearly 2 meters (6.6 feet) in length, with a long neck and head and a mouth full of sharp teeth that were probably used for capturing shellfish and fish. *Mesosaurus* figured prominently in the development of the theory of *continental drift* (the movement of continents to new positions on Earth's surface over long periods), because fossils of this species were found in both South America and Africa.

One of the new specimens, found in Uruguay, represents a coiled embryo skeleton, about 12 centimeters (4.7 inches) long, apparently encapsulated in an egg. This specimen provided the oldest direct fossil evidence of embryonic development in a so-called amniotic egg. All land reptiles have eggs with a shell and special membranes, including the amnion, that permit gas exchange while preventing water loss by evaporation. Unlike the small gelatinous eggs of frogs and other amphibians, the amniotic eggs of reptiles allow embryos to grow inside the egg to a well-developed stage capable of dwelling on land. This contrasts, for example, with frog tadpoles, which must live in water.

The other new fossil specimen, found in Brazil, appears to be of a pregnant adult mesosaur with a similar embryo skeleton within her abdominal cavity. This specimen suggested that the animal may have been

FOSSIL STUDIES continued

ovoviviparous—that is, the female may have retained eggs within her body until they hatched and then given birth to live young. If that is an accurate interpretation of the fossil evidence, it would push back the oldest-known evidence of live births by about 90 million years.

Earliest placental mammal. Fossils of a previously unknown placental mammal, discovered in 160-million-year-old rocks in China, were reported in August 2011 by a team of paleontologists led by Zhe-Xi Luo of the Carnegie Museum of Natural History in Pittsburgh, Pennsylvania. Placental mammals are those in which pregnant females have a placenta, an organ that provides nutrients to and carries away waste from a developing animal. This report extended the known origin of placental mammals approximately 35 million years earlier than previous reports. The

discovery also showed that the first known members of this group were small animals with limbs adapted to climbing trees.

The presence of a placenta enabled the mammal mother to nourish her young in the womb and, therefore, to nurture young that would be born at a relatively advanced stage of development. This evolutionary advance gave young placental mammals a "head start" on life and may be one reason that placental mammals became more numerous and widespread than more primitive mammal groups, such as the pouched marsupials. The fossil evidence for the earlier origin of placental mammals was in line with predictions made by molecular biologists based on comparisons of genetic differences between placental mammals and more primitive mammals. ■ Carlton E. Brett
See also **ARCHAEOLOGY.**

FISH VS. PTEROSAUR—NEITHER WINS

The jaws of an armored predatory fish appear to grasp the left wing of a *pterosaur* (flying reptile) in a 120-million-year-old fossil, seen in full (A), in close-up (B), and in ultraviolet light (C). This fossil and four similar specimens were unearthed in southern Germany by paleontologists at the State Natural History Museum in Karlsruhe, Germany, and reported in March 2012. The pterosaur, *Rhamphorhychus*, which is distorted in the fossil, was apparently grabbed by the large fish, *Aspidorhynchus*, as it flew just above the surface of a lake looking for small fish to eat. *Aspidorhynchus* then pulled the predatory reptile into the water. However, according to the scientists, the pterosaur, which had a wingspan of about 70 centimeters (28 inches), apparently was more than the fish, which was 65 centimeters (26 inches) in length, could handle. The scientists proposed that the fish could not swallow the reptile, nor could it remove its jaws from the wing—and the entangled animals sank together into the lake bed, where they died and became fossilized.

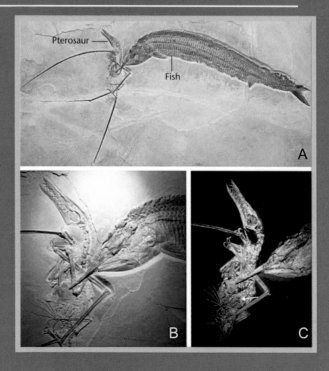

GENETICS

An important discovery about the role that epigenetic factors play in a type of childhood cancer of the eye was announced in January 2012 by a group of researchers led by molecular biologist Michael A. Dyer of Howard Hughes Medical Institute in Chevy Chase, Maryland; physician James R. Downing of St. Jude Children's Research Hospital in Memphis; and geneticist Richard K. Wilson of Washington University School of Medicine in St. Louis. The term *epigenetic,* meaning *above the gene,* refers to heritable changes in gene function that occur without a change in the sequence of the DNA that makes up genes. The scientists found how such changes can lead to the development of retinoblastoma, a rare form of cancer that may result in blindness in one or both eyes of a child.

Previous research had pinpointed the RB1 gene as the underlying problem associated with at least one type of retinoblastoma. The loss of one or both of the copies of the RB1 gene leads to the development of cancer in the cells of the retina, the light-sensitive membrane at the back of the eye. However, additional genetic mechanisms were also suspected of promoting the formation of these cancers.

The researchers first carried out a detailed examination of the genetic material derived from cells in retinoblastoma tumors. The examination method they used, called whole genome sequencing, involves determining the complete linear sequence of chemical units called bases that make up the DNA of cells. The genome sequences found in the tumor cells were then compared with the genome sequences found in other, noncancerous cells from the same patients. The analysis revealed that, other than in the RB1 gene, there were few *mutations* (changes in base sequence) in the tumor cells compared with the noncancerous retinal cells. This suggested that epigenetic changes could be involved in the disease process.

The researchers found a number of epigenetic changes in the tumor cells compared with the noncancerous retinal cells. The most profound change involved the activity of a gene known as SYK. The investigators reported that in cases of retinoblastoma, the activity of the SYK gene prevented the cancerous cells in retinal tumors from self-destructing. The failure of these cells to die was the main factor causing the rapid growth of the retinal tumors in patients.

In preliminary experiments with mice, the researchers showed that a regimen of chemotherapy could be used to interfere with the activity of the SYK gene. In those mice, the tumor cells began to die off in increasing numbers, leading to increased survival of the mice. The scientists were hopeful that this experiment might lead to new treatments for children with this devastating disease. They also noted that the research highlighted the importance of investigating the various, complex epigenetic factors that influence gene activity and function.

Cardiomyopathies. A discovery about genetic mutations that cause about 25 percent of cases of a heart disorder known as idiopathic, or dilated, cardiomyopathy was reported in February 2012 by an international group of researchers led by geneticist Christine E. Seidman of the Harvard Medical School in Boston. This disorder accounts for almost one-third of all cases of congestive heart failure. It most commonly occurs in people between the ages of 20 and 60, though it can affect individuals of any age.

In all types of cardiomyopathies, the heart has diminished function because of problems with its muscles. Researchers had previously identified a molecule known as titin as a likely source of the muscle problems in idiopathic cardiomyopathy. Titin is a protein found in virtually all muscles of the heart, as well as in many other parts of the body. It is one of the largest proteins in the human body, made up of more than 33,000 individual subunits called amino acids. TTN, the gene that codes for the production of the titin protein, is so large that scientists had previously been unable to relate its base sequences to disease states.

Seidman's team used two newer methods, called targeted capture and next generation sequencing, to study the TTN gene.

GENETICS continued

The targeted capture method allows researchers to analyze only the parts of a gene, known as exons, that function in the construction of proteins. Introns, the gene parts that do not code for proteins, can be easily ignored with this method. Once the exons are identified, researchers can use the next generation sequencing method to rapidly obtain detailed information about the sequences of bases in the exons.

The scientists used these two methods to compare the TTN gene of individuals who had idiopathic cardiomyopathy with the TTN gene of individuals who had a heart problem called hypertrophic cardiomyopathy—and the TTN gene of individuals with no heart problem. They found that specific mutations occurred in the TTN gene of more than 25 percent of the individuals with idiopathic cardiomyopathy, compared with only 1 to 3 percent of the other individuals. These mutations all affected the size or structure of the titin protein, causing it to be too short or too long or made of the incorrect amino acid subunits.

The investigators were optimistic that their findings could be used to develop more sensitive tests for detecting mutations in the TTN gene. Such genetic tests, in turn, could allow for earlier diagnosis and identification of patients with idiopathic cardiomyopathy, leading to earlier treatment.

Uterine fibroids. In August 2011, a group of geneticists led by Lauri A. Aaltonen of the University of Helsinki in Finland described mutations in a gene found in approximately 70 percent of tumors known as uterine leiomyomas, also called uterine fibroids. These fibroid tumors develop in about 60 percent of women by the time they are 45 years old. Although the growths are usually *benign* (noncancerous), they may cause severe abdominal pain. These tumors are also a major cause of infertility, and they are the most common reason for women to have hysterectomies, surgical removal of part or all of the *uterus* (womb).

The researchers identified the mutations in a gene known as MED12, a type of regulatory gene. A regulatory gene plays a key role in controlling the activity of many other genes. Using a method called whole exome sequencing, Aaltonen's team focused on analyzing only the exons of MED12, those parts of the gene actively used in the tumor cells. This method allowed the scientists to identify the MED12 mutations in 18 uterine fibroids obtained from 17 patients.

To validate their findings, the researchers then analyzed genetic material from an additional 207 uterine fibroids obtained from 80 patients. This analysis revealed that 70 percent of the tumors had mutations in the MED12 gene, and nearly all of these mutations were of the same type and were found in the same part of the gene. The geneticists said that their research suggested that the altered protein produced by the mutated MED12 gene would not be able to properly do its job of regulating the expression of other genes. This lack of regulation, in turn, would lead to the development of fibroid tumors.

Mutations in other parts of MED12 had previously been identified as the underlying cause for two rare disorders known as Opitz-Kaveggia and Lujan-Fryns syndromes. Patients with these disorders exhibit impaired mental development and some physical abnormalities, but they are not usually predisposed to tumor development. The findings by Aaltonen's team indicated that the MED12 gene plays a larger and more complex role in many aspects of cell activity than previously appreciated.

Ten types of breast cancer. "Breast cancer is not 1 disease, but 10 different diseases," said geneticist Carlos Caldas of the University of Cambridge in England in April 2012. Caldas described the findings of a study in which his research group analyzed genetic changes in breast cancer tissue obtained from about 2,000 women in Canada and the United Kingdom. Their analysis showed that the many ways in which breast cells change when they become cancerous can be grouped into 10 categories. They named these categories IntClust 1 through IntClust 10. The various cellular changes are caused by such genetic changes as particular mutations, overactivity of some genes, and suppressed activity of other genes.

Experts in cancer noted that further research into these findings could lead to the precise targeting of treatments to match particular categories of breast cancer. However, any clinical benefits from the research was expected to take several years.

Personalized treatment for asthma. Genetic information that could help improve predictions of how individuals will respond to the most widely prescribed asthma medications was described in September 2011 by a group led by Kelan G. Tantisira, professor of medicine at Harvard University in Cambridge, Massachusetts. Up to 40 percent of asthma patients do not respond well to inhaled glucocorticoids, the medications that are most widely used for managing this condition. Tantisira's study is one of many in the emerging field of pharmacogenomics, in which scientists search for connections between the genetic makeup of individuals and their response to medications. Researchers in this field usually look for single nucleotide polymorphisms (SNP's), which are individual changes in the chemical bases of DNA.

Using genetic material from 935 people, Tantisira's team analyzed more than 500,000 SNP's as potential candidates for a pharmacogenomic association with glucocorticoids. The researchers identified one SNP that seemed to have such an association. This SNP was either within, or very close to, a gene known as GLCCI1. When this SNP was present in cells grown in laboratory culture, it was associated with a reduction in the level of activity of GLCCI1. The reduced level of GLCCI1 activity coincided with the finding that people with this particular SNP showed a poor response to the use of glucocorticoids in asthma treatment.

The researchers hoped that the identification of this SNP would make it easier to design a genetic test that might predict which patients with asthma would respond well to glucocorticoid therapy and which would not. However, they acknowledged that asthma is a multifaceted disorder that will require more research for the development of more effective treatments.

Mutations and autism. Several mutations that appear to increase the chances that a child will have autism were described

BLACK DEATH BACTERIAL DNA ISOLATED FROM SKELETONS OF VICTIMS

Skeletal remains of individuals who died from the Black Death (an epidemic that killed millions of people in Europe and Asia in the mid-1300's) lie in part of a mass grave excavated in London. In August 2011, archaeologist Johannes Krause of the Institute for Archaeological Sciences in Germany and colleagues reported that they had isolated bacteria from these skeletons and analyzed the DNA of the microbes. The analysis revealed that the bacteria were a strain of *Yersinia pestis,* long suspected of causing the Black Death. In October, the same research team published details of the *genome* (genetic information of a species) of the ancient *Y. pestis* microbes, showing that the ancient strain bore many similarities to modern strains of *Y. pestis.* The genetic analysis suggested that *Y. pestis* caused so many deaths in the mid-1300's because it had recently evolved from an ancestral bacterial species. It was able to spread quickly as a result of lack of human immunity, unhealthy social conditions, favorable climate conditions, and other factors.

GENETICS continued

by two independent groups of geneticists in April 2012. One group was led by Evan E. Eichler of the University of Washington in Seattle, and the other group was led by Matthew Slate of the Yale University School of Medicine in New Haven, Connecticut.

Researchers have long suspected that genetic mutations contribute to the development of autism, which consists of several disorders characterized by a limited ability to communicate and interact with other people. However, scientists had previously encountered difficulty in identifying these varied mutations.

In the new research, both groups of scientists took advantage of the whole exome sequencing method to quickly process and analyze large amounts of genetic material, focusing on examining the makeup of the exons. The investigators compared the exome information obtained from different individuals within hundreds of families. Some of these individuals had autism and others did not. These comparisons allowed the scientists to eliminate all the genetic information that was common to family members and to target the genetic differences that

might explain why one person in a family had autism and another did not.

The team led by Eichler reported that most of the mutations they associated with autism were inherited from the father, and that autism was increasingly likely to occur in offspring as the age of the father increased. These researchers identified two genes, named CHD8 and NTNG1, that were most strongly associated with the occurrence of autism. In addition, Eichler's team reported autism associations for certain SNP's in other genes that had previously been identified as candidates for causing autism.

The study led by Slate also identified a number of SNP's that were associated with autism disorders. Most importantly, these researchers described how some of the SNP's result in the production of proteins that affect cellular activity in the brain, helping to explain the mechanics of these disorders. Both research groups noted that their findings helped to clarify the genetic basis of autism, while highlighting the variety of autism-associated genetic factors.

■ David S. Haymer

See also **BIOLOGY.**

▌ GEOLOGY

The first comprehensive map showing the movement of the ice that covers most of the Antarctic continent was presented in September 2011 by geologists in California. The immense weight of this ice causes it to spread outward and flow toward the coasts. In identifying and describing the major streams of ice across the continent, they found that the East Antarctic ice sheet, which covers 90 percent of Antarctica, is not behaving as expected.

The Antarctic ice sheets contain 30 million cubic kilometers (7.25 million cubic miles) of ice, amounting to 90 percent of all the ice on Earth. Although the ice appears to be solid, it actually moves like a very

viscous (thick) fluid. Glaciologists, geologists who study glaciers, had first studied ice movement by examining mountain glaciers. By measuring the movement of rocks and other debris in glacial ice, glaciologists had calculated that the mountain glaciers usually move less than 330 meters (1,083 feet) per year. At times, the glaciers may not move at all or they may surge to speeds of almost 12 kilometers (7.4 miles) per year. However, Antarctica is so vast that the ice movement across most of the continent had not been directly measured. Many scientists had assumed that the extremely low temperatures of Antarctica meant that most of the continent's ice hardly moves at all.

From 2007 to 2009, as part of the International Polar Year, a number of international agencies directed their satellites to make interferometric synthetic aperture radar (InSAR) measurements of Antarctica's ice. In the InSAR process, microwaves transmitted from a satellite are bounced off Earth's surface and reflected back to the satellite. Measurements of the timing and strength of the returning signals reveal information about the changing *topography* (surface features).

Based on these InSAR measurements, a team led by glaciologist Eric Rignot of the University of California at Irvine and NASA's Jet Propulsion Laboratory in Pasadena, California, found that the speed of some of the nonglacial Antarctic ice is more than 1 kilometer (0.6 mile) per year. The most rapid movements were found in the Weddell Sea area south of the Atlantic Ocean; along the Antarctic Peninsula; along the West Antarctic margin south of the Pacific Ocean; and

DRILLING MILLIONS OF YEARS INTO ANTARCTICA'S PAST

After years of drilling under brutal conditions, Russian scientists announced in February 2012 that a probe had penetrated 3,769 meters (12,366 feet) to the surface of Lake Vostok, a huge, ice-buried, freshwater lake in Antarctica. Lake Vostok, the largest of the hundreds of subglacial lakes on the continent, has been sealed off from the outside world since an ice sheet covered it an estimated 14 million years ago. The water itself, which has circulated through the overlying ice sheet, could be about 1 million years old. The water remains a liquid because it is under enormous pressure from the overlying ice, which reduces the water's freezing point. When the drill broke through a layer of *accretion ice* (water frozen to the bottom of the ice sheet), water from the lake surged 30 to 40 meters (100 to 130 feet) up the borehole. The scientists planned to return to the drilling site, called Vostok Station, in 2013, during the Antarctic summer, to retrieve and analyze that water, which formed an "ice plug" in the borehole. Scientists hope that an analysis of the water might reveal unknown species of microbes or other life forms that have developed in the isolation of the dark, cold lake.

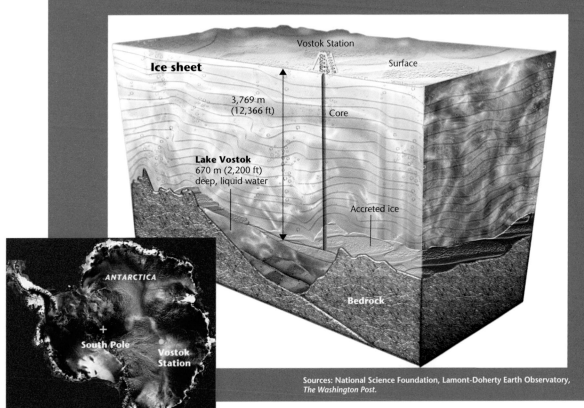

Sources: National Science Foundation, Lamont-Doherty Earth Observatory, *The Washington Post*.

GEOLOGY continued

around the Ross Sea south of New Zealand. The scientists said that much of this moving ice is responding to recent breakups of ice shelves as a result of warming ocean waters.

Glaciologists had long thought that the base of the East Antarctic ice sheet is often frozen to the ground beneath the ice—and that most of the motion takes place in the middle of the ice, between the ice surface and base. However, the InSAR data suggested that much of the ice is moving all the way down to the base—meaning that the basal ice is not frozen to the ground but is moving over a slippery ground surface. Furthermore, the motion of the ice is not always downhill, as might be expected, but is sometimes uphill.

The report by the California team means that glaciologists will need to revise their concepts of how large ice sheets behave. The new understanding could be applied not only to investigations of today's ice sheets, but also to research models of the ice that covered large areas of the Northern Hemisphere during the most recent ice age, which ended about 11,500 years ago. Glaciologists planned additional research to better understand the ice movement across Antarctica.

Permian mass extinction. European scientists reported in September 2011 that the volcanoes of the "Siberian Traps" could have released enough carbon dioxide into the atmosphere about 250 million years ago to cause the mass extinction of marine and *terrestrial* (land) species that occurred at that time. The Siberian Traps are a vast field of preserved prehistoric *basalt* (dark rock formed by volcanic lava) that constitutes the remains of the longest-known continuous eruption of volcanoes. The eruptions of these volcanoes lasted for at least 1 million years.

The Siberian Traps are the largest of areas known as large igneous provinces (LIP's), where enormous amounts of basalt poured out onto Earth's surface in geologically brief periods. Geologists believe that many LIP's developed over plumes of *magma* (partially melted rock) rising from Earth's *mantle* (layer of rock beneath the crust). These basalt lavas released huge amounts of the greenhouse gas carbon dioxide into the

atmosphere when they erupted, leading to a "hothouse" climate in which warm temperatures extended to the polar regions. Such climate changes could have contributed to mass extinctions of organisms on land and in the sea, according to many scientists.

The volcanoes of the Siberian Traps erupted near the end of the Permian Period, between 299 million and 251 million years ago. Their eruption coincided with the greatest extinction event in history, when 96 percent of marine species and 70 percent of terrestrial *vertebrate species* (animals with backbones) became extinct, according to fossil evidence.

The most likely cause of this mass extinction, in the view of many scientists, was the rapid warming of the planet to a hothouse state, with an average global temperature rising above 30 °C (86 °F). By contrast, the present average global temperature is about 15 °C (59 °F). Such high temperatures would occur only if Earth experienced a major increase in the concentration of atmospheric carbon dioxide, which, as a greenhouse gas, "blocks" radiated surface heat from escaping into space. A major question has been whether the volcanoes of the Siberian Traps could have released enough carbon dioxide into the atmosphere to cause the Permian mass extinction.

Geologist Stephan Sobolev of the Deutsches GeoForschungsZentrum in Potsdam, Germany, with collaborators from other institutions in Germany, France, and Russia, analyzed the chemical makeup of rocks associated with the basalts in the Siberian Traps. From this analysis, the team concluded that the volcanoes of the Siberian Traps erupted over a mantle plume that contained as much as 15 percent recycled ocean crust. This marine crustal material contained not only enough carbon dioxide to account for the mass extinction event, but also large amounts of hydrochloric acid, which would have acidified the ocean, contributing to the die-off of marine species during the Permian mass extinction.

Newly found rock layer. Evidence for a previously unknown layer of melted rock at the top of the asthenosphere was reported

EAST COAST EARTHQUAKE

A rare 5.8-magnitude earthquake that struck central Virginia on Aug. 23, 2011, caused shaking as far north as Montreal, Canada; as far south as central Georgia; and as far west as Illinois, as shown in a diagram (below) from the United States Geological Survey (USGS). The last moderate quake in the region occurred in 1875. Small quakes that cause little or no damage (magnitude 4 or less) occur in the area every one to two years. The *epicenter* of the August quake (point on Earth's surface from which earthquake waves radiate) was in the town of Mineral, about 88 kilometers (55 miles) northwest of Richmond. The quake struck 5 kilometers (3 miles) below the surface along the Spotsylvania Fault, a geologic break in the North American tectonic plate (shown right in a diagram prepared by geologist Christopher M. Bailey of the College of William & Mary in Virginia). The USGS describes this region as an area of bedrock "assembled as continents collided to form a supercontinent [Pangaea] about 500 [million]-300 million years ago, raising the Appalachian Mountains." Geologists believe the area is riddled with many small faults.

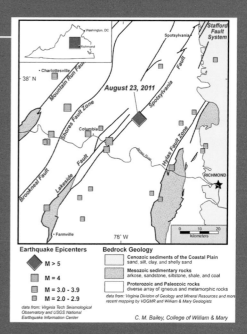

INTENSITY	1	2–3	4	5	6	7	8	9	10+
SHAKING	Not felt	Weak	Light	Moderate	Strong	Very strong	Severe	Violent	Extreme
DAMAGE	none	none	none	Very light	Light	Moderate	Moderate/Heavy	Heavy	V. Heavy

Source: United States Geological Survey.

GEOLOGY continued

in March 2012 by a research team led by geophysicist Nicholas Schmerr of the Department of Terrestrial Magnetism at the Carnegie Institution of Washington in Washington, D.C. The asthenosphere is the layer of hot, partially melted mantle rock beneath the tectonic plates, the approximately 30 rigid pieces of Earth's crust and upper mantle. Earth's continents are embedded within the tops of these plates. As the plates slowly drift over the hot, flowing rock, they carry the continents into ever-changing positions. The scientific study of these changes is called plate tectonics.

Schmerr's team, which was sponsored by NASA, detected the previously unknown melted layer by analyzing the arrival times of earthquake-generated seismic waves at seismometers around the world. By comparing the arrival times, heights, and shapes of these seismic waves at various locations, the team was able to estimate the depth and properties of layers under the Pacific Ocean basin. The scientists concluded that a molten layer,

possibly including water, lies on top of the partially melted asthenosphere, enhancing the ability of the continents to drift about. This molten layer varies in depth from about 55 to 75 kilometers (34 to 47 miles), is only a few kilometers thick, and is present in only some locations. This new clue about the planet's outermost layers was expected to help scientists gain a better understanding of the dynamics of plate tectonics.

Mexico earthquake. On March 20, 2012, a magnitude 7.4 earthquake struck central and southern Mexico, centered near Acapulco. The quake killed at least two people and destroyed thousands of homes. Despite the low loss of life, it was one of the strongest quakes to occur in Mexico since an 8.1-magnitude temblor in 1985. The 2012 quake, which generated powerful aftershocks, occurred as a result of *thrust faulting* (in which the edge of one tectonic plate is thrust beneath an adjoining plate) at or near the boundary between the Cocos and North America tectonic plates.   ■ William Hay

GREAT CENTRAL U.S. SHAKEOUT DRILL

Students practice taking shelter under their desks during "The Great Central U.S. ShakeOut Drill" on Feb. 7, 2012. More than 2.4 million people at schools, workplaces, homes, and other locations in nine central U.S. states participated in the earthquake-awareness event, sponsored by the Federal Emergency Management Agency and other federal and state agencies. The annual event is meant to educate the public on how best to seek protection during an earthquake. Organizers recommend that people drop to the ground when they feel an earthquake, take cover under a sturdy desk or table, and hold onto the desk or table until shaking stops. If there is no such shelter nearby, people are urged to get on the ground next to an interior wall or low-lying furniture and to cover their heads with their arms and hands. Other recommendations are provided for different circumstances. Similar "shakeouts" are held each year in other parts of the United States and in other countries.

Get Ready to Shake Out.

DROP! COVER! HOLD ON!   ShakeOut
The Great Central U.S.
February 7, 2012
10:15 a.m.
Register at www.ShakeOut.org/centralus

Rare Earths: The Essential Modern Metals

From iPods to electric cars to pilotless military drones, many of the most important technologies of the 21st century are made possible by the special properties of chemical elements known as "rare earths." Rare earth elements are a group of 17 chemically similar metals. Fifteen of these metals make up a series of elements called lanthanides, which are grouped in the periodic table under the *atomic numbers* 57 through 71. The atomic number of an element is the number of *protons* (positively charged particles) in the *nucleus* (core) of an atom. The lanthanides, in order of atomic number, are lanthanum (La), cerium (Ce), praseodymium (Pr), neodymium (Nd), promethium (Pm), samarium (Sm), europium (Eu), gadolinium (Gd), terbium (Tb), dysprosium (Dy), holmium (Ho), erbium (Er), thulium (Tm), ytterbium (Yb), and lutetium (Lu). The other two rare earths are scandium (Sc, atomic number 21) and yttrium (Y, atomic number 39). These metals have similar properties to lanthanides and are often found in the same deposits of *ore* (accumulations of metal-rich rock).

Rare earths tend to lose three *electrons* (negatively charged particles) when forming chemical compounds. In addition, the electrons in rare earth atoms tend to exist in complex patterns, with variations in the number of electrons in the inner shell of the atom (rather than in the outermost shells, where most other elements vary in electron number). The unique chemical characteristics of rare earths can influence the chemical states of other elements and enhance the magnetic properties, electrical conductivity, light absorption, strength, high temperature tolerance, and other useful properties of materials.

Aside from a few exceptions, such as lutetium and terbium, rare earths are not actually rare. However, they are difficult to find in sufficient quantities in any one location. These metals are dispersed in tiny amounts throughout Earth's crust and are often surrounded by other minerals, such as bastnaesite and monazite. Separating rare earth metals from extracted ore is a complex, expensive process. Only a few locations in the world have rare earth deposits that are concentrated enough to make mining profitable. Approximately 35 percent of the world's rare earth deposits are found in China, while the United States contains an estimated 13 percent. Australia also has economically significant rare earth reserves.

A wide range of cutting-edge technologies use components made from rare earths. These components are used in televisions, smartphones, and laptop computer batteries. They can also be found in medical diagnosis equipment, fiber-optic cables, and aircraft engines. The special conductive properties of rare earths enable hard drives to store increased amounts of information in a smaller-than-typical space. Rare earths are also important ingredients in "clean energy" technology. For example, cerium is used in fuel additives to reduce pollution emissions from vehicles by *catalyzing* (enhancing) the burning of carbon particulates, as well as in solar panels to absorb ultraviolet light. In another example, the Chevrolet Volt, an extended-range

The Rare Earth Group

The rare earths consist of 17 chemical elements, 15 of which are known as lanthanides. The lanthanides have atomic numbers from 57 through 71. The rare earth elements with the atomic numbers 21 and 39 are chemically similar to lanthanides. Rare earths can enhance the magnetic properties, electrical conductivity, strength, and other useful properties of materials.

Element	Atomic Number
Lanthanides	
Lanthanum (La)	57
Cerium (Ce)	58
Praseodymium (Pr)	59
Neodymium (Nd)	60
Promethium (Pm)	61
Samarium (Sm)	62
Europium (Eu)	63
Gadolinium (Gd)	64
Terbium (Tb)	65
Dysprosium (Dy)	66
Holmium (Ho)	67
Erbium (Er)	68
Thulium (Tm)	69
Ytterbium (Yb)	70
Lutetium (Lu)	71
Others	
Scandium (Sc)	21
Yttrium (Y)	39

electric car produced by General Motors Company of Detroit, uses 3.2 kilograms (7 pounds) of rare earth elements in magnets inside the motor. A large wind turbine capable of providing electric power to 2,400 homes uses about 300 kilograms (661 pounds) of neodymium in its magnets.

The government of China, the world's primary producer of rare earths, cut its annual export quotas for these elements by almost 40 percent in 2010, arguing that the restrictions were necessary because of the severe environmental impact of rare earth mining. The complicated process of extracting ore and treating it with toxic acids to separate minerals from the ore produces millions of tons of wastewater and harmful chemical by-products. In 1998, chemical processing was halted at the Mountain Pass mine—a mine in California's Mojave Desert that had formerly been the United States' leading producer of rare earths—after radioactive wastewater flooded nearby Ivanpah Dry Lake. Half of China's rare earths come from a mine in the Inner Mongolian city of Baotou, where mining has contaminated the landscape and resulted in reservoirs full of toxic wastewater.

The United States, European Union, and Japan——all of which depend on China's supply of rare earths—maintained that China's trade policies gave that nation an unfair economic advantage by limiting the ability of electronics manufacturers in other countries to compete with Chinese companies. China's production of electronics technology was soaring in 2012 as a result of the government's financial support and the unfettered supply of rare earth resources, as well as minimal environmental regulations in that nation.

Restricted access to China's rare earths is not only an economic disadvantage for the United States; it also has national security implications. Much U.S. military technology, such as Predator drones, night-vision goggles, and smart bombs, depends on China's rare earth supply. In 2011, the U.S. Department of Defense announced several measures to ensure access to China's rare earths, such as authorizing U.S. defense contractors, which are exempt from China's export restrictions, to purchase rare earths on behalf of the Pentagon. Nevertheless, many market observers advocated for renewed domestic production of rare earths in the United States to meet the defense industry's needs.

Mountain Pass Mine

Mountain Pass mine, a rare earth mine in the Mojave Desert of California, was reopened in 2012 after being closed since 1998 because of radioactive pollution problems. The operator of the mine—Molycorp Inc. of Greenwood Village, Colorado—renovated and modernized the facility to meet environmental standards of the federal government. Molycorp scientists estimated that the mine contained 1.33 billion kilograms (2.94 billion pounds) of proven or probable rare earth reserves.

The mining company Molycorp Inc. of Greenwood Village, Colorado, reopened the Mountain Pass rare earth mine in 2012. Renovation and modernization of the facility to meet U.S. environmental standards cost more than $1 billion. In April 2012, Molycorp estimated that the Mountain Pass mine contained 1.33 billion kilograms (2.94 billion pounds) of proven or probable rare earth reserves. According to Rare Element Resources Ltd. of Lakewood, Colorado, its rare earth mine under development in Bear Lodge, Wyoming, in 2012 was capable of producing as much as 10,000 metric tons (11,023 tons) of ore annually. At a mine on Mount Weld

in Australia, Lynas Corporation Ltd. hoped to produce 22,000 metric tons (24,250 tons) of rare earth ore annually starting in 2012. A Lynas-operated rare earth refinery in Malaysia was expected to help ease the international tension over China's export restrictions.

Some technology firms are embracing alternative methods to meet their rare earth needs. Several Japanese companies have "urban mining" programs to recover rare earths from discarded cell phones and other electronic devices. Japanese electronics manufacturer Hitachi Ltd. began a recycling program in 2010 to recover rare earths contained in computer hard drives and air conditioners. In 2012, Japanese automaker Honda Motor Co. Inc., together with Japan Metals and Chemicals Co. Ltd., began a program to recover certain rare earth elements, including lanthanum, from used car batteries.

The potential scarcity of rare earths has inspired important research in the field of magnetics. Magnets account for about one-fifth of global rare earth consumption. When iron is magnetized, its magnetic field is vulnerable to disruption from temperature or electrical changes. Some of the strongest magnets blend iron with boron and the rare earths neodymium, which helps iron resist demagnetizing forces, and dysprosium, which reshapes the magnetic field to strengthen it against heat. Magnets made with rare earths can reach a power of about 56 megagauss-oersteds (MGOe, the measure of magnetic field strength). By contrast, the strongest magnets without rare earths typically reach a power of about 10 MGOe. Some researchers are developing ways of using fewer rare earths in magnet *alloys* (metal mixtures) or investigating metal substitutes for rare earths.

At General Electric Company's Global Research Center in Niskayuna, New York, scientists in 2011 and 2012 researched nanocomposite magnets, which are quiltlike composites of nanoparticles that interact in ways that boost magnetic properties. (A *nanoparticle* is roughly 300 to 500 times the diameter of a single atom.) General Electric scientists hoped to develop a nanocomposite magnet for use in wind turbines that would both decrease the amount of rare earths needed by 80 percent and boost magnetic strength by 40 percent.

The government of Japan devoted $150 million to magnet research in 2011. Scientists at the National Institute for Materials Science in Tsukuba, Japan, developed fine-grain magnets free of dysprosium that are 60 percent more stable than other dysprosium-free, neodymium-based magnets. Japanese automaker engineers at Toyota Motor Corporation have worked on a program to rid the company's cars of rare earth magnets by developing a motor based on electromagnets.

Rare earth metals will continue to be essential ingredients in components of high-tech gadgetry and clean-energy technology. With the opening of new rare earth mines, the implementation of rare earth recycling programs, and innovations in the field of magnetics, multinational technology industries may soon become less dependent on China for their supply of these special, valuable metals. ■ Scott Witmer

Wind Turbine Magnets

Large, powerful wind turbines typically contain substantial amounts of rare earth elements, such as neodymium and dysprosium, inside their magnets. Neodymium helps the iron in magnets resist demagnetizing forces, and dysprosium reshapes the magnetic field to strengthen it against heat. Magnets made with rare earths can reach much greater powers than magnets without rare earths. The extra magnetic power helps make the wind turbines capable of producing greater amounts of electric current.

■ MEDICAL RESEARCH

Success in transforming stem cells taken from human umbilical cord tissue into a type of cell found in the central nervous system was reported in January 2012 by biochemist James Hickman and colleagues at the University of Central Florida (UCF) in Orlando. Stem cells are immature cells that can *differentiate* (develop) into other kinds of cells, such as skin cells or brain cells or any of the hundreds of other different cell types in the body. The UCF researchers' achievement marked the first time that scientists had induced stem cells taken from umbilical cord tissue to change into mature, specialized cells.

The use of stem cells to treat disease has been the subject of considerable controversy. Most stem cell research has involved cells taken from human embryos provided by fertility clinics. But many people have opposed the use of such cells on ethical grounds. Thus, researchers have been searching for new sources for stem cells that perform as well as the embryonic stem cells.

SEE ALSO   THE SPECIAL REPORT
KNOCKING HEADS: THE DANGERS OF CONCUSSION
PAGE 70

One possibility is stem cells taken from adults. These cells are found in many kinds of human tissue However, they are difficult to locate and to harvest. Moreover, adult stem cells are not able to naturally produce every kind of human cell, a capability known as *pluripotency.*

Scientists have found ways to make adult stem cells pluripotent, but these transformed stem cells are often damaged and can give rise to cancer. Researchers prefer to work with cells that are naturally pluripotent and do not have the risks associated with adult stem cells. Stem cells from the umbilical cord seem to meet these requirements.

Production of nerve cells called oligodendrocytes *(AH lih go DEN dro sites)* from stem cells could yield future dividends in

TINY MICROSCOPE FITS ON A FINGERTIP

A fluorescing microscope for studying *neurons* (nerve cells) in the brains of mice, announced in September 2011, is so tiny that it easily fits on a fingertip. The device was developed by researchers at Stanford University in California. A fluorescing microscope detects light given off by objects that have briefly become *fluorescent* (light-emitting) by being infused with a special dye. Stanford scientists strap the tiny microscope to a mouse's head after boring a hole in the skull and covering the hole with a transparent protective layer. The scientists can then view neurons in action as the mouse walks, runs, or performs other actions. The recorded images can be downloaded to a computer for viewing. The scientists suggested many other uses for the microscope, including screening for the tuberculosis bacterium at remote clinics and onsite analysis of microorganisms in soil.

neural (of the nervous system) medicine, the UCF researchers noted. Oligodendrocytes produce a substance called myelin, which insulates nerve cells. This insulation makes it possible for nerve cells to conduct the electrical signals that control body movement and other functions.

The loss of myelin can cause electrical "short-circuiting" in nerves, which can lead to malfunctioning of the nervous system. Technology for producing oligodendrocytes, as demonstrated by the UCF research team, is likely to spur research into potential treatments for multiple sclerosis, spinal injuries, and other myelin-related disorders, analysts predict.

Multiple sclerosis research. In September 2011, researchers at the University of California at San Diego (UCSD) reported the results of a study involving inflammation in myelin. Such inflammation is associated with multiple sclerosis (MS), an often-progressive disease of the nervous system that can lead to spasms, muscle weakness, and loss of balance. Disease symptoms in advanced cases may include paralysis and vision loss. MS is an autoimmune disease, in which the cells of the immune system mistakenly attack the body's own tissues. In MS, the tissue under attack is myelin, which becomes inflamed and, over time, breaks down.

Working with mice that had been genetically altered to develop a condition simulating MS, the investigators examined how immune cells in the nervous system use fatty acids as an energy source when glucose— sugar in the blood—is in short supply. Glucose shortages can occur in inflamed tissue such as myelin affected by MS.

The scientists discovered that blocking the action of a single enzyme (a molecule that speeds up a chemical reaction) rendered the immune cells unable to metabolize (derive energy from) the fatty acids. The cells then starved and died, preventing them from further inflaming myelin tissue.

The agent used by the UCSD researchers to inhibit the enzyme was a prescription drug used to treat people with congestive heart failure. The scientists said that further research was needed to determine whether the drug would suppress the fatty acid-metabolizing enzyme in human MS

patients and reduce myelin inflammation.

In November 2011, researchers with the University of California at San Francisco (UCSF) reported significant results from a Phase II clinical trial of ocrelizumab, an anti-MS compound designed by scientists with the pharmaceutical company Roche. A Phase II drug trial is conducted among a group of human volunteers to determine if a drug works as intended. It follows a Phase I trial, which is conducted among a smaller group to evaluate the drug's safety and to identify possible side effects.

The UCSF scientists tested ocrelizumab in 220 patients with MS over a 24-week period at hospitals in the United States, Canada, and Europe. The volunters were randomly divided into four groups: one group that received interferon-beta, a standard, FDA-approved drug for MS patients; two groups that received ocrelizumab but at different doses; and a control group that received a placebo (an inactive substance).

To gauge the effectiveness of the treatments, doctors performed monthly magnetic resonance imaging (MRI) brain scans of the patients. The researchers counted the number of lesions (abnormal structures) in the scans; such lesions indicate inflamed areas. They also compared the severity and frequency of symptom relapses in study subjects among the four groups.

The results of this trial showed that patients who received ocrelizumab fared better and showed fewer signs of the disease than patients who received interferon-beta or a placebo. Overall, the trial found that ocrelizumab led to an 89-percent reduction in the formation of inflamed areas in nerve tissue and reduced the number of relapses in study subjects. Neurologist Stephen Hauser, lead author of the study, described the finding as "remarkable," but noted the importance of testing the drug in a larger group of subjects over a longer period of time. Such testing was planned for the Phase III trials, for which recruitment of study subjects was already in progress.

Breath test for MS. In October, scientists with Technion, the Israel Institute of Technology in Haifa, announced that they had successfully tested a device capable of detecting chemical compounds associated

MEDICAL RESEARCH continued

with MS in the breath of test subjects. The device consists of an array of highly sensitive sensors.

In current medical practice, there are two widely accepted methods of diagnosing MS: an MRI scan of brain and spinal tissue and a spinal tap to extract and analyze the fluid that bathes the brain and spinal cord. Both methods have drawbacks. The MRI scans are complex and expensive, and spinal taps are an invasive procedure with some associated risks. Investigators have long sought a simpler, noninvasive test to confirm the presence of MS.

The researchers tested their device on 34 MS patients and 17 healthy volunteers. They found that the breath sensors confirmed the presence of MS just as accurately as a spinal tap.

Technion scientists have also been working on breath tests to detect cancers of the lung, colon, breast, and prostate gland, as well as cancers of the head and neck. The scientists recommended further research to develop clinical breath tests for cancer, MS, and other diseases.

Autism and brain organization. Researchers have long sought to understand how the brains of people with autism differ from those of normal people. In December, researchers at Children's Hospital in Boston reported evidence that people with autism have disorganized bundles of *neurons* (nerve cells) in their brains. Such structures carry signals to and from various parts of the nervous system.

Autism is a developmental disorder that emerges in the first three years of life. Individuals with the disorder are unable to develop normal social and communications skills. Children with autism are typically withdrawn and do not form friendships or engage in interactive games or other activities.

Scientists have long theorized that autism is caused by chemical and biological abnormalities in the brain. Some genetic and brain-cell studies indicate that autism is caused by abnormalities in the ways in which neurons in the brain connect with one another. The researchers at Children's Hospital designed their study to test that theory.

The research team conducted MRI brain scans of 40 patients with a condition called tuberous sclerosis complex (TSC) and 29 healthy control subjects. TSC is a genetic disorder of the brain that can cause thinking and behavioral problems. About 50 percent of children with TSC also develop autism.

Using a special MRI technique called diffusion tensor imaging (DTI), the researchers

CELLS SNAG BACTERIA

A "cage" of special protein (red, below) entraps toxic Shigella bacteria (green) inside a cell that has been invaded by the germs. Shigella can cause intestinal illness in people. Scientists with the Pasteur Institute in Paris announced their discovery of the entrapment phenomenon in December 2011. The scientists explained that a Shigella bacterium hijacks cellular proteins to make a cometlike tail soon after it invades a cell. The microbe needs the tail to propel itself through the host cell. The invaded cell may respond to the invader's protein-snatching by producing other proteins that ensnare the microbe in a cagelike mesh. Still other proteins then digest the invader. The Pasteur scientists noted that because the cellular mechanism for entrapment is complex, invaded cells corral Shigella invaders only about 10 to 30 percent of the time. They speculated that further research into the cellular "cage building" might eventually lead to a new class of antibiotics.

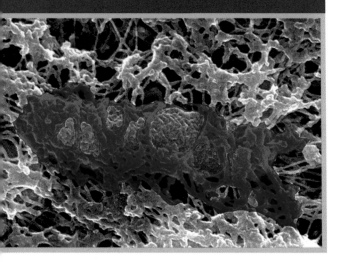

examined the corpus callosum, a large bundle of nerve fibers that enables the right and left halves of the brain to communicate with each other. In DTI, an MRI scan measures the *diffusion* (spread) of water molecules through living tissue. Because the molecules travel relatively easily along bundles of nerve fibers in the corpus callosum, the technique highlights the neurological connections and *orientation* (direction) of the nerve fibers.

The scans revealed considerable nerve-pathway disorganization in the TSC patients with autism. The TSC patients who were not autistic had only a slight disorganization compared with the control subjects, whose corpus callosum neurons exhibited normal orientation and organization. The scans also revealed evidence of damaged myelin in nerve tissue of the subjects with autism but little or no such evidence in the other volunteers.

The researchers noted that the ability to identify distinctive structural differences in the brains of infants and toddlers with autism could lead to earlier diagnosis of autism. According to medical experts, medical and other interventions are most likely to be effective in individuals with autism when begun at an early age.

New light on blood cell production. In research published in January 2012, a study of progenitor cells—cells that can change into various types of blood cells and immune system cells—yielded new knowledge about how red blood cells are produced in the body. The research was reported by scientists at the Walter and Eliza Hall Institute of Medical Research in Melbourne, Australia.

The research team studied progenitor cells in mice. At times of bodily stress, the progenitor cells respond by increasing blood cell production. For example, serious bleeding, infections, or the side-effects of cancer chemotherapy can push progenitor cells into action.

The scientists were especially interested in a subset of progenitors called *myeloid* (within bone marrow) progenitor cells. These cells produce *megakaryocytes* (MEHG uh KAR ee uh sytz), cells that are known to give rise to platelets, the colorless blood cells that play an important role in blood clotting.

The researchers discovered that megakaryocytes can themselves develop into red blood cells. This was an entirely unexpected finding. In additional research, the investigators found that other kinds of progenitor cells are also able to develop into red blood cells.

The investigators were able to prompt progenitor cells to develop into red blood cells by stimulating them with specific *cytokines* (SY tuh kynz), hormonelike substances, or combinations of cytokines. Cytokines are secreted by certain cells of the immune system to produce effects on other cells.

The researchers expressed the hope that their findings would lead to a better understanding of genetic changes that set the stage for the onset of certain blood diseases. Further research, they speculated, could in time yield improved treatments for such diseases.

Devious leprosy bacterium. The bacterium that causes leprosy—*Mycobacterium leprae*—has a remarkable ability to evade the defenses of the human immune system. It does so by inhibiting the body's ability to respond to the infection, scientists at the University of California at Los Angeles (UCLA) reported in January.

Leprosy is a *chronic* (long-lasting) infectious disease that affects the skin, the peripheral nervous system—the nervous system outside the brain and spinal cord—the upper respiratory tract, and the eyes. The condition can lead to the disfigurement of the hands, face, and feet. According to the World Health Organization, an agency of the United Nations, more than 200,000 new cases of leprosy are reported each year in developing countries.

The UCLA investigators studied tiny bits of genetic material called micro-RNA's. These are small segments of RNA, the large molecules that encode proteins to carry out the various activities in a living cell. The micro-RNA's do not *code for* (produce the instructions for) proteins; instead, they bind to particular segments of RNA and block their replication during protein *synthesis* (formation).

The research team discovered that a particular micro-RNA associated with *M. leprae*,

MEDICAL RESEARCH continued

GUT MICROBES WITH INFLUENCE

A major study of gut microbes in three distinct communities of human subjects indicate that these microbes—which inhabit the human digestive system and, particularly, the intestines—may interact with the human brain in surprising ways. The study, led by biologist Jeffrey Gordon of Washington University in St. Louis and reported in the May 9, 2012, online issue of *Nature,* analyzed feces from people in Malawi, Venezuela, and several large American cities to determine the microbial populations in their intestines. The microbes varied from community to community because of different diets. They also varied among people within communities. For example, the researchers found that obese people host different gut microbes than people of average or low weight. The scientists theorize that the microbes in the obese people may send "eat more" messages to their brains. The scientists also discovered a correlation between certain gut microbial populations and depression in people. They speculated that further research might yield treatments for such health problems as obesity and depression based on manipulating populations of gut microbes.

called hsa-mir-21, blocked the functioning of a human gene that enables macrophages, a type of cell in the immune system, to utilize vitamin D to fight infection. When the researchers neutralized the activity of hsa-mir-21 in macrophages, the cells regained their ability to exploit Vitamin D and were again able to fight infection.

Dermatologist Robert Modlin, a senior member of the research team, said of this finding, "The leprosy pathogen was able to effectively evade the host's immune response by regulating critical immune-system genes. It's like having the enemy sending a decoy message to your combat troops and telling them to lower their weapons." He and the other members of the team said that they were amazed by the devastating effects that just a single micro-RNA had on the ability of immune-system cells to fight infection.

To determine if hsa-mir-21 might have the same effect on other infectious diseases, the researchers introduced the micro-RNA into human macrophages that they then infected with *Mycobacterium tuberculosis,* the type of bacteria that causes tuberculosis. They found that the micro-RNA blocked the disease-fighting activity of the macrophages just as it had when *M. leprae* was the infectious agent.

Discovery of micro-RNA's role in TB infection could eventually lead to new treatments that by-pass the problem of bacterial resistance to antibiotics, speculated immunologist Barry Bloom of Harvard University in Cambridge, Massachusetts. Many strains of TB have developed resistance to currently available antibiotics, and medical researchers are seeking novel approaches to treating the disease.

The UCLA researchers recommended more studies to examine the role of hsa-mir-21 in infection by disease pathogens. They also recommended further investigation into the ways that micro-RNA's might be involved in the onset and progression of such noninfectious diseases as cancer and heart disease. ■ David L. Dreier

NEUROSCIENCE

A novel technique for electronically converting brain waves created as an individual thinks into words was reported in January 2012 by scientists at the University of California, Berkeley, and three other institutions. The scientists said that further development of the technology might lead to a device that can generate the sounds of words that are imagined by people who are unable to speak.

SEE ALSO THE SPECIAL REPORT KNOCKING HEADS: THE DANGERS OF CONCUSSIONS PAGE 70

NEURAL PATHWAYS IN BRAIN

Details of the organization of *neural* (nerve cell) pathways in the brain are revealed in an image created with a technique called diffusion spectrum magnetic resonance imaging. This technique allows researchers to trace the movement of water molecules along the intersections of nerve fibers to show the orientation of each fiber at each intersection. The imaging technique, developed by neuroscientist Van Wedeen of Harvard Medical School, showed that the organization of the brain's neuron network is simpler than previously believed. Rather than forming a spaghetti-like jumble of nerve fibers, the neurons are arranged in an orderly three-dimensional grid-like structure with different pathways (shown as different colors) that crisscross each other.

A team led by Berkeley neuroscientist Brian N. Pasley worked with 15 patients, each of whom had a hole cut in their skull as part of a surgical procedure for determining the place in their brain where their epileptic seizures began. Surgeons had positioned electrodes on the surface of each patient's *cerebral cortex* (outer "gray matter," responsible for higher mental functions) to monitor their brain activity for a week. While the patients were in the hospital for this procedure, Pasley's team visited them to study the functions of Wernicke's area, a part of the cerebral cortex associated with speech and language.

The neuroscientists monitored the electrical activity of the patients' Wernicke's areas as they listened to 5 to 10 minutes of recorded conversation. The researchers found that each word heard by the patients corresponded to a particular pattern in an auditory *spectrogram* (a visual representation of the brain's electrical activity spread into *frequencies* [wavelengths]). Plugging the frequency data into a computer model allowed the scientists to match each pattern to a particular spoken word—and then to reproduce the sounds of the words electronically.

Although this experiment involved the reproduction of words that were heard by the volunteers, Pasley said that similar technology could be applied to words thought by people—because the same areas of the brain are likely activated in both cases. Pasley added that further investigation might make it possible to use the technology to accurately reproduce the sounds of imagined words. Such a breakthrough would allow people who cannot speak because of a stroke, paralysis, or some other neurological condition to communicate verbally.

Translating thoughts into walking. Research published in July 2011 shed light on how the brain's electrical activity controls

NEUROSCIENCE continued

the motions of walking. The research also raised the possibility that a special electronic "brain cap" could help restore walking ability to paralyzed people.

The research was the latest in a series of studies led by Jose Contreras-Vidal, professor of *kinesiology* (the science of human motion) at the University of Maryland in College Park. Contreras-Vidal investigated the use of a sensor-lined cap that can read electrical signals in the brain and translate those signals into body movement. The inside of the cap is lined with electrodes that can detect the brain's electrical signals without being surgically connected to the brain's surface (as is needed in most other research into brain signals).

The Maryland team used an electroencephalograph (EEG) to record the brain activity of cap-wearing individuals as they moved their legs on a treadmill. The team then matched specific patterns of EEG-recorded signals with specific movements of the ankles, knees, and hip. The scientists noted that further research could allow them to develop brain-computer *interfaces* (electronic connections between the brain and a computer) that would translate thoughts into electronic instructions for leg movement. These instructions, in turn, would prompt prosthetic devices worn by paralyzed individuals to move the individuals' legs in a normal human gait.

Contreras-Vidal's team previously reported the experimental results of using this technology to enable computer users to control a computer curser with their thoughts. These cap-wearing computer users were able to control the cursor just as well as the volunteers who had electrodes surgically implanted in their brains.

These results and the results reported in July were encouraging to Contreras-Vidal, who was collaborating with several institutions to develop thought-controlled robotic prosthetic devices. These devices would permit people with paralysis to move their arms and legs without the need for surgically implanted electrodes.

Clairvoyance. In one of the first studies of its kind, scientists in August 2011 reported how the brain makes the numerous predictions it makes every day about events that will happen seconds in the future. Examples of such predictions—which are a form of *clairvoyance* (keenness of mental perception)—include knowing whether a dropped glass will break, whether a splash of water will hit you, and where a car will stop when brakes are gradually applied.

The scientists, led by psychologist Jeffrey M. Zacks of Washington University in St. Louis, analyzed the brains of volunteers by using functional magnetic resonance imaging (fMRI), a brain-imaging technology that shows areas of increased activity in the brain as represented by increased blood flow. The scientists focused on the mid-brain dopamine system (MDS), in which brain activity is heightened by sudden, unexpected events.

The volunteers' brain activity was examined as they watched videos of people performing such everyday tasks as washing a car or washing clothes, and as they were asked to predict what would happen next when the video was suddenly stopped in the midst of the task. As the individuals made their predictions, the fMRI images revealed noticeable activity in several mid-brain regions, including a region called the substantia nigra. This region is damaged in individuals with Parkinson disease, Alzheimer's disease, and certain other neurological disorders.

Zacks explained that successful predictions about everyday events require a smooth stream of consciousness about circumstances at the present time. When circumstances suddenly and unexpectedly change, the stream of consciousness may be broken, and the brain's MDS, including the substantia nigra, may become more active in an attempt to adapt. If this brain region is damaged, the individual may have difficulty adapting to the constantly changing events of everyday life. Zacks said that his team's findings could lead to improved diagnoses of neurological disorders in early stages, allowing for earlier treatment interventions. ■ A. J. Smuskiewicz

PIGEONS CAN LEARN MATH SKILLS

A pigeon pecks at a computer touch screen in an experiment testing the bird's ability to learn abstract mathematical concepts, including sequencing numbers. In December 2011, psychologist Damian Scarf of the University of Otago in New Zealand described how his team first taught pigeons how to correctly order images representing the numbers 1 through 3 on a computer screen. The birds were rewarded with snacks when they pecked on the correct images with their beaks. The scientists next taught the pigeons to sequence pairs of images representing the symbols 1 through 9. The results led the researchers to conclude that pigeons are more capable of understanding mathematical concepts than expected. In fact, the skills of the birds are similar to those of rhesus monkeys. Scarf and his colleagues noted that if pigeons—which are not considered a particularly intelligent bird—have these math skills, other birds probably possess them as well.

NOBEL PRIZES

The 2011 Nobel Prizes in science were awarded for research on the immune system; for the discovery that the universe is expanding at an accelerating rate; and for the discovery of quasicrystals, a previously unknown form of matter. Each prize was worth about $1.4 million.

The Nobel Prize in physiology or medicine. American biologist Bruce A. Beutler shared the 2011 Nobel Prize in physiology or medicine with Jules A. Hoffman of Luxembourg and Canadian-born scientist Ralph M. Steinman for their research on the immune system. Working individually, the three scientists made key discoveries that answered fundamental questions about how the body defends itself against infection. The discoveries paved the way for research that resulted in the development of new treatments for infections, cancer, and inflammatory diseases.

Beutler, a scientist at the Scripps Research Institute in La Jolla, California, shared one-half of the prize with Hoffman of the National Center of Scientific Research in Strasbourg, France. The two scientists made key discoveries on how the immune system first recognizes such infectious microbes as viruses and bacteria and activates the body's defenses against them.

Steinman was awarded the other half of the prize for his discovery of dendritic cells, a type of white blood cell that helps adapt the immune system to react to different infectious agents. The fundamental research by these three scientists has led to the development of vaccines and drugs that treat disease by boosting the body's natural defense systems.

The Nobel Assembly at the Karolinska Institute in Stockholm, which awards the prize in physiology or medicine, announced the prize on Oct. 3, 2011. At that time, the Assembly was unaware that Steinman had died on September 30. The Nobel Assembly has a long-established policy of not awarding prizes posthumously (after death). However, in this case, the Nobel Assembly issued a statement that the prize would be awarded to Steinman, because he was alive when the Assembly had chosen to honor him.

The Nobel Prize in physics. Three United States-born astronomers won the Nobel Prize in physics for their revolutionary discovery that the universe is expanding at an accelerating rate. The scientists theorized that the mysterious antigravitational force known as dark energy is the cause of the acceleration. The prize winners were Saul Perlmutter of the University of California, Berkeley; Adam G. Riess of the Space Telescope Science Institute and Johns Hopkins University; and Brian P. Schmidt of the Australian National University. Schmidt is also a citizen of Australia.

The finding by the three astronomers expands on another revolutionary discovery made in 1929 by American astronomer Edwin Hubble. He had observed that the farther apart galaxies are from one another, the faster they are moving away from one another. From this, Hubble determined that the universe is expanding at a uniform rate. Later scientists found evidence that the expansion began 13.7 billion years ago with a cosmic explosion known as the big bang. For many decades, astronomers believed that the expansion was slowing down because of the counter force of gravity on the universe.

Then in 1998, Perlmutter, Riess, and Schmidt shocked the scientific community with their finding that galaxies are actually speeding away from each other at a faster and faster rate. Studies of the light from *supernovae* (exploding stars) indicate that this expansion began about 5 billion years ago. To account for the acceleration, scientists concluded that the universe was full of some kind of invisible energy, which was named dark energy. Later measurements confirmed that approximately 70 percent of the *mass* (amount of matter) of the universe consists of dark energy.

The Nobel Prize in chemistry was awarded on Oct. 5, 2011, to Israeli chemist

THE EXPANDING UNIVERSE

Three scientists were awarded the Nobel Prize in physics in 2011 for their discovery that the universe is expanding at an accelerating rate. The scientists theorized that a mysterious, antigravitational force called dark energy is causing the acceleration. Physicists generally agree that dark energy and dark matter make up most of the universe. Dark matter is an invisible form of matter that does not give off or reflect radiation. They estimate that the "normal" matter in stars, planets, and living things comprises only about 5 percent of the universe (right). Scientists do not know what dark energy is or what causes it.

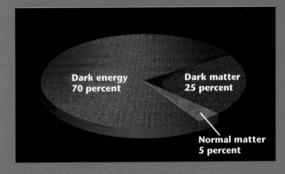

Dark energy
70 percent

Dark matter
25 percent

Normal matter
5 percent

The scientists arrived at their conclusion about the acceleration of the universe by studying a number of Type 1a supernovae (left). A supernova is an exploding star. All Type 1a supernovae are thought to be of a similar size and brightness, so scientists can accurately measure their relative distance from Earth. Supernovae that are from 4 billion to 7 billion light-years from Earth are dimmer—and thus, farther away—than they would be if the expansion rate of the universe were slowing.

From their supernova observations, the scientists concluded that about 5 billion years ago, the universe began to expand at a faster rate. About 10 billion years ago—about 4 billion years after the big bang—the rate of expansion had slowed. The big bang is the cosmic explosion that scientists think began the expansion of the universe. Some scientists had predicted that the expansion would eventually stop and gravity would pull all galaxies back together. Now scientists are convinced tha the universe will continue to expand forever.

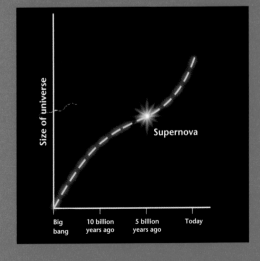

Size of universe

Supernova

Big
bang

10 billion
years ago

5 billion
years ago

Today

NOBEL PRIZES continued

Dan Shechtman of Technion—The Israeli Institute of Technology. Shechtman received the award for his 1982 discovery of quasicrystals. Quasicrystals are a previously unknown form of matter with a structure that scientists had believed was impossible.

Crystals are substances that are made of atoms arranged in an ordered repeating pattern. Most solid materials consist of crystals. However, the atoms of a quasicrystal are ordered *but not repeating.* It was later discovered that a quasicrystal's structure closely follows a mathematical principle called the golden section. The golden section—or "phi"—is a special number approximately equal to 1.618; it appears many times in geometry and is often used in art and architecture.

Shechtman's discovery first met with strong resistance from fellow scientists. After more examples were brought to light, a belief in the existence of the quasicrystal gained wide acceptance. The Royal Swedish Academy of Sciences characterized Shechtman's discovery as fundamentally changing the way scientists look at solid matter. Scientists and educators note that basic chemistry textbooks have had to be revised to accommodate the concept of quasicrystals.

■ Barbara Mayes

DAN SHECHTMAN, DISCOVERER OF QUASICRYSTALS

Research chemist Dan Shechtman appears at a press conference at Technion (The Israel Institute of Technology, Haifa) on Oct. 5, 2011. The Royal Swedish Academy of Sciences had just announced its decision to award Shechtman the Nobel Prize in chemistry for his 1982 discovery of quasicrystals. In quasicrystals, atoms align in regular patterns according to mathematical rules. However, unlike all other known crystals, the pattern does not repeat. The difference is obvious when the pattern is rotated: The inherent pattern of atoms in a crystal looks the same in any rotation, but the pattern in quasicrystals looks different in rotation. Years after Shechtman's discovery, other scientists began to look for quasicrystals. Scientists in Sweden discovered them in certain kinds of steel. Until 2009, most scientists believed that quasicrystals could only occur in *synthetic* (human-made) materials. But in that year, scientists in Russia found the remnants of a meteorite (right) in a riverbed. Inside the rock, they detected quasicrystals. The discovery confirmed that quasicrystals can occur in nature and can long remain stable.

■ NUTRITION

Young children will eat more vegetables and reduce the amount of calories they consume in a meal when vegetables are *puréed* (finely mashed) and hidden in food. A research team at Pennsylvania State University (Penn State) in University Park published this finding in the September 2011 issue of the *American Journal of Clinical Nutrition*.

The research team recruited children attending a day care center on the campus of Penn State to participate in a meal study. The test group included boys and girls ranging in ages from 3 to 6 years with the following racial profile: 72 percent white; 23 percent Asian; and 5 percent African American.

The researchers scheduled the study for three days on which the children were served breakfast, lunch, a snack, and dinner in the daycare center. The meals were designed to vary the energy content—the calories—while keeping the serving sizes the same.

On the first day of the study, the children ate regular meals that had with no hidden vegetables and relatively high calorie contents. On the second day, the meals had enough mashed-up, hidden vegetables in the entrées to reduce calories by 15 percent. On the third day, meals with more hidden vegetables reduced total calories by 25 percent. Examples of altered foods included zucchini bread containing varying amounts of puréed zucchini (breakfast); puréed broccoli, cauliflower, and tomato incorporated into pasta sauce for spaghetti (lunch); and puréed cauliflower and squash mixed into a chicken noodle casserole (dinner). Whether original recipes or recipes with hidden vegetables, the dishes looked the same and had a consistent texture.

Using a computer randomization program, the researchers scheduled the meals for each child so that the test subjects would not all be served the same food mixtures at the same time. The children were able to eat as much or as little as they pleased. All leftover food was weighed to determine how much the children ate.

A few days after completing the meal study, the children were given food sam-

SEE ALSO CONSUMER SCIENCE THE "SKINNY" ON GLUTEN PAGE 101

ples similar to the entrées they had eaten during the study. The children were asked to taste each sample and rate the food by pointing to cartoon faces representing "yummy," "okay," or "yucky." About 70 percent of the children rated all the entrées "okay" or "yummy."

The researchers determined that the children ate consistent amounts of food across the three test days. Thus, the children ate more vegetables and fewer calories when the entrées contained more hidden vegetables. Vegetable intake was 0.8 serving per day when standard meals were served. However when puréed vegetables replaced 15 percent of calories, daily vegetable intake was 1.5 servings; and when vegetables replaced 25 percent of calories, daily vegetable intake was 1.9 servings.

Noting that the study lasted only three days, the researchers acknowledged that these findings may not reflect outcomes for longer periods of time. However, the results provide encouragement to children's caregivers, the researchers asserted, to experiment with hiding vegetables in familiar foods with the intent of decreasing children's calorie intake and increasing their vegetable intake.

Iodine deficiency. In a study sponsored by the Society for Endocrinology in the United Kingdom (U.K.) researchers found that young girls selected from geographically representative regions of the United Kingdom excreted low levels of iodine in their urine. This finding suggests that many adolescents in the United Kingdom may be iodine-deficient. Endocrinologist Mark Vanderpump and colleagues published their findings in the journal *Lancet* in June 2011.

Iodine deficiency is the leading preventable cause of mental retardation, particularly for babies of iodine-deficient mothers. Iodine deficiency also causes learning disabilities in growing children. In people of all ages, the deficiency can cause

NUTRITION continued

goiter, the enlargement of the thyroid gland.

The researchers selected nine locales in England, Northern Ireland, Scotland, and Wales. They recruited 810 schoolgirls ages 14 and 15 from these locales for the study, which was conducted during the midsummer and early-winter months of 2009. Participants collected urine samples each morning and answered survey questions about their dietary habits.

Data about levels of iodine in the girls' urine indicated that 69 percent of the study volunteers had an iodine deficiency and that 17 percent were moderately to severely iodine-deficient. Diet data collected during the study indicated that girls who reported drinking the most milk excreted the highest levels of urinary iodine. The data also showed that urinary iodine levels were higher in winter than in summer.

These findings, the Vanderpump researchers noted, matched feeding patterns in U.K. dairy cattle. The cattle eat iodine-enriched commercial feed as a supplement to pasture-feeding or as a replacement in the coldest winter months. Iodine passes from the feed into the cows' milk and, through dietary intake, into the bodies of people. Therefore, girls in the study who drank the most milk were likely to exhibit higher levels of iodine, the investigators reasoned.

According to standards established by the World Health Organization (WHO), a population is considered deficient in iodine if the median urine iodine excretion is less than 100 µg/L (micrograms per liter). In the Vanderpump study, the median concentration was 80.1 µg/L, raising concerns for their health and for the health of the British population at large.

Vanderpump and colleagues noted that in such countries as the United States and Switzerland, iodine is added to the food supply in the form of iodide-treated table salt. By contrast, commercial production of iodized salt is not common in the United Kingdom. Given the importance to public health of adequate iodine intake, Vanderpump and colleagues urged that more comprehensive studies of iodine status be conducted in the United Kingdom. They also recommended that U.K. authorities consider taking steps to add iodine to the food supply.

■ Catherine J. Klein and Amy Schweitzer

GOOD FOOD FOR GOOD HEALTH

New federal guidelines in 2012 mandated more health-conscious school lunches featuring increased selections of vegetables and fruits as well as low-fat, low-sodium foods. The guidelines apply to all school lunches that are subsidized by federal funds, affecting some 32 million schoolchildren, according to the U.S. Department of Agriculture. Secretary of Agriculture Tom Vilsack, accompanied by First Lady Michelle Obama, unveiled the new guidelines at a public elementary school in Alexandria, Virginia, on January 25. Mrs. Obama has championed improved nutrition and regular exercise for young people in her "Let's Move!" campaign. Nutrition experts and other health professionals have warned of a growing epidemic of childhood obesity in the United States. According to the Centers for Disease Control, more than one-third of all children and adolescents in the United States are overweight or obese.

OCEANOGRAPHY

The Canadian motion picture director James Cameron joined an exceptionally exclusive club in March 2012. In a submarine of his own design, Cameron became just the third person to visit the Challenger Deep, the deepest part of the world's oceans. The only previous such dive was performed in 1960 by the Swiss oceanographer Jacques Piccard and Lieutenant Don Walsh of the United States Navy.

The Challenger Deep is a depression in the floor of the Mariana Trench, a deep cut in the seabed of the Pacific Ocean off the east coast of the Philippines. The bottom of the Challenger Deep is about 10.9 kilometers (6.8 miles) below the surface. If Mount Everest, the world's tallest mountain, were placed in this depression, the top of the mountain would still be about 1.6 kilometers (1 mile) under water.

Cameron performed his dive in the *Deepsea Challenger*, a submersible he designed and built. He spent about three hours on the sea floor after a descent of about two hours. Cameron had hoped to collect samples of sea creatures and rocks. This proved impossible, however, when his sub's robot arm failed due to a hydraulic fluid leak. However, he was able to shoot some video.

Cameron is widely known for directing such Oscar-winning films as *Titanic* and *Avatar*. He has also made several undersea documentaries, including *Expedition: Bismarck* and *Ghosts of the Abyss*. Cameron announced that he planned to make still more dives to the Challenger Deep.

Oldest living organism. In February, Carlos Duarte, a professor at the University of Western Australia, announced the discovery of the oldest living organism—a 200,000-year-old sea grass. Called *Posidonia oceanic*, the sea grass is found throughout the Mediterranean Sea. It is also known as Neptune grass and Mediterranean tapeweed. The previous record for the oldest known living organism was held by a shrub native to Tasmania, Australia. It was estimated to be 43,000 years old.

Sea grass, unlike kelp and other seaweeds classed as algae, is a complex multicellular plant with roots, leaves, and flowers. A single patch of the sea grass can grow up

NEW SPECIES OF SEA LILY

Members of a previously unknown species of sea lily cling to a *seamount* (undersea mountaintop) off the coast of Antarctica. The discovery of the species, named *Ptilocrinus amezianeae,* was reported in September 2011 by French scientists. A sea lily is a flower-shaped sea animal with a cup- or fan-shaped body and a stalk that attaches it to a surface. The scientists photographed the sea lilies using a remotely operated vehicle at a depth of 1,600 meters (5,250 feet). The largest individuals, the scientists reported, are about 0.5 meter (1 ¾ feet) long. Evidence found by the scientists—including stalk remains and video of sea urchins and sea stars feeding on the sea lilies—suggests that this newly discovered species is in decline.

OCEANOGRAPHY continued

JACKSON THE SEAL

Jackson, a southern elephant seal, became a celebrity in 2011, after swimming some 29,000 kilometers (18,000 miles) in South Pacific waters off the coast of Chile in an 11-month period ending in November. Scientists with the Wildlife Conservation Society tagged Jackson in December 2010 with a satellite transmitter so they could learn more about the habits of elephant seals. The scientists said that the data they gathered would help conservationists advise authorities on how to manage fisheries and where to establish protected areas for the seals and other sea mammals.

to 16 kilometers (10 miles) long and weigh as much as 4,000 kilograms (9,000 pounds).

Duarte determined the sea grass's age by analyzing the DNA of various specimens sampled from all over the Mediterranean Sea. The plant grows by *cloning* (copying) itself. As a result, all new plants have the same DNA as the original. Although the plant has spread widely, Duarte says the original plant is still alive and thriving after some 200,000 years.

Elephant seal's journey. In December 2011, a team of scientists with the nonprofit Wildlife Conservation Society revealed that a young male elephant seal traveled 29,000

kilometers (18,000 miles) in a single year. The animal, nicknamed Jackson, was tagged with a small satellite transmitter in 2010. From December 2010 to November 2011, the seal looped up and down the coast of Chile, sometimes venturing as far as 640 kilometers (400 miles) out into the Pacific.

The goal of the study was not only to learn more about elephant seal habits, but also to better understand the Chilean coastal ecosystem as a whole. The information gathered will help scientists recommend areas to set aside as protected wildlife reserves.

Strange Antarctic hydrothermal vents. The discovery of several hydrothermal vents at the bottom of the Southern Ocean, the ocean that surrounds Antarctica, was reported in January 2012 by a team of British scientists. Their findings were published in the January 3 issue of the science journal *PLoS Biology*. Hydrothermal vents are places where heated water flows out from beneath the sea floor. Scientists believe that almost all hydrothermal vents are the result of volcanic activity under the oceans.

The researchers sent a remotely operated vehicle (ROV)—a kind of robotic submarine—to examine the vents, sited at depths of between 2,400 meters (7,874 feet) and 2,600 meters (8,530 feet). The ROV captured images of a vent system teeming with life. Among the many newly discovered organisms was a large population of a previously unknown species of yeti crab. (Yeti crabs, first discovered in 2005, are pale whitish vent-dwelling crabs that have dense patches of hairlike filaments on parts of their bodies.) The crabs lived in surprising densities of up to 600 per square meter. (A square meter is 10.8 square feet.)

The research was also notable for what the scientists did not see. Animals typically found around vents in the other oceans—tubeworms, vent mussels, vent shrimps—were not found around the Southern Ocean vents. The missing species suggest that the Southern Ocean may have a barrier, possibly the cold ocean current around Antarctica, which keeps these species out.

Penguin count. In April 2012, a team of British, U.S., and Australian scientists revealed a new population count for emperor penguins in Antarctica. Their findings, which disclosed a higher population than previous estimates, appeared in the April 13 issue of the science journal, *PLoS ONE*.

The scientists used imagery from the orbiting Very High Resolution Satellite to scan Antarctica for the penguins. In the images, scientists were able to view the 44 known emperor penguin colonies as well as 7 previously unknown colonies. Based on this data, they estimated a population of about 600,000 birds. Previous estimates had put the emperor penguin population at around 300,000.

Double tsunami. A NASA study has found evidence of a long suspected phenomenon called a "double" or "merging" tsunami, which is capable of producing waves of unparalleled destructive power. Scientists Y. Tony Song and C.K. Shum announced this discovery at the December 2011 meeting of the American Geophysical Union, an international association of scientists specializing in Earth and space science. Song is a research scientist at NASA's Jet Propulsion Laboratory (JPL) in Pasadena, California; Shum is a professor of earth sciences at Ohio State University in Columbus. The scientists found evidence of the double tsunami in satellite images of the March 11, 2011, tsunami along the coast of Japan.

A useful way to conceptualize a tsunami is to consider the metaphor of a pebble dropping into a puddle. When the pebble hits the surface, smooth, circular waves move outward in all directions from the point of impact. Similarly, a tsunami wave starts out as a long, smooth wave radiating from the epicenter of an underwater earthquake. The wave is circular with one smooth arc or wave front.

As the wave moves farther away, the single wave front begins to break into many smaller wave fronts, due to interference caused by uneven features on the sea floor. The single arc begins to appear as several smaller arcs running next to each other. Under certain conditions, two or more smaller arcs can overlap along their ends. Where the two waves overlap, a single wave forms that is equal to the two smaller waves combined. This is a so-called double tsunami.

The taller wave front of a double tsunami helps explain how some areas of the Japanese coast showed signs of a much larger wave than a single tsunami wave. Scientists speculated that areas with the most

"ALIEN MOTHER SHIP" ON OREGON BEACH

Part of a dock from the Japanese port of Misawa that was encrusted with tons of alien species sits along a beach in Oregon in June 2012. The structure was swept to sea during the devastating March 2011 tsunami in northern Japan. Scientists examining the dock fragment found numerous Asian species of crabs, sea stars, algae, and barnacles, some of which are highly threatening to native species. One scientist described the dock as "a large, dirty needle that just got stuck into our ecological arm, into our ecosystem." Workers quickly moved to scrape the dock and bury the alien animals. But many animals were scrapped off the bottom of the structure by sand and water as it was carried to shore.

OCEANOGRAPHY continued

extreme devastation likely suffered the impact of a double tsunami.

Tsunami debris. Environmentalists reported in December 2011 that debris from the March Japanese tsunami had reached the Alaska coast. In early 2012, tsunami debris, including a large abandoned Japanese fishing boat, was spotted off the coast of British Columbia. Scientists predict that the debris will continue washing up along the Pacific Coast of North America from Alaska to Mexico for several years. Estimates of the quantity of tsunami debris in the oceans range from 5 million to 20 million metric tons (5.5 million to 22.0 million tons).

The scientists identified the Kuroshio Current as a major steering mechanism for the seaborne tsunami debris. This current sweeps northward off Japan's east coast, ultimately merging with the eastward flowing Alaska current. The current then flows southward along the western coasts of British Columbia and the Pacific coastal states of the United States. This system of directional currents carries much of the debris in a wide, semicircular sweep around the North Pacific basin.

However, some of the debris ends up in an area called the Great Pacific Garbage Patch in the middle of the North Pacific Ocean. This area, twice the size of Texas, is a floating carpet of garbage held in place by swirling Pacific currents.

Scientific and government organizations, including the Scripps Oceanographic Institute of La Jolla, California; the U.S. Navy; and the National Oceanic and Atmospheric Administration monitor the Great Pacific Garbage Patch. The garbage is harmful to maritime traffic, and it poses environmental threats to a variety of marine organisms.

Sea animals and plastic flotsam. Seagoing vessels and scientific expeditions in recent years have encountered huge areas of floating plastic garbage in the oceans, particularly in the Great Pacific Garbage Patch. The presence of the plastic—mostly in pieces the size of a fingernail or smaller—is affecting animal behaviors, researchers from the Scripps Institute discovered.

During an ocean expedition, the scientists studied an ocean insect, *Halobates sericeus,* a type of *water strider* (insect that stays on the water surface). They discovered that the bugs have altered their behavior by using floating plastic as sites to lay eggs instead of the flotsam of wood, plant remains, and other natural debris they would normally use. The adaptation has led to an increase in egg densities of *H. sericeus* in the North Pacific, the researchers reported.

The researchers also examined the stomach contents of fish during their expedition. They reported that 9 percent of the sampled fish had some amount of plastic in their stomachs. Plastic is toxic to many forms of life. The scientists speculated that chemicals from the plastic are being passed up the food chain as larger and larger ocean animals—and eventually, people—eat the fish.

Adaptive coral. For several years, many scientists have spoken out about the dangers posed to coral reefs by mounting atmospheric carbon dioxide (CO_2) and rising temperatures. In two studies released in April 2012, researchers revealed that certain species of coral may be better able to cope with these changing conditions than others.

Higher concentration of CO_2 in the atmosphere has the effect of increasing the acidity of the oceans. This is because the CO_2 molecules react chemically with water molecules on the ocean surfaces. Greater acidity makes it difficult for corals to form the hard calcium carbonate skeletons they need to survive.

Rising temperatures can also pose a threat to corals by harming the algae that live in *symbiotic* (mutually dependent) relationships with the coral organisms. Many species of coral depend on symbiotic algae and will die without them. Such death is known as coral bleaching, because algae provide the coloration in coral, and their death leaves the coral a lifeless gray or white color.

In one study, a team of scientists found that certain species of coral are able to counteract the effects of acidified seawater.

Team members included scientists affiliated with Australia's Centre of Excellence for Coral Reef Studies and France's Laboratory of Climate and Environmental Sciences.

Corals depend on water that is not too acidic to *synthesize* (make) their hard calcium carbonate skeletons. Overly acidic water may soften or even dissolve the hard skeletal material. One group of coral species, called aragonite corals, have "molecular pumps" inside their cells that enable them to regulate their internal acid balance and synthesize their skeletons successfully even when the overall environment is somewhat acidic. Molecular pumps are proteins that allow or prevent compounds from entering cells.

A different group of coral species, called calcite corals, do not have such cellular pumps. Thus the calcite corals are more vulnerable to ocean acidification than are the aragonite corals.

In the other study of corals, scientists with the University of Miami's Rosenstiel School of Marine and Atmospheric Science discovered that some corals may be able to adapt to warming waters by relying on species of symbiotic algae that are relatively heat-resistant. Previously, scientists believed that a coral species hosted only one particular algal species. But the Rosenstiel researchers found that some corals can host more than one species. The implication of this discovery is that such corals might be able to adapt to rising temperatures by hosting more heat-resistant symbiotic algae.

■ Michael DuRoss

ADAPTING TO GLOBAL WARMING

A group of corals called argonite calcifying corals may be better able to adapt to global warming than previously thought, according to research reported in April 2012. These corals may be able to maintain strong shells even as Earth's oceans grow more acidic. Ocean acidification occurs when a buildup of carbon dioxide in the atmosphere—a major feature of and chief cause of global warming—gradually causes the oceans to become more acidic. Since 1750, the oceans have become about 30 percent more acidic, according to a 2009 report by the Secretariat of the Convention on Biological Diversity in Montreal, Canada. Acidifying waters interfere with the shell-building activities of corals, clams, oysters, and other shell-bearing sea animals. Without strong shells, these animals are more vulnerable to environmental changes or *predation* (being eaten by other animals). Argonite calcifying corals have proteins known as molecular pumps that allow them to maintain a proper internal acid balance even in increasingly acidic seawater.

Exploring the Challenger Deep

Packed into a deep-sea vessel described as a "vertical torpedo," filmmaker and explorer James Cameron on March 25, 2012, became the first solo explorer to reach the Challenger Deep at the bottom of the Mariana Trench in the Pacific Ocean. At nearly 11 kilometers (7 miles) down, the Challenger Deep is also the deepest known spot in the world. In 1960, Swiss engineer Jacques Piccard and United States Navy Lieutenant Don Walsh in the submersible *Trieste* became the first humans to penetrate that remote and forbidding spot. Cameron reached the Challenger Deep in a submersible named *Deepsea Challenger,* which he helped design. Submersibles are built to withstand the crushing pressures and near-freezing temperatures found in the ocean depths. The seafloor, Cameron said, looked as bleak and barren as the moon. It was "devoid of sunlight, devoid of any heat, any warmth." He said that the only organisms he saw were tiny, shrimp-like *arthropods* (animals with jointed legs and no backbone).

Cameron planned to spend six hours taking videos and collecting samples. But his mission was cut short by leaking hydraulic fluid that clouded his window and an inability to get the submersible's robotic claw working. However, he was able to collect about 50 milliliters (1.7 ounces) of muddy sea water, which scientists planned to examine for unknown forms of microbial life.

James Cameron, a Canadian-born motion-picture director and screenwriter, has made some 70 deep-sea dives in *submersibles* (deep-sea research vehicles). Many of these dives have been to the wreckage of the *Titanic,* which struck an iceberg and sank in the North Atlantic Ocean in 1912. That disaster was the basis for a 1997 film written and directed by Cameron that became the second most commercially successful film ever made.

The Chinese submersible *Jiaolong* is lifted from the water after completing a 7,020-meter (23,000-foot) test dive to the Mariana Trench in June 2012. The voyage was the submersible's fourth and deepest dive into the trench. The three "oceanauts" in the *Jiaolong* spent several hours collecting water samples and sediment.

The *Trieste*, a two-person bathyscaph, was the first piloted submersible to descend to the Challenger Deep. On Jan. 23, 1960, Swiss engineer Jacques Piccard and U.S. Navy Lieutenant Don Walsh spent 20 minutes at the site. When the *Trieste*'s searchlights were turned on, Walsh and Piccard saw living forms moving through the cold, black waters. The dive confirmed that sea life could withstand the awful pressure of the water at such a depth and that the deep ocean had enough oxygen to support marine life. But Piccard and Walsh saw little because the submersible stirred up so much silt as it touched down.

The manipulator arm of the *Nereus,* a robotic deep-sea vehicle, collects sediment from the Mariana Trench in 2009. The *Nereus,* developed by the Woods Hole Oceanographic Institute in Woods Hole, Massachusetts, was the second remotely operated vehicle (ROV) to penetrate the Challenger Deep. In 1995, Japanese researchers lowered the ROV *Kaiko* to the floor of the trench.

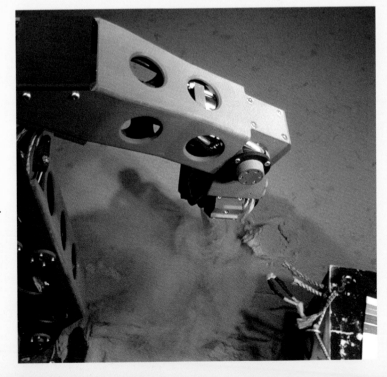

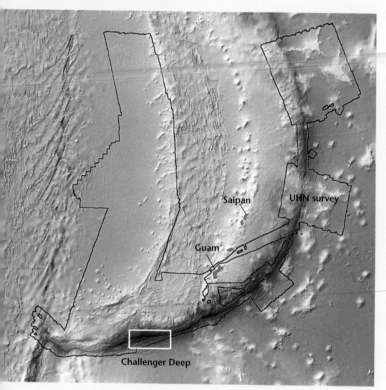

Saipan

UHN survey

Guam

Challenger Deep

The Challenger Deep lies at the bottom of the Mariana Trench, about 320 kilometers (200 miles) southwest of Guam in the Pacific Ocean. Challenger is the deepest of the more than 100 known deeps. (A deep is an ocean area that has a depth of at least 5,490 meters [18,000 feet].) Various shades of blue indicate degrees of depth in a map of the region made using sound waves by researchers with the United States Center for Coastal and Ocean Mapping/Joint Hydrographic Center at the University of New Hampshire (UNH). (The areas outlined in black indicate the locations surveyed by the UNH researchers.)

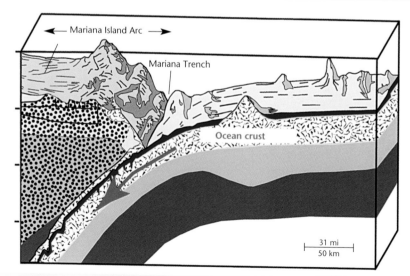

← Mariana Island Arc →

Mariana Trench

Ocean crust

31 mi
50 km

Island arc crust, including rocks from contemporary volcanism and from older, rifted volcanic arcs.

Basaltic crust, including old crust on the Pacific Plate and young crust formed in the back-arc spreading center.

The Mariana Trench is one of a number of deep narrow valleys in the ocean floor. Trenches are created where the edge of one tectonic plate is *subducting* (being thrust) beneath the edge of another plate. As oceanic crust plunges deep into the Earth at the Mariana Trench, it melts, turning to magma. Magma rising through the overlying rock has created an island arc, a narrow, curving chain of volcanic islands called the Mariana Islands.

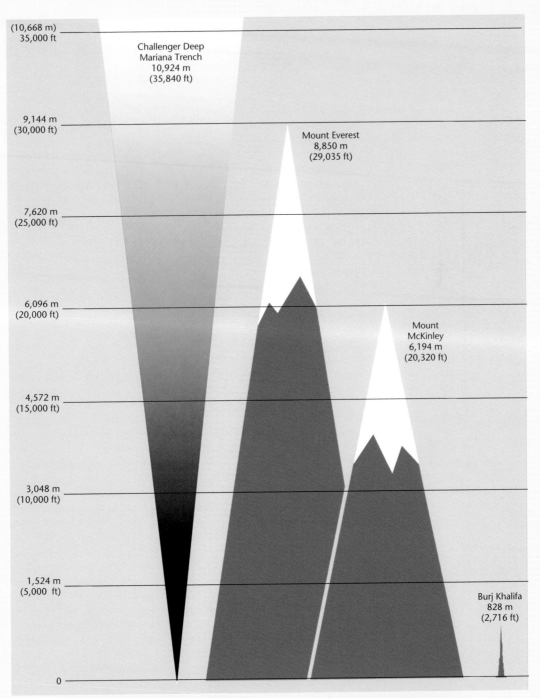

(10,668 m)
35,000 ft

Challenger Deep
Mariana Trench
10,924 m
(35,840 ft)

9,144 m
(30,000 ft)

Mount Everest
8,850 m
(29,035 ft)

7,620 m
(25,000 ft)

6,096 m
(20,000 ft)

Mount
McKinley
6,194 m
(20,320 ft)

4,572 m
(15,000 ft)

3,048 m
(10,000 ft)

1,524 m
(5,000 ft)

Burj Khalifa
828 m
(2,716 ft)

0

Both Mount Everest—the highest mountain in the world—and Mount McKinley (in Alaska's Denali National Park)—the highest peak in North America—would be completely submerged if placed in the Challenger Deep. The deep is so far below the surface of the ocean that it could hold 14 stacked Burj Khalifa's—a skyscraper in the United Arab Emirates that ranks as the tallest building in the world.

PHYSICS

Evidence for the elusive Higgs boson was reported in December 2011 by physicists working with the world's highest-energy particle accelerator, the Large Hadron Collider (LHC), at CERN, a center for international nuclear research near Geneva, Switzerland. The LHC consists of two rings, with a circumference of 27 kilometers (17 miles), in which *protons* (positively charged subatomic particles) are accelerated to high energies and collided to reveal information about properties of matter. The Higgs boson is a theoretical particle thought to be the source of the mass of all other particles.

The Higgs boson is the principle missing component of the Standard Model, the theory that describes the particles that make up matter and how those particles interact by means of forces. The Standard Model can be used to predict the rate at which the Higgs boson would be produced in collisions of protons in such particle accelerators as the LHC. Physicists expect that the Higgs boson is unstable, quickly *decaying* (breaking down) into other particles, including *photons* (elementary particles that makes up light and other forms of electromagnetic radiation). Given a particular possible value of the *mass* (amount of matter) of the Higgs boson, the Standard Model can be used to predict the length of time it takes for the Higgs to decay into these particles.

The main challenge faced by the LHC researchers in detecting the Higgs boson was that production of the particle is expected to occur in only one of trillions of proton collisions. In addition, a small fraction of the collisions are expected to mimic signals suggestive of the Higgs boson—even if the Higgs was not produced.

The researchers reported the most persuasive evidence to date for the Higgs boson is the detection of pairs of high-energy photons generated in the proton collisions. They noted that the decay of the Higgs into photons provided a "cleaner" signal than other possible breakdown products—a signal that was more readily recognized among the mix of background signals generated in the LHC. The measured energy levels of the detected photons indicated certain possible masses for the Higgs—most likely a mass of approximately 125 times the mass of a proton. Physicists describe this amount of mass as 125 gigaelectronvolts. With this amount of mass, the Higgs would be expected to decay into a type of *quark* (elementary "building block" of matter) known as the bottom quark, into pairs of photons, or into certain other particles.

The data reported in 2011 were not strong enough for the CERN scientists to definitively claim a discovery of the Higgs boson. However, the researchers hoped to have results of more comprehensive—and statistically more convincing—tests available in 2012. Plans in 2012 called for technological upgrades of the LHC to double the maximum energy level of the particle accelerator. Physicists investigating the Higgs boson and other phenomena of particle physics expected the energy upgrade to reap great benefits in their cutting-edge research.

Neutrino oscillation. An analysis of a previously little understood neutrino phenomenon was described in March 2012 by physicist Yifang Wang of the Institute of High-Energy Physics in China. Wang was Chinese project manager of the Daya Bay Neutrino Experiment, a multinational research collaboration using neutrino detectors in southern China. Neutrinos are subatomic particles with no electric charge. Their masses are so tiny, and they interact with other particles with such weak forces, that they can pass through a large amount of matter without interacting with other particles. Neutrinos are produced in situations as varied as nuclear reactions in the sun, the decay of unstable particles, and collisions of cosmic ray particles with atoms in the upper atmosphere. They are also produced in collisions of elementary particles at high energies. The Daya Bay Neutrino Experiment analyzes neutrinos produced by the reactors of a local nuclear power plant.

There are three forms, called flavors, of neutrinos—the electron-neutrino, the muon-neutrino, and the tau-neutrino. In addition, neutrinos occur as combinations, or mixtures, of different flavors and as combinations with antineutrinos, which are the antimatter equivalent of neutrinos. Antimatter resembles ordinary matter but with certain properties of its particles reversed. In the case of antineutrinos, they spin in the opposite direction of neutrinos. Neutrinos of one flavor or mixture can transform into other flavors or mixtures in a process called oscillation. The relative proportions of each flavor in a mixture can be described in terms of three mixing angles. Information about two of these mixing angles was previously known from experiments. The Daya Bay researchers filled in the gap by characterizing the third mixing angle, known as theta one-three. Measuring and understanding this third mixing angle helped physicists explain how electron-neutrinos and their antineutrino counterparts mix and change into neutrinos of other flavors.

The researchers noted that their findings would aid further investigations into neutrino physics, including studies of which neutri-

ANTIPROTON RING DETECTED AROUND EARTH

A long-theorized ring of antiprotons around Earth has finally been found, according to an August 2012 report by a team headed by physicist Piergiorgio Picozza of the University of Rome Tor Vergata in Italy. Antiprotons are similar to protons but have a negative rather than a positive charge. The team used PAMELA, a cosmic-ray detector on a Russian Earth-observation satellite, to find the antiprotons within the inner of the two Van Allen radiation belts, zones where electrically charged particles are trapped by Earth's magnetic field and directed toward the magnetic poles. The PAMELA detector recorded 28 antiprotons in one small area of the inner belt, from 350 to 600 kilometers (220 to 375 miles) above the planet's surface. The scientists proposed that billions of antiprotons probably exist in the lowest part of the inner belt.

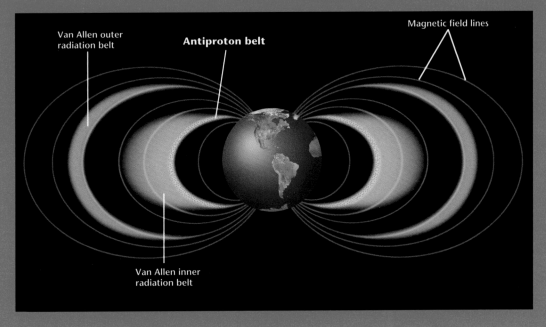

PHYSICS continued

no flavors are the most massive, whether there is a difference between neutrino and antineutrino oscillations, and why there is far more matter than antimatter in the universe today. Scientists believe that both matter and antimatter existed in equal amounts immediately after the big bang, the explosion of matter and energy that marked the birth of the universe some 14 billion years ago.

Neutrinos as geologic tool. The use of neutrinos as a scientific tool for understanding Earth's interior was highlighted by research reported in July 2011 by a team of scientists led by physicist Itaru Shimizu of Tohoku University in Japan. Using an underground neutrino detector in Japan known as the Kamioka Liquid-Scintillator Antineutrino Detector (KamLAND), the researchers gathered data on neutrinos generated in the radioactive decay of uranium, thorium, and other materials in Earth's core.

The neutrino measurements suggested to the investigators that 29 *terawatts* (trillion watts) of the total 44 terawatts of heat generated inside Earth result from radioactive decay in the core. The heat generated inside Earth is responsible for magnetic fields, volcano activity, seafloor spreading, and the movement of *tectonic plates* (chunks of Earth's outermost layer into which the continents are embedded). The heat estimates based on the neutrino findings were in line with the expectations of geologists.

Faster-than-light neutrinos? Preliminary findings reported by CERN physicists in September 2011 suggested that neutrinos might be able to travel faster than light. If confirmed, such a finding would overturn one of the main principles of modern physics—that nothing can move faster than light. That principle was established by the special theory of relativity published by physicist Albert Einstein in 1905.

A group of physicists with the Oscillation Project with Emulsion-tracking Apparatus (OPERA) collaboration conducted an experiment in which neutrinos produced at CERN, near Geneva, were sent 732 kilometers (455 miles) through the ground to a detector in

Italy that was part of that country's Gran Sasso National Laboratory. When the neutrino beam reached the detector, a few of the neutrinos interacted with the detector and generated signals. By measuring the time between this signal detection in Italy and the production of the neutrinos in Switzerland, the scientists could calculate the speed at which the neutrinos traveled. Because neutrinos have mass—though only a tiny amount of mass—physicists expected their speed to be somewhat less than that of the massless photons of light. However, the calculations of the OPERA scientists indicated that the neutrinos arrived at the detector in Italy approximately 60 *nanoseconds* (billionths of a second) sooner than light would have arrived.

This report of faster-than-light neutrinos generated a great deal of skepticism within the international physics community. The OPERA researchers carefully reevaluated all aspects of their experiment and, in February 2012, they reported possible problems that could have led to an incorrect conclusion about the speed of the neutrinos. Specifically, they explained that a loose fiber-optic cable may have affected their timing measurements. Casting further doubt on the original OPERA results, physicists with the Imaging Cosmic and Rare Underground Signals (ICARUS) experiment in March 2012 described their own measurements of the speed of neutrinos traveling between CERN and the Gran Sasso detector. These investigators reported that the neutrinos in their experiment did not move faster than light. Thus, most physicists in mid-2012 were convinced that the faster-than-light neutrino findings were flawed.

CP violation. In November 2011, physicists working with the LHC reported some of the best evidence to date that charge-parity (CP) violation may defy accepted principles of particle physics. CP violation refers to a phenomenon in which CP symmetry does not occur. According to CP symmetry, any process involving a particle should be identical to the same process involving its corre-

DA VINCI EXPLAINS: HOW TREES WITHSTAND WIND

The pattern of branches in a tree is ideally suited to withstand breakage that could be caused by wind, according to a computer *model* (simulation) described in November 2011 by physicist Christophe Eloy of the University of Provence in France. Artist and scientist Leonardo Da Vinci (1452-1519) had observed that "all the branches of a tree at every stage of its height when put together are equal in thickness to the trunk." To discover the reason for this relationship, Eloy conducted experiments with a computer model of tree structure. In simulations of bending forces caused by wind, the model revealed that the branch pattern noted by da Vinci was best at allowing trees to survive strong gusts of wind without breaking.

sponding antiparticle. For example, a particle and its corresponding antiparticle should decay at exactly the same rate. Although a small degree of CP violation is incorporated into the Standard Model, the new evidence suggested that the observed violation was larger than would be expected from the Standard Model.

A group of physicists led by Mat Charles and Guy Wilkinson of the University of Oxford in England presented their analysis of the decay of subatomic particles called charm mesons and anticharm mesons (also called charm quarks and anticharm quarks). Mesons include some 150 kinds of unstable subatomic particles. Evidence for CP violation in charm mesons had previously not been clearly documented. However, CP violation had previously been documented with two other types of mesons. In both of those

cases, the decay measurements agreed well with expectations from the Standard Model.

In the new analysis, a difference was detected in the decay rates of charm mesons compared to anticharm mesons—a difference that slightly exceeded that predicted by the Standard Model. Should this difference be confirmed by additional research, the physicists noted, it might be evidence for physical phenomena that are not described by the Standard Model.

Majorana fermions. Evidence for the existence of a theoretical particle called the Majorana fermion was reported in April 2012 by a team led by physicist Leo Kouwenhoven of Delft University of Technology in the Netherlands. The Majorana fermion, first proposed in the 1930's by Italian physicist Ettore Majorana, is theorized to be an electrically neutral particle that be-

PHYSICS continued

haves fundamentally differently than other fermions. "Fermion" is a general name for the class of atomic and subatomic particles that make up matter, including electrons, protons, and neutrons. Unlike other fermions, Majorana fermions, if they exist, are identical to their corresponding antiparticles in terms of their wavelike properties. Physicists think of Majorana fermions as a type of "quasiparticle," emerging from the collective motions of atoms in solids.

Kouwenhoven's team found evidence for Majorana fermions while studying materials known as topological insulators. These materials are, for the most part, *insulators* (which conduct almost no electric current), but they can conduct electric current on their surfaces under certain electronic conditions. The investigators placed a topological insulator in contact with a superconductor, a material that conducts electric current without resistance at extremely low temperatures. This contact caused the surface of the topological insulator to become superconducting, but at half the strength of a normal superconductor. Physicists had previously speculated that Majorana fermions might emerge from the electron movement inside such a device and, if so, these exotic fermions would be detectable by their characteristic responses to applied voltages and magnetic fields.

The topological insulator used by the team was a nanowire, a wire of dimensions on the order of a *nanometer* (one-billionth of a meter), made of indium strontium. The nanowire was connected to a superconducting electrode and normal electrode. The device was cooled to temperatures just above absolute zero (−273.15 °C [−459.67 °F]). When the researchers applied a magnetic field or electric current to the device, they found that at two points along the nanowire, electronic "signatures" were detected at the precise places where Majorana fermions were predicted to occur. These signatures showed that the apparent Majorana fermions did not move when the strengths of the magnetic field or electric current were changed—a lack of movement that would

be expected because of their electrical neutrality.

Although the reported findings were suggestive of the emergence of Majorana fermions in the nanowire, the scientists pointed out that additional research would be needed to prove the existence of these particles. Ultimately, if the existence of Majorana fermions could be proven, researchers expected that they would be useful for storing information in so-called quantum computers, computers that function according to the principles of *quantum mechanics* (the branch of physics concerned with atomic structure and function). The usefulness of Majorana fermions in such advanced computer technologies would be based partly on their greater stability—that is, their higher resistance to electronic disturbances—than the electrons used in traditional computers.

Graphene surprise. Graphene, a strong, flexible material consisting of a single layer of densely packed carbon atoms, is surprisingly permeable to water, according to a January 2012 report by scientists at the University of Manchester in England. A group led by Nobel Prize-winning physicist Sir Andre Geim demonstrated that graphene-based membranes are impermeable to all gases and liquids (that is, gases and liquids cannot pass through the membranes)—except for water. The researchers described how water vapor passed though a stack of membranes made of the compound graphene oxide as quickly as if the membranes did not even exist. These same membranes, by contrast, completely blocked other liquids and gases—even helium, which can pass through very tiny openings.

Scientists were previously unaware of this unique property of graphene, which is being investigated for use in making products ranging from flexible electronic devices to ultralight aircraft bodies. Geim's group noted that this property could make graphene useful for various filtration methods or other tasks in which water needs to be separated from a mixture. ■ Michael Dine

See also **NOBEL PRIZES.**

PSYCHOLOGY

A relationship between diet and mental health, with implications for preventing such common conditions as depression and anxiety, was described in September 2011 by a team led by biomedical scientist Felice N. Jacka of Deakin University and the University of Melbourne in Australia. Jacka and colleagues studied some 3,000 adolescent students over a two-year period. In addition to having their height and weight monitored, the students completed questionnaires—at the beginning of the study and later in the study—assessing factors related to their quality of life, including diet, mental and emotional health, and physical activity.

From this information, the researchers computed healthy and unhealthy "diet scores" for each student and investigated the relationship between these scores and such measures of mental health as how often the students felt sad, afraid, angry, or worried. A high healthy diet score meant that the diet included many fruits and vegetables and few processed foods, such as fried foods, sweets, and ice cream. A high unhealthy diet score indicated that the diet was high in snacks and processed foods.

The investigators found that high healthy diet scores at the beginning of the study predicted good mental health later in the study. Conversely, high unhealthy diet scores predicted poorer mental health at follow-up. Jacka's team further reported that if the quality of a student's diet changed over the course of the study, so did the student's mental health. Adolescents whose diets became poorer over the course of the study showed a worsening of mental health scores, whereas those whose diets improved showed improved mental health.

These results were similar to results from previous studies showing that individuals who regularly consumed a diet of vegetables, fruits, whole grains, and high-quality meat and fish had a reduced risk for depression and anxiety disorders, compared with individuals who had a diet high in refined or processed foods and saturated fats.

Although psychologists are not sure ex-

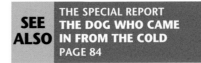

SEE ALSO THE SPECIAL REPORT **THE DOG WHO CAME IN FROM THE COLD** PAGE 84

actly how diet affects mental health, a number of possible mechanisms remain under investigation. According to one possibility discussed by Jacka's group, diet quality may affect the secretion of a protein called brain-derived neurotrophic factor (BDNF). In the brain, BDNF acts on the hippocampus, cerebral cortex, and other structures that influence learning, memory, and higher-order thinking. In laboratory rats, exposure to stress has been shown to decrease BDNF secretion and lead to the *atrophy* (wasting away) of the hippocampus and other brain structures. Atrophy of these structures has also been found in autopsies of people who had suffered from mental disorders. Thus, a high-quality diet might help prevent atrophy and maintain good mental functioning.

Because many psychiatric disorders begin in adolescence or early adulthood, this type of research has implications for the prevention of mental disorders and the treatment of patients with such disorders. However, Jacka acknowledged that a clearer cause-and-effect relationship between diet and mental illness must be established before dietary interventions can be reliably recommended for patients with mental disorders.

Predicting suicide attempts. A questionnaire that measures suicidal thoughts, feelings, and behaviors can be used to accurately predict whether a person will attempt suicide, according to a study published in December 2011. Suicide is the second leading cause of death for Americans aged 25 to 34 years and the third leading cause of death for Americans aged 15 to 24 years. One of the main goals of suicide prevention is to identify individuals at risk for suicide so that appropriate help can be made available to them. The development of a screening tool, such as a brief questionnaire, that can predict who is likely to attempt suicide is vital to accomplishing this goal.

PSYCHOLOGY continued

The Columbia-Suicide Severity Rating Scale (C-SSRS) is a questionnaire that was developed by researchers from Columbia University in New York City and other institutions as part of a previously conducted treatment study of high-risk teenagers. The C-SSRS was used in that study to track changes in participants' suicidal thinking and behavior throughout treatment. The C-SSRS contains questions about the frequency, duration, and controllability of suicidal thoughts; intentions to commit suicide; types of suicide planning; and previous suicide attempts. The C-SSRS had been adopted as a suicide screening tool in many clinical settings, but questions about its reliability in risk assessment remained.

In the study reported in 2011, psychologist Kelly Posner of Columbia University and colleagues examined how well the C-SSRS and other scales had performed in previous studies of depressed teenagers, including teens who had attempted suicide. The researchers found that the C-SSRS had accurately predicted suicide attempts during the studies, while other questionnaire scales had not. Specifically, Posner's team found that teenagers who showed a certain pattern of results on the C-SSRS at the beginning of the studies were more likely to attempt suicide during the studies.

The researchers concluded that the type of predictive information revealed with the C-SSRS could be useful in identifying individuals who are at high risk of attempting suicide—allowing those individuals to be referred to appropriate treatment resources. Posner's team pointed out that another advantage of the C-SSRS is that, with limited training, it can be used by clinicians not trained in mental health. The investigators added that further study with more diverse patient samples and settings was needed to determine if the C-SSRS can ultimately help prevent suicides in at-risk individuals.

Obsessive-compulsive disorder. Children with obsessive-compulsive disorder (OCD) who are taking medications benefit

"CONCHING" THE NEWEST DOLPHIN FAD?

A bottlenose dolphin in Australia's Shark Bay uses a conch shell as a tool to help it capture and eat fish. In August 2011, biologists at Murdoch University in Australia described how dolphins in the bay perform this behavior. First, a dolphin uses its *rostrum* (beak) to push small fish into a conch shell on the seafloor. The dolphin carries the conch to the surface, where it shakes the conch to drain the water and then funnels the fish into its mouth. According to the scientists, this "conching" behavior appears to be spreading from dolphin to dolphin—through imitation—across the population in the bay. The scientists based this preliminary conclusion on an increasing number of reports from people who had observed the behavior from 2007 to 2011. If confirmed, the conching activity would be the first documented spread of a learned behavior through a population of bottlenose dolphins in such a short period. Dolphins rank among the most intelligent of animals, along with chimpanzees and dogs.

most when a type of psychological treatment called cognitive behavior therapy (CBT) is added to their treatment program, according to a study published in September 2011. Individuals with OCD experience obsessions, which are repeated, unwanted, anxiety-provoking thoughts or impulses that the individuals cannot control and that can cause disablement. Many people who experience obsessions also develop compulsions, repeated mental or behavioral acts that, though they are unnecessary, temporarily calm the anxiety produced by the obsessions. An example of a common obsession-and-compulsion combination is the repeated fear of contracting a disease by touching doorknobs (the obsession) and repeated hand washing (the compulsion).

A class of medications called selective serotonin reuptake inhibitors (SSRI's) has been used with some success for the treatment of patients with OCD. However, many children with OCD respond only partially to SSRI treatment. Cognitive behavior therapy has been shown to help both adults and children with OCD perform the behaviors that they fear while refraining from compulsions and managing anxieties. Studies had previously shown that the combination of SSRI's and CBT can improve outcomes in adults with OCD, but no previous studies had examined this combination in children.

To investigate the possible benefits of this approach in children, psychiatrist Martin E. Franklin and colleagues at the University of Pennsylvania in Philadelphia studied three treatment options for 124 patients with OCD between the ages of 7 and 17 years. The three treatment options were: (1) an SSRI alone; (2) an SSRI plus instructions in CBT provided by a physician; and (3) an SSRI plus a full course of CBT provided by a trained CBT therapist.

Results showed that after 12 weeks of treatment, nearly 69 percent of children receiving SSRI plus a full course of CBT responded well to treatment. By contrast, only 34 percent of children receiving SSRI plus instructions in CBT and 30 percent of children receiving SSRI alone showed similar improvements. The researchers concluded that an SSRI alone was relatively ineffective in children and that adding CBT instructions to

SSRI treatment did not improve outcomes noticeably. However, a full course of CBT combined with SSRI treatment benefitted substantially more children than the other two treatment options.

This finding provided further support for the idea that CBT—either by itself or when combined with an SSRI—is an effective treatment for patients with OCD. The researchers recommended making CBT widely available to both children and adults with OCD.   ■ Timothy J. Bruce

See also **MEDICAL RESEARCH; NEUROSCIENCE.**

LIZARDS WITH LEARNING SKILLS

An anole lizard, native to Puerto Rico, investigates a disc-covered well during a test of the reptile's *cognitive* (thinking) abilities and memory. In July 2011, researchers led by biologist Manual Leal of Duke University in Durham, North Carolina, described putting the anoles on a platform with two wells—one containing food and the other empty. The wells were covered with discs of different colors and patterns. In repeated tests, four of the six lizards learned to remove the disc covers and to correctly associate certain disc colors and patterns with the well containing food. Leal noted that the test results demonstrated more flexibility in anole thinking and food-finding behavior than the researchers had expected. In nature, anoles find prey by scanning for movement and striking from above. But the anoles in the experiment obtained food from the wells by biting the discs then pulling them away or by pushing the discs away with their snouts.

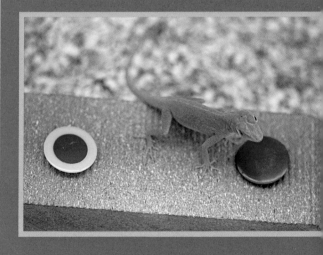

PUBLIC HEALTH

In March 2012, United Nations (UN) Secretary-General Ban Ki-moon announced that one of the UN's Millennium Development Goals (MDG), concerning the availability of clean drinking water, had been met. In 2000, the UN had set eight MDG's to be achieved by 2015. Goal seven, Environmental Sustainability, encompasses the subgoal of reducing by half the number of people who lack access to safe drinking water.

Survival, health, and quality of life depend upon the availability of clean, safe drinking water. Today, 2 billion more people have access to clean drinking water than in 1990. By the end of 2010, 89 percent of the world's people obtained their drinking water from such clean sources as piped supplies and protected wells, according to the WHO/UNICEF Joint Monitoring Programme for Water Supply and Sanitation (JMP).

However, about 780 million people still lacked sustainable sources of safe drinking water in 2012, according to the UN, and access to clean water was not equal across regions in the developing world. In its report *Progress on Drinking Water and Sanitation 2012*, JMP estimated that 61 percent of people living in sub-Saharan Africa did not have regular access to clean, safe drinking water. Among people living in developing nations outside Africa, by contrast, 90 percent enjoyed such access.

When medicines kill. In January, the Centers for Disease Control and Prevention (CDC) reported that prescription drug abuse is the fastest growing drug problem in the United States. The CDC reported that prescriptions for opioid analgesics—commonly referred to as pain pills—increased more than sevenfold between 1997 and 2007. Since 2003, the agency reported, more people have died from overdosing on prescription pain pills than on cocaine and heroin.

The spike in prescription rates, however, is only one facet of the prescription drug abuse problem. In separate studies conducted in Ohio, Utah, and West Virginia, researchers found that from 25 to 66 percent of people who died from opioid analgesic overdose used pills that had been pre-

SEE ALSO THE SPECIAL REPORT **KNOCKING HEADS: THE DANGERS OF CONCUSSION** PAGE 70

scribed for someone else or pills obtained through channels other than licensed pharmacies. The same studies uncovered data suggesting that from 16 to 28 percent of these overdose victims had engaged in "doctor-shopping"—that is, seeking prescriptions from multiple doctors.

The damage inflicted by the abuse of prescription pain killers extends far beyond deaths by overdose. For every person killed by overdose, nine people are admitted to hospitals or rehab centers for substance abuse treatment, according to Leonard Paulozzi, a medical epidemiologist with the federal government's Substance Abuse and Mental Health Services Administration in Rockville, Maryland. Additionally, 35 people visit hospital emergency rooms, 161 report drug abuse or dependence, and 461 report nonmedical uses of prescription pain pills. In this last category, a mere 20 percent reported obtaining the drugs from their own doctor.

In the deadliest outbreak of foodborne illness in the United States in a decade, 30 people died between August and October 2011 after eating cantaloupe contaminated with *Listeria*. Another 146 people in 18 states reported related illnesses. Most who died were older than 60 years old.

Listeria is a species of bacteria that can cause a type of food poisoning called listeriosis. The bacteria spreads easily from the digestive system into the bloodstream or to other body sites, according to the CDC. Persons infected with *Listeria* may suffer diarrhea or other gastrointestinal symptoms followed by fever and muscle aches. More severe symptoms, generally experienced by older adults or those with weakened immune systems, can include attacks on muscle and spinal cord tissues. Pregnant women may have a miscarriage, or their unborn babies may suffer birth defects.

It may take as long as two months to fall

ill after eating *Listeria*-contaminated food. This lag between eating the food and the onset of symptoms often poses challenges to researchers attempting to identify the cause of a stricken individual's illness.

Agents of the U.S. Food and Drug Administration (FDA) eventually found the strain of *Listeria* responsible for the outbreak on equipment at Jensen Farms in Colorado. The FDA prompted recalls of cantaloupes processed at Jensen Farms and of such cantaloupe products as cut-up cantaloupe or mixed fresh fruit that might be implicated. The agency also urged consumers to wash cantaloupes and other raw produce carefully under running water and to dry the produce with clean paper towels.

In another outbreak of foodborne illness involving produce, several thousand people, mostly in Europe, became sick between May and July from eating food contaminated by *Escherichia coli*, a species of bacteria. Investigators traced the contamination to fenugreek sprouts raised on a farm in Germany. (Fenugreek sprouts are typically used as ingredients in salads.) Over 800 people, mainly in Europe but also including 6 people in the United States, developed kidney failure as a result of the *E. coli* infection. At least 32 people died.

Violence and pregnancy. In the United States, the violent acts of *homicide* (the killing of a person) and suicide kill more pregnant and *postpartum* (immediately after childbirth) women than do many of the medical complications of pregnancy. A research team led by Christie Palladino, an obstetrician-gynecologist with the Georgia Health Sciences University, Augusta, reported this conclusion in the journal *Obstetrics & Gynecology* in November 2011.

Between 2003 and 2007, the rate of pregnancy-associated violent deaths—classified by the CDC as death during pregnancy and the following year—was 2.9 for every 100,000 live births, the researchers reported. The rate of death by suicide in the same period was 2.0 per 100,000. Taken together, these acts of violence kill more mothers than the medical conditions of hemorrhage, preeclampsia, eclampsia, and placenta previa combined.

Violence from a current or former intimate partner accounted for 45 percent of homicides. A slightly larger proportion of the suicides—54 percent—were associated with problems with a current or former intimate partner. ■ Deborah Kowal

ANTISMOKING CAMPAIGN WITH TEETH

An advertisement featuring a child threatened by cigarette smoke is one in a series of hard-hitting antismoking ads launched in March 2012 by the Centers for Disease Control (CDC) in Atlanta. The campaign marked the first time that an agency of the United States government directly sponsored antismoking ads in nationwide media. The ads, for use in both print publications and on television, were designed to appeal to the emotions of smokers. Some of the ads featured victims of smoking-related disease in frank, shocking presentations. Analysts noted that the ad campaign began only weeks after a federal court struck down a 2009 federal law requiring tobacco manufacturers to include expanded health warnings on their products. The judgment was rendered in a lawsuit brought by tobacco companies on the basis of an alleged violation of their First-Amendment right to free speech. The U.S.Department of Justice appealed the decision, and analysts predicted that the case would eventually end up in the Supreme Court. According to the CDC, more than 440,000 Americans die annually from diseases linked to tobacco use.

SCIENCE AND SOCIETY

The United States National Science Advisory Board for Biosecurity (NSABB) reversed itself on March 30, 2012, by recommending that the complete papers of two scientists who had altered the H5N1 influenza virus—the "bird flu" virus—be published in their entirety. Just three months before, the NSABB set off a storm of controversy by asking the scientists to edit out details of experiments they had submitted for publication because of risks to the public.

The story began on Sept. 12, 2011, when Dutch virologist Ron Fouchier presented a paper at a scientific meeting describing how he and his colleagues had altered the H5N1 virus to make it capable of being transmitted between ferrets. Fouchier's group, and another research team led by Yoshihiro Kawaoka at the University of Wisconsin, had been studying the question of how flu virus is passed between humans. Scientists use ferrets for this research because viral behavior in ferrets is quite similar to viral behavior in humans.

Deadly in birds, the H5N1 virus has caused the destruction of thousands of poultry flocks around the world. Since the virus's identification in 1997, it has also infected nearly 600 humans, more than half of whom died. In almost all cases, the victims caught the virus from birds. By studying the transmission of the virus, scientists hoped to learn what makes it so deadly and how to prevent it from infecting people.

Scientists and health officials feared that the virus might accidentally escape from the lab or that terrorists might replicate the scientists' experiments to develop new bioweapons. When Fouchier and Kawaoka submitted papers based on their research to the scientific journals *Science* and *Nature*, the U.S. Department of Health and Human Services asked the NSABB to review the work for potential risks. The NSABB, in turn, asked the journals to reconsider their publication plans, though the board did not have the power to require them to do so.

In December 2011, the NSABB asked Fouchier and Kawaoka to edit their papers, omitting information about the methodologies used in their experiments. This was the first such request ever made by the NSABB.

Fouchier and Kawaoka agreed to comply with the request as long as the journals were willing to provide the omitted information to responsible researchers and public health officials. As *Science and Nature* prepared to publish the edited papers in March 2012, an influential international group of scientists, public health officials, and journal editors, meeting at the World Health Organization in Geneva, Switzerland, issued a statement calling on the two journals to publish the full, unedited texts of the papers.

This statement—as well as additional research data suggesting that the altered virus was less dangerous than previously believed—led the NSABB to reverse its recommendation. The board declared that the benefits of publishing outweighed the risks. In May, the journal *Nature* published in full the scientific paper of the Kawaoka team. At the same time, editors of *Science* were preparing to publish the complete version of the Fouchier paper.

Italian geologists on trial. Six prominent geologists and an official of the Italian government went on trial for manslaughter in L'Aquila, Italy, on Sept. 20, 2011. They were accused of negligence for failing to alert residents of L'Aquila of the risk of an impending earthquake. The magnitude-6.3 quake struck in the early morning of April 6, 2009, killing 309 people. Many others were injured, and thousands of buildings in the medieval town were destroyed. The geologists, including the president of Italy's National Institute of Geophysics and Volcanology (INGV), were members of the National Commission for Forecasting and Predicting Great Risks.

L'Aquila, located in one of the most earthquake-prone areas of Italy, began experiencing increasingly frequent small tremors in October 2008. By March 2009, there were an average of more than three tremors a day. Though hardly new to the residents of L'Aquila, the daily tremors were making many people nervous. In addition, a retired laboratory technician was receiving local media attention for earthquake predictions based on his readings of radon gas emissions, a technique most scientists regard as unreliable.

In view of the increasing uneasiness in L'Aquila, the head of Italy's Department of Civil Protection called a special meeting of the Risks Commission in L'Aquila on March 31, 2009, to provide citizens with the latest information about the seismic activity. The meeting lasted just one hour andwas followed by a press conference at which Bernardo De Bernardinis, vice-director of the Department of Civil Protection, spoke reassuringly, saying the situation posed no danger. The commission did not issue a formal statement and made no recommendations of precautions that citizens might take.

After the quake struck, six days later, citizens reacted angrily. Many claimed that the commission's reassurances were the reason they did not take such protective measures as spending the night outside—a common response to earthquake threats.

The public prosecutor alleged that the commission had been irresponsible and, in

SCIENCE ON TRIAL

Italians protest in the streets of L'Aquila, a city in central Italy, in September 2011 as a trial of seismologists and government officials begins. Italian government prosecutors charged the seven defendants with manslaughter for their alleged mishandling of public communications regarding the likelihood of an earthquake in L'Aquila in 2009. Shortly before a devastating earthquake struck on April 6 of that year, the scientists and officials had issued a public announcement minimizing the quake threat. More than 300 residents of the city died in the disaster, and many citizens claimed that the officials' statement had dissuaded them from taking appropriate precautions. The large sign held by the September 2011 protestors, who demanded the conviction of the accused, memorializes some of the young people who died in the quake. Scientists in Italy and abroad, however, petitioned the Italian government to stop the trial, warning that the legal action would have a chilling effect on scientists.

SCIENCE AND SOCIETY continued

June 2010, he indicted some of its members. After nearly a year of delays, the prosecutor and the lawyer for the defendants finally appeared before a judge. Although the prosecutor conceded that the scientists had no way of predicting the earthquake, he claimed that they should have been more diligent in warning citizens of the risks. He based his accusation on De Bernardinis's statement: "The scientific community tells me there is no danger because there is an ongoing discharge of energy. The situation looks favorable." Although the statement was disputed at the time by some *seismologists* (scientists who study earthquakes), the judge decided to bring the case to trial.

Scientists around the world expressed alarm and outrage. More than 5,000 signed an open letter to the president of Italy opposing the trial.

As the trial stretched into early 2012, it took a couple of strange twists. At a hearing on February 15, the former head of the Department of Civil Protection, who had been De Bernardinis's supervisor, was questioned about a telephone conversation in which it appeared that he had set up the March 2009 meeting to reassure the public regardless of the scientists' opinions. Originally expected to serve as a witness, he was notified that he might in fact become a defendant. Also at the Feb. 15, 2012, hearing, the former chief seismologist for the California Department of Transportation testified for the prosecution, claiming that the Italian scientists failed to use their scientific knowledge to warn the public in L'Aquila. Analysts predicted that, with 300 witnesses to be heard from, the trial would last through 2012.

Gold vs. Salmon. A major environmental battle continued in 2012 over a proposal to construct a huge mine in a remote part of Alaska. Although the project is not widely known in "the lower 48" (as Alaskans call the rest of the United States), it has generated fierce opposition from environmentalists, fishermen, native Alaskans, and even a group of 200 chefs concerned about the availability of wild salmon.

Located in the Bristol Bay watershed

some 325 kilometers (200 miles) southwest of Anchorage, the Pebble mine site is said to contain some $300 billion worth of minerals—primarily gold and copper—the largest deposit of these minerals ever found in North America. Extracting it would require digging a pit 3.2 kilometers (2 miles) across and 610 meters (2,000 feet) deep in an area that supports sockeye salmon spawning streams. Also slated in the plans for the mine are dams to create containment ponds where mining waste could be dumped.

In October 2011, residents of the sparsely populated region voted 280-to-246 against the mine in a ballot initiative brought by mine opponents. The vote was immediately challenged by the mining company. On Feb. 12, 2012, the company, the Pebble Limited Partnership, released its "Environmental Baseline Document," the result, it claimed, of four years of research costing more than $100 million. The 27,000-page document describing the current physical, biological, and social environment of the region did little to stem the controversy or satisfy the project's opponents.

Critics dismissed the document as biased because it was paid for by the mining company. The mining company noted that the studies were conducted by independent contractors and asked who else would spend such a huge sum of money to study the project. Unanswered by the document are questions about the potential impacts of constructing the huge mine and the roads and other infrastructure needed to bring its products to market.

In May, the Environmental Protection Agency (EPA) issued a report on the proposed Pebble mine. The report warned that the project would, at minimum, destroy or degrade salmon-spawning habitat on several streams in the Bristol Bay watershed. Meanwhile, analysts predicted that the legal and political battle over the mine would take several years to play out.

Budget woes and space exploration. NASA's budget and program plans suffered a series of setbacks in fiscal 2012. With intense pressure on the federal government to reduce the budget deficit, many uncertainties remain about the future of both human space flight and space science. On July 6, 2011, a committee of the U.S. House of Representatives released its fiscal year 2012 budget plan for several key science agencies. The committee proposed cutting nearly $2 billion from President Obama's request for NASA. The bill terminated funding for NASA's flagship James Webb Space Telescope (JWST), which is intended to replace the Hubble Space Telescope. The committee described the JWST project as "billions of dollars over budget and plagued by poor management."

Although NASA's overall budget was ultimately cut—by more than $500 million—the agency did, in the end, receive full funding for the JWST. In return, the administration of President Barack Obama agreed to slash funding for planetary exploration by more than 20 percent. Support for two Mars lander missions being developed with the European Space Agency was eliminated. NASA programs in aeronautics, astrophysics, and education also incurred cuts.

The one area of NASA's budget that did grow is space technology. Congress allocated funding for a heavy-lift rocket—the Space Launch System (SLS). Funding also came through for the Orion Multi-Purpose Crew Vehicle—a capsule intended to carry astronauts to deep space. However, both projects are many years and billions of dollars from completion.

The human space flight program also faced challenges in 2011 and 2012. The launch of the Atlantis space shuttle on July 8, 2011, marked the end of the 30-year shuttle program, leaving the United States without a vehicle capable of carrying humans into space. NASA, hoping that private companies will help bridge the gap, is providing nearly $1 billion to subsidize development of spacecraft by several firms, including SpaceX, Virgin Galactic, and Boeing. None of these is expected to provide a spacecraft capable of carrying astronauts into orbit before 2017. Until then, NASA is dependent on Russian Soyuz spacecraft to carry astronauts to and from the International Space Station. ■ Albert H. Teich

DEADLY GERMS

Workers in hazmat suits dispose of dead chickens at a poultry market in Hong Kong in December 2011. The chickens were killed because they were infected with *avian* (bird) flu. Researchers first identified avian flu in 1997. The virus, exceptionally lethal in humans, has, to date, infected only people in close contact with birds. In 2012, scientists published studies explaining how the virus could mutate and develop the ability to infect people more easily. The research was intended to help scientists battle a potential epidemic, but many experts worried that rogue states or terrorist groups might use the information to make a biological weapon.

SPACE TECHNOLOGY

The three remaining space shuttles flew their final missions in 2011 and then were sent for permanent display to different museums in the United States. NASA, other spacefaring nations, and private companies planned the next steps in human space flight in 2011 and 2012, while a fleet of robotic explorers continued humankind's quest for knowledge of the solar system.

End of the shuttle era. The last flight of the 30-year space shuttle era ended on July 21, 2011, as Atlantis dropped from the predawn sky over Kennedy Space Center in Florida and rolled to a stop on the shuttle landing strip. "It's been an amazing run for the 30 years," said NASA Space Shuttle Program Manager John Shannon. Shannon was one of the NASA officials who had helped determine how to get the shuttle fleet flying safely again after the shuttle Columbia disintegrated, killing all seven crewmembers, during reentry into Earth's atmosphere in 2003.

SEE ALSO THE SPECIAL REPORT **WHEN GALAXIES COLLIDE** PAGE 12

Atlantis carried a smaller-than-normal crew, dubbed the "final four," who spent 13 days stocking the International Space Station (ISS) with enough food, water, spare parts, and other supplies to last the station crew through 2012. By 2013, NASA officials hoped to be using unpiloted, privately operated cargo carriers on a regular basis to deliver supplies to the ISS. The end of Atlantis's final mission left the first gap in the ability of the United States to send astronauts into space since the start of the shuttle era.

On its last mission, Atlantis carried Commander Chris Ferguson, pilot Doug Hurley, and flight engineers Rex Walheim and Sandra Magnus. They worked with the six-member ISS crew to move 8.6 metric tons (9.5 tons) of cargo from Atlantis to the station. The shuttle crew also carried out a

ROBONAUT 2 READY FOR ACTION ON INTERNATIONAL SPACE STATION

United States astronaut Cady Coleman poses with Robonaut 2, a humanlike robot that was officially activated aboard the International Space Station (ISS) in February 2012. The legless robot was designed by NASA and General Motors Company of Detroit to assist ISS crew members with performing such simple but time-consuming tasks as routine maintenance and housecleaning inside the space station. NASA engineers planned to eventually give Robonaut 2 a pair of legs so that it would be able to work outside the station alongside another robot, named Dextre, which rode on the end of the station's robotic arm.

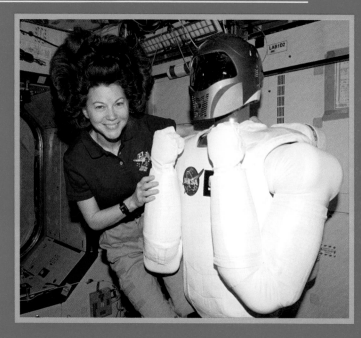

spacewalk to retrieve a pump built to circulate ammonia coolant through the system that regulates temperature in the ISS's pressurized modules. The pump had failed earlier and was replaced with a spare, but engineers on the ground wanted to examine it so they could learn what went wrong. Returning such heavy pieces of hardware to Earth will be difficult or impossible until the hauling capability of the shuttle is replaced.

Commercial vehicles. With the shuttle out of service, NASA and its Canadian, European, and Japanese partners had to rely on Russian Soyuz vehicles to transport their astronauts to and from the ISS. NASA partnered with a number of private companies to build commercial U.S. "space taxis" designed to take crews to the ISS for a fee, but those vehicles were not expected to be ready until 2017 at the earliest.

Private companies were also developing cargo vehicles to join European, Japanese, and Russian unpiloted spacecraft in keeping the station stocked with supplies. The first such commercial vehicles—named Dragon and Cygnus—started flying to the ISS in 2012. Dragon, developed by Space Exploration Technologies Corp. (SpaceX) of Hawthorne, California, was launched on its first ISS mission on May 22 atop a Falcon 9 rocket. After delivering supplies and equipment to the ISS crew, Dragon splashed down to a parachute-assisted landing in the Pacific Ocean on May 31. This landing technique allows station crews to send scientific samples and worn-out equipment to Earth for analysis or repair, though Dragon cannot match the huge "down-mass" capability of the shuttles. Cygnus, operated by Orbital Sciences Corp. of Dulles, Virginia, was scheduled to take off on its first mission by the end of 2012. It was to be launched on a rocket named Antares, which Orbital also made available for satellite launches.

ISS research. With more than 10 years of construction work on the ISS completed in May 2011, station crews had much more time to spend on scientific research, working with scientists on Earth via video and radio links. Most of that research took advantage of the "weightless" environment in orbit, where the influence of gravity is reduced to almost zero. Such conditions give researchers an opportunity to conduct studies that are not possible on Earth, including analyzing how materials mix and how the human body functions in *microgravity* (conditions of little gravitational influence). This type of research could lead to the development of new drugs and other materials, as well as improved knowledge on how to keep astronauts healthy during long missions in space—such as a trip to Mars.

Other research performed on the ISS in 2011 and 2012 involved robots designed to assist crew members with dangerous or repetitive tasks. Such robots are envisioned as being important to lengthy future space missions. Two experimental robots on the ISS—Dextre and Robonaut 2—helped engineers study how well such devices could assist humans in space.

Dextre (an abbreviated version of its official name—Special Purpose Dexterous Manipulator) is a two-armed "space handyman," 3.7 meters (12 feet) tall, that rides outside the ISS's modules on the end of the station's long robotic arm. Developed by the Canadian Space Agency, Dextre showed in a series of tests in 2011 that it could serve as a substitute for space-walking astronauts in replacing worn-out parts outside the station. Cameras on Dextre were used to assist with the initial berthing of the Dragon cargo craft to the ISS.

NASA astronauts officially activated Robonaut 2 for day-to-day use in February 2012. This humanlike robot, designed by NASA and General Motors Company of Detroit, assisted crew members with such interior ISS jobs as routine maintenance and housecleaning. In 2012, Robonaut 2 (called "R2" by the crew) had only an upper body. However, engineers planned to eventually add a set of legs to enable R2 to work outside the station alongside Dextre.

Augmented reality. On the ground, researchers with the European Space Agency (ESA) tested equipment that could help astronauts who are untrained in medical procedures to diagnose and treat injured or ill crewmates on the ISS or on future long-distance space flights. In February 2012, the ESA described tests of its Computer Assisted Medical Diagnosis And Surgery System (CAMDASS).

SPACE TECHNOLOGY continued

An astronaut using CAMDASS wears a headset equipped with a stereoscopic display combining the wearer's natural view of surroundings with computer-generated graphics. An infrared camera tracks the position of an ultrasound probe or other examination or surgical tool used by the wearer. Three-dimensional "cue cards" shown in the stereo display guide the wearer in performing the steps of a surgical or other medical procedure. In tests of a prototype CAMDASS at Saint-Pierre University Hospi-

PRIVATE ENTERPRISE ENTERS SPACE

In the first private, commercial launch to the International Space Station (ISS), a Falcon 9 rocket blasts off from Cape Canaveral, Florida, on May 22, 2012, carrying the unpiloted Dragon cargo craft. Both the rocket and unpiloted spacecraft were designed, owned, and operated by Space Exploration Technologies Corp. (SpaceX) of Hawthorne, California. Dragon carried food and other important supplies and equipment to the ISS crew. After delivering these supplies, Dragon—packed with such time-sensitive payloads from the ISS as biological experiments and refrigerated samples—splashed down to a parachute-assisted landing in the Pacific Ocean on May 31. This successful test mission cleared the way for SpaceX to begin fulfilling its $1.6-billion ISS resupply contract for NASA, which involved 12 flights through 2015.

The robotic arm of the ISS pulls the Dragon cargo capsule toward a docking port.

tal in Brussels, Belgium, medical and nursing students demonstrated that they could use the system to successfully perform difficult procedures in which they had not previously been trained.

ESA engineers planned to conduct further tests of CAMDASS in remote sites on Earth, including Antarctica, before moving it into orbit for use on the ISS.

China's mini-station. On Sept. 29, 2011, China launched the Tiangong 1 laboratory module, a pressurized target with which Chinese astronauts can practice docking maneuvers in preparation for the space station that China hopes to launch between 2020 and 2022. Although not designed for full-time occupancy, Tiangong 1 was to carry experiments tended occasionally by visiting astronauts.

In a test conducted in November 2011, Shenzhou 8, an unpiloted version of a spacecraft that had previously carried astronauts into orbit, successfully docked with Tiangong 1. Carrying a crew of three, Shenzhou 9 launched on June 16, 2012, and successfully docked with the Tiangong 1 mini-station on June 18. With the maneuver, China joined the United States and Russia as the only countries to complete a piloted docking in space. The crew included the first Chinese woman astronaut.

Mars Science Laboratory. In November 2011, NASA launched the Mars Science Laboratory (MSL), a continuation of the agency's series of remotely controlled Mars rovers. Scheduled to land inside the red planet's Gale Crater in August 2012, the MSL rover was to explore a carefully selected stretch of Martian terrain for chemical and physical evidence of past or present water and life.

Powered by a radioisotope thermoelectric generator, which converts the heat from radioactive plutonium into electric current, the MSL rover, named Curiosity, was not dependent on sunlight to keep it moving, as were previous Mars rovers. The size of a small automobile, Curiosity was much larger than the previous golf-cart-sized rovers, Spirit and Opportunity.

Twin video cameras gave Curiosity's remote-control drivers at the Jet Propulsion Laboratory (JPL) in Pasadena, California, a stereoscopic view of the rover's surround-

EARTH-LIKE LAVA FLOWS ON MARTIAN SURFACE

Ancient, dried, coil-shaped lava flows create intriguing patterns in a photograph of the surface of Mars released by NASA in April 2012. The volcanic formations are the first detected on a planet other than Earth. Located near the Martian equator, the formations are the result of volcanic activity sometime within the past 20 million years, according to an analysis conducted by Andrew Ryan, a graduate student in planetary geology at Arizona State University in Tempe. Ryan explained that after lava from volcanic eruptions flowed through valleys into a broad basin, it settled into coil shapes in the basin, where it hardened and became preserved. Such twisted lava formations are also found on the Big Island of Hawaii and on the floor of the Pacific Ocean.

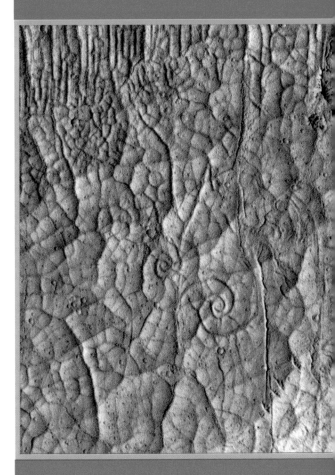

SPACE TECHNOLOGY continued

ings, enabling them to steer the vehicle clear of large rocks and steep slopes.

The rover's advanced robotic arm included a tool kit that allowed it to drill into rocks and scoop up soil for analysis. In one of the analytical techniques, a laser was designed to vaporize the soil so that a device called a spectrometer could analyze the colors in the resulting flash of light. Different colors rep-

resent different chemicals in the soil. Results of the analyses were to be relayed to Earth.

Curiosity was so large and heavy that it could not land on airbags, as did its smaller predecessors. Instead, engineers at the JPL designed a "sky crane" approach to lower the rover on cables from a platform suspended by the blasts of rocket engines above the landing site. Once the rover

DAWN BRAKES AT VESTA

The rugged, heavily cratered surface of Vesta comes into focus in one of the first close-up images of this rocky body taken by NASA's Dawn spacecraft. Data from Dawn, which went into orbit around Vesta in July 2011, confirmed earlier suspicions that Vesta is not an asteroid but the solar system's only known surviving planetesimal. Also known as protoplanets, planetesimals were asteroid-sized objects that collided and stuck together to form the planets, moons, and other solid or mostly solid objects of the solar system. Vesta has survived in the rough-and-tumble environment of the Main Belt since the formation of the solar system more than 4 billion years ago. The Main Belt is a region of millions of asteroids between the orbits of Mars and Jupiter. Vesta was on its way to becoming a planet when it was stopped near its present size by the gravitational pull of the gas giant Jupiter, which probably prevented Vesta from combining with other planetesimals to form a full-sized planet.

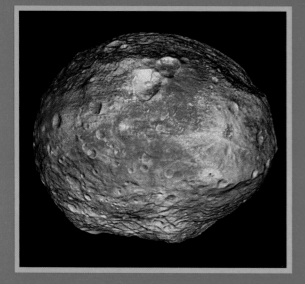

The variety of minerals on Vesta's surface glow in a kaleidoscopic image made with photographs taken in visible and infrared light by a camera on Dawn. In the image, taken from an animation, green represents areas with a concentration of iron. Scientists continued to study the planetesimal to identify the minerals represented by other colors.

touched the ground, the cables were to be released, and the platform was to fly off to crash a safe distance away. This previously untried landing technique was risky.

Robotic probes. In 2012, data continued to pour in from NASA's MESSENGER (Mercury Surface, Space Environment, Geochemistry, and Ranging) probe, which began orbiting Mercury, the planet closest to the sun, in March 2011. MESSENGER's data raised questions regarding previous ideas on how Mercury formed. Scientists previous-

ly thought that the planet's rich supply of iron was left over after the sun's heat boiled away lighter chemical elements. However, MESSENGER's instruments detected such lighter elements as sulfur and potassium—elements that would not be present if previous ideas about Mercury's formation were correct. The discovery of the lighter-than-expected elements illustrated the value of using robotic space probes to get "up close and personal" with the distant bodies of the solar system.

Evidence from Dawn that Vesta has a largely iron core surrounded by a rocky crust and mantle—like Earth and the other inner planets of the solar system—helped confirm the protoplanet's true identity. Asteroids usually consist of the same material throughout. The existence of the core, which is about 220 kilometers (140 miles) in diameter, suggests that Vesta melted completely early in its history. The iron in this magma ocean sank to form the core and produced a *basaltic* (volcanic rock) crust.

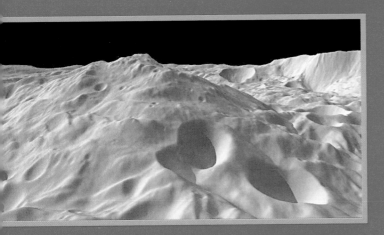

Vesta's south pole mountain, the largest on the protoplanet, rises from about 20 to 25 kilometers (12 to 15 miles) above the average height of the surrounding terrain, nearly three times as high as Earth's Mount Everest. The mountain faces a steep cliff (right in photo) that is 15 to 20 kilometers (9 to 12 miles) tall with a jumble of rocks at its base. Dawn scientists think this rugged area was probably created by landslides. In the image, the surface has been flattened to provide a view of both features at once. A person standing on Vesta, which has a diameter of only about 525 kilometers (325 miles), would not be able to see both because one would be over the horizon.

SPACE TECHNOLOGY continued

Dawn, a NASA probe that began orbiting the giant "near-planet" Vesta in July 2011, discovered a volcanic mountain larger than any on Earth—and almost as large as Olympus Mons on Mars (the largest known volcano in the solar system). Analysis of the discovery helped planetary scientists refine their understanding of the way that volcanic action shapes planets and undeveloped planets such as Vesta. Dawn was scheduled to move on to the asteroid Ceres after completing its study of Vesta.

Launched in August 2011, NASA's Juno probe was to be the first probe powered by solar cells to orbit Jupiter. After it arrives at Jupiter in 2016, Juno is to spin its three long solar arrays like a giant windmill as it orbits the solar system's largest planet. The probe's main mission was to study the composition of Jupiter's upper atmosphere to learn more about aspects of the solar system's formation. For example, by measuring how much water is in the clouds of Jupiter's atmosphere, researchers may be able to estimate how much of the water came from comets—revealing, in turn, clues about where Earth's water originated.

NASA launched the GRAIL (Gravity Recovery and Interior Laboratory) mission to the moon in September 2011. The mission consisted of two identical spacecraft, named Ebb and Flow, designed to map tiny variations in the moon's gravitational field. The crafts conduct this mapping exercise as they precisely measure their changing altitudes while passing over surface materials of different densities. The data generated from these measurements helped scientists calculate details about the structure of the moon beneath the lunar surface.

DUST DEVIL ON MARS

A dust devil swirls more than 800 meters (2,625 feet) above the surface of northern Mars in February 2012, in a photograph taken by a high-resolution camera on NASA's Mars Reconnaissance Orbiter. Dust devils, which also form on Earth, are whirling columns of air similar to small tornadoes. They occur most frequently in deserts, where the sun heats the air near the dry ground, and the warm, rising air carries sand and dust along with it. However, the NASA photo was taken during the time of year when Mars is farthest from the sun. Thus, scientists found it surprising that, despite the reduced exposure to the sun's rays, such a large, powerful dust devil could still develop on Mars.

Special payloads riding piggyback on the Ebb and Flow spacecrafts provided fifth- to eighth-grade students with opportunities to explore the moon from their classrooms. The "MoonKAM" cameras collected photographs of the cratered surface below the spacecraft, and these photos were posted online. Students were then able to send online requests regarding which features in the photos they wished to explore in greater detail. Sally Ride, the first U.S. woman in space, managed the MoonKAM program for NASA.

■ Frank Morring, Jr.

See also **ASTRONOMY.**

Rediscovering Mercury

Until the MESSENGER space probe began its examination of Mercury in 2011, the first rock from the sun was widely considered uninteresting. Scientists believed that hot, barren Mercury had remained nearly unchanged since its formation more than 4 billion years ago. But data from MESSENGER, the first probe to orbit Mercury, has revealed that the planet is both strange and dynamic.

After making flybys in 2008 to reduce its speed, MESSENGER (short for Mercury Surface, Space Environment, Geochemistry, and Ranging) settled into orbit around Mercury in March 2011. Later in the year, the solar system's smallest planet began revealing some big surprises. It has mysterious surface features unknown elsewhere in the solar system. Its core is unlike that of any other planet. Perhaps most interesting of all, the planet's geologic history is much more exciting than anyone expected. In November, NASA announced that it was extending the MESSENGER mission to at least 2013, a move expected to yield even more surprises.

A bulging plateau (whittish area at lower left) surrounded by narrow ridges (pink areas) rises above ancient volcanic plains in Mercury's northern hemisphere, in a false-color image created using altitude measurements made by MESSENGER. The altitude data also revealed that Mercury is relatively flat. The difference between the highest points (white) and lowest points (the floors of impact craters, shown in purple) is only about 2.3 kilometers (1.4 miles), significantly less than that on the moon or Mars.

The smooth plains covering much of Mercury's northern hemisphere (outlined in yellow) resulted from volcanic activity that was more violent and widespread than scientists had suspected, MESSENGER data have revealed. From 4 billion to 3.5 billion years ago, thick rivers of lava gushed from cracks up to 25 kilometers (15 miles) long in Mercury's already scorching surface. The lava flows filled impact craters and flooded low-lying areas around the north pole "like a bathtub," one scientist said. The plains cover an area equal to about 60 percent of the continental United States.

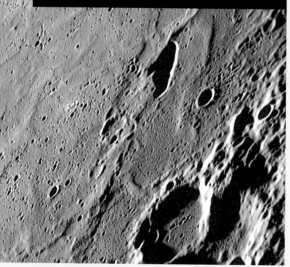

A small, irregularly shaped pit on the floor of the Tolstoj basin is one of a number of similar unexplained holes in Mercury's surface. The absence of a rim around the pit suggests that these so-called pit-collapse features are not impact craters. Scientists speculate the pits may have formed when magma drained from a shallow chamber beneath the crater, weakening the rock above and causing it to collapse.

Only the rim of an ancient impact crater (lower left in photo) survived the massive lava flows that buried Mercury's northern hemisphere early in its history. Such "ghost craters" have helped scientists determine the volume of the volcanic flood, as some of these craters were more than 2 kilometers (1.2 miles) deep. More recent craters in the lava beds (upper right in photo) are evidence of the continuing bombardment of the planet by asteroids and meteorites since volcanic activity ended.

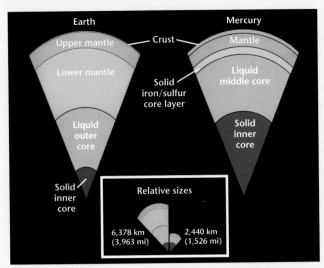

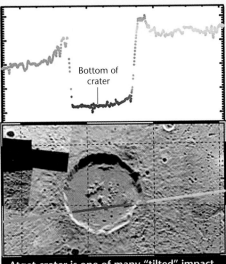

Gravitational measurements suggest that Mercury's core is larger, relative to its size, than the core of any other planet in the solar system. Mercury's core takes up an estimated 85 percent of the interior of the planet—leaving the crust and mantle only about 300 kilometers (185 miles) thick. Earth's core, in contrast, occupies about 50 percent of the interior. Scientists speculate that Mercury has a third layer of solid iron and sulfur that lies between the liquid portion of the core and the mantle above. This proposed "outer layer" of the core may explain one of the planet's greatest mysteries—how it could be so small and still have a greater *mass* (amount of matter) than the other inner planets—Venus, Earth, and Mars—for its size.

Atget crater is one of many "tilted" impact craters on Mercury, with one side higher than the other (drawing at top). Scientists believe that the uneven floors of the craters suggest that tectonic movements linked to the shrinking of the core continue to shape the surface.

A huge cliff called the Victoria Rupes cuts across a section of Mercury's northern hemisphere, in a mosaic made from MESSENGER images. Arc-shaped rupes (Latin for *cliff*) are the most common *tectonic* (structural) feature on the surface. Rupes may be up to 1.5 kilometers (1 mile) high and 550 kilometers (350 miles) long. Scientists believe these "wrinkles" in Mercury's thin crust formed when one block of crust was pushed up against another block as the core cooled and shrank.

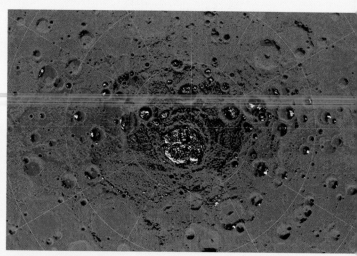

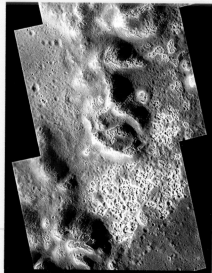

Water ice may be lurking in deep craters on hot, barren Mercury, a composite false-color image of the area around the south pole suggests. In the image, "bright" patches that strongly reflect radar waves—a common sign of water ice—imaged by an Earth-based telescope correspond to areas of permanent darkness mapped by MESSENGER. Compounds other than water could reflect radar waves to the same extent, however.

Holes known as hollows (blue dots in image) may be the strangest landforms discovered on Mercury. These mysterious structures, which appear in clusters, are widespread on the floors, walls, and peaks of craters and have not been seen on any other planet or moon in the solar system. Rimless and irregularly shaped, they range in size from 18 meters to 1.6 kilometers (60 feet to 1 mile) across and from 18 to 37 meters (60 to 120 feet) deep. Scientists think hollows formed recently because the structures have not been reshaped by tectonic forces or impacts, but their origin is unknown. Some scientists think they may have been created as sulfur or other minerals common on Mercury vaporized in the heat and solar wind bombarding the planet, weakening the surface rock and causing it to crumble and collapse.

Water ice could survive in kilometers-deep craters around Mercury's poles, even though the surface temperature on the planet may reach 450 °C (840 °F) during the day. Permanently shielded from sunlight, the floors of the craters could become "cold traps" that capture vapor from space. The temperature in the deeply shadowed cold traps would never get high enough to melt the ice, which, some scientists speculate, could be several meters thick.

SUPPLEMENT

New encyclopedia articles are
devoted to the following topics:

© Minden Pictures/Masterfile

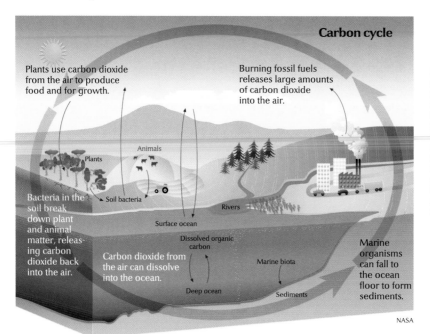

Carbon cycle

Plants use carbon dioxide from the air to produce food and for growth.

Burning fossil fuels releases large amounts of carbon dioxide into the air.

Animals

Plants

Bacteria in the soil break down plant and animal matter, releasing carbon dioxide back into the air.

Soil bacteria

Surface ocean

Rivers

Dissolved organic carbon

Carbon dioxide from the air can dissolve into the ocean.

Marine biota

Marine organisms can fall to the ocean floor to form sediments.

Deep ocean

Sediments

Carbon cycles between the atmosphere, land, and oceans. Plants and certain other organisms use the energy from sunlight to convert carbon dioxide (CO_2) into a form that is usable by other animals. Human activity also contributes to the cycle. Burning fossil fuels for energy has added a significant amount of CO_2 into the atmosphere. The additional CO_2 is slowly warming Earth's surface.

NASA

Carbon cycle is the circulation of the element carbon among Earth's atmosphere, land, oceans, interior, and *organisms* (living things). Carbon is an essential element of living creatures. It is also a major ingredient in the natural energy resources: coal, natural gas, and petroleum. The carbon cycle helps to determine levels of heat-trapping carbon dioxide (CO_2) gas in the atmosphere. The cycle thus has a major effect on Earth's climate. The total amount of carbon on Earth is constant. The cycle does not create or destroy carbon. Instead, it simply exchanges carbon among different places and forms.

On land, certain organisms draw carbon, in the form of carbon dioxide, from the air. This carbon is then used in *photosynthesis*, a process in which plants, algae, and some other organisms use energy from sunlight to make food and the building blocks for growth. The carbon thus becomes part of the plants' bodies.

When plants die or shed leaves, they deposit their trapped carbon into the soil. There, certain bacteria may break down some of the plant matter. These bacteria release carbon back into the atmosphere as CO_2. Animals also eat some plant matter for energy and growth. The animals exhale some of the carbon from the plant matter as CO_2. When animals die, as with plants, soil bacteria may consume them, releasing CO_2 back into the atmosphere. Animals' remaining carbon can become buried.

In the oceans, algae, plants, and other organisms use CO_2 from the atmosphere for photosynthesis. These organisms may be broken down by bacteria or consumed by other organisms, or they may sink to the bottom.

CO_2 can also dissolve directly into the oceans from the atmosphere. Some organisms, such as coral and oysters, can use this carbon to create shells. When these organisms die, the shells may settle to the ocean floor and form limestone. Limestone sediments represent Earth's largest store of carbon. Ocean currents can bring dissolved carbon from the deep ocean back to the surface. There, it may return to the atmosphere.

Over millions of years, once-living matter that remains in the ground can transform into the fossil fuels coal, natural gas, and petroleum. When people burn fossil fuels for energy, the carbon that was captured by plants or eaten by animals millions of years ago is returned to the atmosphere. Since the mid-1800's, human activity has significantly altered the carbon cycle. Fossil fuels that would have remained deep underground are instead burned for energy. Burning fossil fuels has raised the concentration of CO_2 in the atmosphere. It has also raised the acidity of the oceans.   C. Adam Schlosser

Forensic pathology is the study of disease and injury as it applies to legal matters. Forensic pathologists often conduct their studies through a procedure called *autopsy.* An autopsy is an external and internal examination of a dead body.

There are two main branches of forensic pathology. They are *anatomic pathology* and *clinical pathology.* Anatomic pathology deals with the study of tissues obtained from living or dead people. A forensic pathologist may perform an autopsy on a body to determine the cause of death. This procedure is usually done in cases where a death cannot be otherwise explained. Clinical pathology involves the collection and study of body fluids, such as blood or saliva. Laboratory analysis of these materials can help determine the cause of a death.

Legal officials may insist on an autopsy when a person's death results from suicide, homicide, or unknown causes. Forensic pathologists may also gather other kinds of evidence from a crime scene to help determine the cause of a death. In some cases, experts can learn why someone died from a detailed review of medical records.

In the United States, the American Board of Pathology first recognized forensic pathology as a separate branch of medical pathology in 1959. Today, many countries require that a medical examiner or coroner be trained in forensic pathology.   Jason H. Byrd

© Gianni Muratore, Alamy Images

The Internet makes possible communication that reaches around the world. In this Internet cafe in India, Buddhist monks access the Internet from laptop computers and mobile phones. People everywhere use the Internet to research, shop, watch television, play games, and talk with friends.

Internet

Internet is a system of computer networks that links together billions of computers, mobile phones, and other electronic devices around the world. People using such devices have rapid access to vast stores of information. They can also quickly communicate with one another. Nearly a third of the world's population has access to the Internet. In developed countries, many people use the Internet every day. In less developed countries, most cities have Internet cafes or kiosks. At such places, people can pay to use a computer with Internet access.

The amount of information stored on the Internet dwarfs that in the world's largest libraries. This information can take the form of text, sounds, images, videos, or *interactive* computer programs. Interactive programs enable the user to take part in and help guide the action.

Much of the Internet's information is organized into the World Wide Web. The Web is the part of the Internet that contains—and links together—millions of websites. But the Internet does not just store information. It also enables people to work, shop, play games, form online communities, and share their artwork and ideas. A tremendous amount and variety of activity takes place *online* (on the Internet).

The Internet works through a combination of *hardware* and *software*. The hardware includes all of the computers, wires, and other physical structures and devices that make up the network. The software includes sets of rules called *protocols*. Protocols determine how the hardware sends, receives, and displays information. The Web and its contents are another layer of software.

The Internet originated in the United States in the 1960's. At first, only the armed forces and computer experts used it. The World Wide Web developed during the 1990's, making the Internet much easier to use. By the 2000's, ordinary people could easily find information, communicate, and publish content on the Internet.

Widespread use of the Internet has reshaped society. Since the Web developed, new industries have sprung up to take advantage of the Internet's capabilities. Other industries have struggled to adapt. Ideas have spread quickly through the Internet. The Internet enables marketers, politicians, and ordinary people to send messages far and wide. People have used the Internet to organize political movements and even revolutions.

Uses

For hundreds of millions of people around the world, Internet use is part of daily life. Computers, mobile phones, video game consoles, televisions, and even some automobiles can connect to the Internet. Each of these devices thus serves as a gateway to a huge store of information. The Internet makes possible many forms of communication. Any Internet-connected device can link together individuals, businesses, and other organizations across the globe.

Information and media. Computers have an enormous capacity to store information. In a computer, information exists in *digital* format. This means that the information is encoded in patterns of numbers. Virtually any kind of *media* can be stored as a digital computer file. Media include text, sounds, images, and videos. Software programs, such as electronic games and word processors, are also stored in digital files.

Glossary of Internet terms

Blog, a contraction of *web log,* is an online journal in which people can easily publish writing, photos, and other media.

Broadband is high-speed, wired connection to the Internet. Cable and digital subscriber line (DSL) are types of broadband.

Cloud computing is the storage of data and use of software on the Internet, rather than on a user's computer.

Cookie is a piece of data distributed by a website and stored by a user's web browser. Cookies often contain information that websites use to personalize content or advertising.

Domain name is a group of letters and symbols—often words—that forms part of a web page's URL address. Websites are typically organized around easily recognized domain names, such as *worldbook.com.*

Firewall is an electronic barrier that protects an Internet-connected computer or private network from intrusion.

Hyperlink is a highlighted word or icon on a web page that "links" to another page, enabling the user to access its content.

HyperText Markup Language (HTML) is the technical language used to write web page files.

HyperText Transfer Protocol (HTTP) is the set of rules that governs how the World Wide Web works.

Internet Protocol (IP) address is a unique identification number assigned to each device connected to the Internet.

Internet service provider (ISP) is a business or other organization that provides users with access to the Internet's wires and transmitting equipment.

Malware is harmful software programs, such as *viruses* and *worms,* that can spread easily over the Internet.

Modem is a device, often provided by an ISP, that enables computers to send and receive Internet data.

Peer-to-peer (P2P) networking involves the direct transfer of files between the computers of Internet users.

Phishing is the criminal technique of posing as a bank or other legitimate institution or person on the Internet to gain passwords or other personal information from users.

Router is a device that directs the flow of data in a computer network. For example, a home router can pass Internet data from a modem to several home computers and vice versa.

Search engine is a program that enables a user to find information on the Internet by typing in key words. The search engine returns a list of web pages relevant to the key words.

Server is a computer specialized for sending data to a large number of other devices on the Internet or a private network. Much web content is stored, or *hosted,* on servers.

Spam is unsolicited e-mail or other online messages sent to hundreds or even millions of recipients.

Spyware is software that gathers information about Internet users' identities and habits, often without their knowledge.

TCP/IP, short for Transmission Control Protocol/Internet Protocol, is a set of rules that governs how data move over the Internet.

Uniform Resource Locator (URL) is a web page's address.

Web browser is a software program on computers and other Internet-connected devices that enables a user to access and view web pages.

Wiki is a website that enables multiple people to quickly and easily edit its content.

World Wide Web is a system of computer files called *web pages* that are linked to one another on the Internet. *Websites* are collections of web pages.

It is difficult to state how much information exists on the Internet. New information is constantly *uploaded* or added to the Internet. In 2010, for example, people uploaded an average of about 24 hours of video to a popular website called YouTube every minute.

Some of the Internet's information primarily serves local communities. For example, people might use the Internet to look up their local school's cafeteria menu. But much of the Internet's information links people and cultures separated by vast distances. For example, Internet users can easily listen to music from performers living across the world.

File sharing. Before the Internet, people had extremely limited access to files not stored on their own computers. By linking the world's computers together, the Internet created a global storage space for digital files.

Much of the Internet's information is available on the Web. Nearly any Internet user can access most websites. Some sites require people to log in or to pay for access to certain content. Internet users can also share digital files on their computers directly with one another. Such sharing is called *peer-to-peer* (P2P) networking.

Search engines. Without some system for organizing and finding information, the vast amount of data on the Web would be largely useless. It would be much like a library full of unshelved books. Some web pages, called *portals,* attempt to collect and organize information available on the Internet. They provide lists of links to other related web pages, such as news articles or entertainment sites.

However, Web users chiefly find information using a *search engine,* such as Google or Bing. Most search engines feature a box in which the user types *key words.*

The search engine then displays a list of web pages related to those key words.

Search engines determine and rank the web pages they return in a number of ways. For example, a search engine may return a list of web pages with the key word in their text or title. Search engines often count the links that lead to a certain web page. If many other places link to that page, the search engine may assume that the page is more desirable to the searcher. It may thus rank the site higher in the list. Many search engines can also help users narrow their search to images, news articles, shopping sites, or other types of content. They can also suggest similar key words that the user might not have considered.

Communication is a major use of the Internet. Some forms of Internet communication work much like older forms. For example, e-mails can take the place of written letters delivered by the post office. Voice over Internet Protocol (VoIP) enables people to make calls through their Internet connection instead of over a telephone. People can also *videochat* using computers or phones equipped with special cameras. Videochatters can watch each other while having a conversation.

Entirely new forms of communication have also emerged through the Internet. *Listservs* are electronic mailing lists. They make it easy to send e-mails to long lists of people. A listserv enables an organization to quickly send announcements to a large group. The people on the listserv can also form a discussion group to talk about various topics with one another. With *instant messaging,* or *IM,* people can quickly exchange typed messages in a back-and-forth conversation. *Blogs* are journallike websites that take advantage of the ease of publishing on the Internet. Blog is short for *web log.* Blog authors can easily *post* (publish) written entries, photographs, or other media. Readers can also post comments on blog entries.

Online communities. People with similar interests often participate in online communities. Some online communities are organized around sports, celebrity gossip, health information, or other topics. In many online communities, people can create discussions on a virtual message board and post replies. Other communities are virtual spaces in which people play games together. In *multi-user domains* (MUD's), people can organize and play text-based *role-playing games.* A role-playing game involves taking on the role of an imaginary character, often in a fantasy setting. *Massively multiplayer online role-playing games* (MMORPG's) are more elaborate online fantasy worlds. They include complex *graphics* (visual elements) and sound.

Social networking websites are a special type of online community. People on social networks can connect with other people on the network by *friending* or *following* them—that is, by asking them to become friends or followers. Friends can see each other's *profiles.* A profile could include personal information, blogs and comments, photos, videos, and music. Users can thus share personal information and photos with all their friends or followers at once. They can also post short messages called *status updates.* Facebook, Tumblr, and Twitter are popular social networks. They have millions of active users. Another social network, LinkedIn, serves mostly for business dealings or job searches. Togetherville is a social network for young people and their parents.

Commerce. Almost all businesses have websites. Many such commercial sites function as online stores. Some large companies—notably Amazon.com, Inc.—exist entirely as online retailers. Other sites connect sellers with potential buyers. For example, eBay is a popular auction website. Craigslist is a nonprofit site that enables people to post classified advertisements for free.

Internet users can typically purchase items online with a credit card. Some services, such as PayPal, enable people to make payments from online accounts. Traditional banks also run websites on which people can pay bills and manage their accounts. Many businesses, such as utility services and credit card companies, offer an option called *online bill pay.* With online bill pay, customers can arrange to pay their bills electronically.

Some Internet services employ *virtual currency.* People use such currencies to purchase imaginary items in social networks or online games. Some virtual currencies can be used to *download* or take from the Internet movies or other electronic content.

Advertising is a common feature on many websites. *Banner ads* run above or beside a web page's main content. They often include video or interactive elements. *Pop-up ads* generate a new window to attract attention. Many advertisers buy small, text-based ads that run alongside search results for certain key words. These ads are called *contextual ads.* For example, someone who searches for baseball statistics might see a contextual ad for a sporting goods store. Advertising games or *advergames* take advantage of the Internet's interactivity. They encourage Internet users to play product-related

games or to spread messages about products.

By 2008, advertising companies spent more money on Internet advertising than on such traditional media as newspapers, radio, and television. Many Internet ads, like traditional ads, simply encourage people to buy something. But Internet advertisers have more power to target potential buyers. Some companies use *cookies*—files stored on Internet users' computers—to track people's purchases and online behavior. By collecting such data, advertisers can more effectively target customers.

Cloud computing enables people to store data and use software programs on the Internet, rather than on their own computers. For example, people might use a word processor on a website, instead of a word processing program installed on their own computer. People can also store music, photo collections, and other large files on an Internet account. They can then access such files and programs from any computer. The term *cloud computing* refers to the diffuse manner in which computing tasks and resources on the Internet are spread among various computers. Multiple people can easily collaborate on a single document stored on "the cloud."

How the Internet works

The Internet is a global network of computers and other devices. At a basic level, the Internet consists of hardware. Hardware includes every computer, phone, and other device on the Internet. It also includes the cables, wires, and wireless broadcasting equipment that enable electronic signals to travel from device to device.

The Internet's hardware would be useless without a set of rules that control how electronic signals are sent and received. These rules are the Internet's software protocols. Every device on the network has an Internet Protocol (IP) address. The IP address is a number somewhat like a home address. The software protocols enable IP addresses to efficiently send data to one another.

The Internet's hardware, together with its software protocols, determines how information moves through the network. But there is yet another layer of organization to the Internet, the World Wide Web. The Web has its own set of protocols. Before the Web existed, people found it difficult to access and view information on the Internet. The Web provides a meaningfully connected structure for the Internet's information.

Hardware. The Internet's hardware includes all the physical structures that send and process electronic data. The data travel in the form of electronic signals. Such signals can move over copper telephone lines. Fiber optic cables, which consist of tiny glass fibers, can carry large amounts of data. Radio waves can also transmit the signals through the air and from satellites orbiting Earth.

People typically purchase access to the Internet's wires and transmitting equipment through an Internet service provider (ISP). Many ISP's are telecommunication companies. Universities and national governments also provide Internet access.

The Internet was originally built to use the lines and connections of the telephone network. *Dial-up* connections use this type of technology. *Broadband* connections transfer data much faster than do dial-up connections. Broadband became increasingly popular during the 1990's. One type of broadband, called a *digital*

How data move over the Internet

Data move over the Internet according to a concept called *packet switching*. This simplified illustration shows how packet switching might be used to transmit a piece of data—in this case a photo of a cat—from a smartphone to a distant computer.

WORLD BOOK diagram

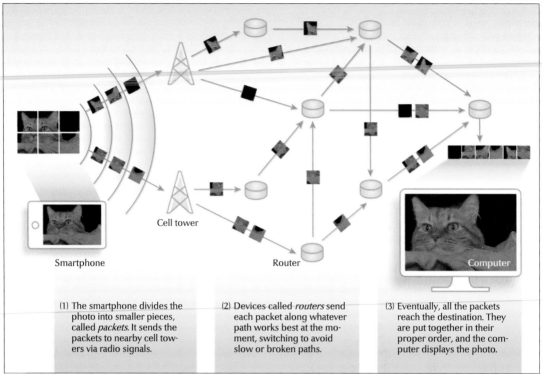

Smartphone

Cell tower

Router

Computer

(1) The smartphone divides the photo into smaller pieces, called *packets.* It sends the packets to nearby cell towers via radio signals.

(2) Devices called *routers* send each packet along whatever path works best at the moment, switching to avoid slow or broken paths.

(3) Eventually, all the packets reach the destination. They are put together in their proper order, and the computer displays the photo.

tions transfer data much faster than do dial-up connections. Broadband became increasingly popular during the 1990's. One type of broadband, called a *digital subscriber line* (DSL), increases the amount of data copper telephone wire can carry. Cable companies also sell broadband connections through high-capacity wires or fiber-optic lines.

Mobile phones and some portable computers access the Internet through radio waves. Such *wireless connections* use a number of technologies, including 3G (third generation), 4G (fourth generation), and LTE (Long Term Evolution). These technologies can approach the speeds of broadband.

The Internet's "net" connects all the IP addresses together. Any personal computer, mobile phone, or other device with an IP address can typically send data to any other device on the Internet. But certain computers, called *servers,* are specialized for sending data to a large number of other devices. The data that make up websites are usually stored on servers. *Data centers* are compounds that house large numbers of server computers. Large Internet and technology companies own and operate most data centers. Such companies may offer space on their servers to *host* (store and distribute) other people's data or websites.

Software. The Internet's hardware operates according to a software protocol—that is, a set of rules called Transmission Control Protocol/Internet Protocol (TCP/IP, or IP for short). The rules determine how data move

from one IP address to another.

TCP/IP employs a concept called *packet switching.* This concept makes the Internet work much differently from the telephone network. When two people talk on the telephone, the two phones must maintain a constant, direct connection. But when a computer sends a file to another computer over the Internet, the file does not have to travel directly, or in one piece. Instead, the file's digital code is split up into smaller chunks, called *packets.* Each packet contains a numerical code for its source IP address, its destination IP address, and information about how it fits together with other packets.

Packets do not have to travel through the network on the same path, or in their original order. If parts of the network become overloaded, damaged, or blocked, the packets switch to another route. When the packets all arrive at their destination, they are reassembled into the complete file.

TCP/IP makes the Internet a stable, efficient means of transmitting information. It ensures that information can always flow over the network, even if parts of the network are not working properly. Splitting and reassembling files takes a fraction of a second. However, users sometimes notice the delay as a lag in instant messaging conversations and other applications.

Other software protocols operate on top of TCP/IP. For example, e-mail works through either of two protocols—Internet Message Access Protocol (IMAP) or Post Office Protocol (POP). These protocols control how e-

The World Wide Web is perhaps the most recognizable portion of the Internet. The Web is not the same as the Internet. If the Web did not exist, people could still use the Internet to e-mail each other and exchange files. However, the Web makes a huge amount of information easily accessible to Internet users. Websites can also make use of other software protocols. For example, many people use the Web to e-mail each other and to transfer files.

People use programs called *web browsers* to access and interact with web pages. Popular web browsers include Chrome, Firefox, Internet Explorer, and Safari. Many computers, *smartphones,* and other devices come with browsers already installed. Smartphones combine the features of a cellular phone and a handheld computer. Other programs—for example, certain applications, or "apps," on smartphones—can also access and display Web content in a more limited fashion.

HTTP. The Web works through a set of rules called HyperText Transfer Protocol (HTTP). *HyperText* refers to the linking of words or images among web pages. The visual image of a "web" is based on this system of links between web pages. But unlike the Internet's "net" of physical hardware devices, the Web exists entirely as electronic code.

Web pages are simply digital files. They are typically stored on server computers. Each web page has a unique address, called a URL (Uniform Resource Locator). For example, the URL for World Book Encyclopedia's home page is http://www.worldbookonline.com. The URL tells the web browser how to locate the web page on the Internet.

Websites are collections of individual web pages. A site is organized under a certain *domain name*—for example, the term "worldbookonline" in the above URL. A domain name is somewhat like a street name. Each house on the street corresponds to a URL address.

World Book's website has a home page along with thousands of other web pages for individual encyclopedia articles and other features.

The ".com" in a typical URL is called a *top-level domain.* The letters in this case stand for *commercial.* Other top level domains include ".gov" for the United States government; ".ca" for Canadian websites; ".au" for Australian sites; and ".edu" for universities.

HTML. Web page files are written in a special technical language called HTML. The letters stand for Hyper-Text Markup Language. HTML tells a web browser how to display a web page on the screen.

Before the Web, information on the Internet was largely limited to simple text displays. People could transfer images and other files, but they had to use special programs to view the files. HTML, on the other hand, provides web pages with rich, interactive designs. HTML files can contain text, image, and video files, and display them on a user's web browser. HTML can also make use of certain *programming languages,* such as Flash and Java. A programming language is an artificial language used to write instructions for computers. By using such languages, web pages can act like word processors, spreadsheets, electronic games, and other software programs.

ICANN, the Internet Corporation for Assigned Names and Numbers, helps administer many of the Internet's software protocols. It serves as a registry for IP addresses and website domain names. Thus, the organization sees to it that no two devices share the same IP address. ICANN also ensures that no two organizations or individuals control the same website domain. ICANN is an international nonprofit organization formed in 1998.

The Internet and society

Like earlier revolutionary technologies, such as the printing press and the steam engine, the Internet has

Data centers filled with specialized *server computers* form an important part of the physical structure of the Internet. This data center in Switzerland supports scientific research at the CERN research center. Other data centers hold the digital files and do the computer work necessary for social networks, video sharing, e-mail, and other popular Internet activities.

© George Grassie, ZUMA Press

transformed human society. Nearly all businesses, governments, universities, and other organizations maintain websites. Hundreds of millions of people also have their own social networking pages or websites. Mobile phones with video cameras and Internet access enable ordinary people to publish information about events as they unfold. Such events would once have required professional journalists and camera crews to document.

Every day, the Internet transfers more data than all voiced phone calls and post office mail combined. In the United States, online books and news sources have become more popular than traditional printed versions.

The Internet has spread throughout the world. English was the primary language of the early Internet. But websites now exist in almost every language.

The Internet economy. Many businesses established themselves online during the 1990's. At that time, the Internet first became widely available to the public. Many such companies failed. But several survived to become major economic powers. The successful companies capitalized on the Internet's ability to easily—and cheaply—connect buyers and sellers around the world.

Connected customers. Online stores, marketplaces, and auction sites reach beyond the geographic limitations of traditional stores. Before the Internet, people typically purchased largely from local stores. Such stores, in turn, stocked mostly items that were broadly popular. Many obscure or specialty items—known as *niche products*—could not attract enough buyers in a particular region to be sold at a profit. But the Internet easily connects niche product sellers to a vast pool of potential buyers. This fact enabled online retailers, such as Amazon.com and Apple's iTunes Store, to make great profits by selling a wide range of niche products.

Internet users can also review and comment on products and services. This process makes it easier for other customers to find and evaluate new items. Websites that sell digital media, such as music, can offer free samples of content. Such samples make it easier for customers to discover niche works.

Changing industries. Some traditional stores and media companies have declined during the Internet era. In some cases, online upstarts have drawn away their business. For example, the online movie rental service Netflix outcompeted traditional video rental stores. Craigslist displaced many newspaper classified advertisement sections. Such sections had served as a mainstay of revenue for traditional local newspapers.

The Internet's very nature has also challenged traditional companies. The Internet enables people to easily—and freely—share media. People can easily electronically copy and exchange newspaper articles, books, songs, movies, and electronic games. Such items were once much more difficult to copy. They often required multiple users to buy individual copies. Many individuals now illegally copy and distribute such copyrighted media to thousands of other people through P2P networking. However, companies must charge money for these products to stay in business.

The free sharing of copyrighted digital media is often called *software piracy.* Companies take various steps to protect their copyrighted media from piracy. One approach is called *digital rights management.* It involves encoding additional software into a copyrighted file. The extra programming limits how the file can be distributed. Governments also prohibit piracy. They have shut down websites that make copyrighted material freely available.

The Internet culture. The Internet serves as a great cultural library. By shaping the way millions of people around the world interact, it has also helped generate and spread new cultures.

Communication without limits. The Internet has erased traditional communication barriers between people who are far apart. Traditional letters, for example, often take days to reach their destination. E-mails

© Reuters/Landov

Political use of the Internet includes the ability to organize and rapidly spread political movements. This photograph shows an observer with a mobile phone recording video of a protest in Iran. Mobile phones equipped with cameras and wireless Internet connections enable ordinary people to document such events for a global audience.

and IM's, on the other hand, appear almost instantly. VoIP calls are often much cheaper than long-distance or international telephone calls. In a videochat, people on opposite sides of the world can see and speak to one another as if only a window separated them. Online communities can easily connect people beyond national borders.

Some forms of Internet communication are *real time,* or *synchronous.* Synchronous communication takes place in a live, often back-and-forth exchange. It is much like a face-to-face conversation. However, the Internet also enables *asynchronous* communication. In asynchronous communication, participants receive and respond to messages at their leisure. For example, people often leave posts on social networks and other online communities. They then wait for others to read and respond. The result is a "conversation" spread over a longer time.

Businesses and news media can publish information about events live on the Internet as they unfold. But unlike television audiences, Internet users can easily go back and view the published information later.

Many of these types of communication are possible using traditional means. But the Internet makes them widely available and easy to use and combine, contributing to a culture of communication.

Spreading ideas. The word *meme* is often used to describe ideas that spread quickly on the Internet. The term *meme* comes from the British biologist Richard Dawkins. He coined it before widespread use of the Internet to describe the way ideas spread among cultures. Internet memes include jokes and videos. They also include more serious ideas, such as political attacks. Memes typically spread through e-mails, social networks, blogs, and other websites. The way memes spread somewhat resembles the spread of viruses among human hosts. If enough people pass on a meme to others, the message is said to "go viral."

In marketing, memes are related to the idea of *word of mouth,* sometimes called "buzz." Some marketers create *viral marketing campaigns* to promote products by spreading memes. In some cases, people may not even realize they are taking part in viral marketing.

Identity and privacy. The Internet has fundamentally changed how many people express themselves and relate to one another. Social networks and online communities can extend the reach of real-world groups. But people can also form communities and close friendships with people they have never met in person.

The Internet also enables people to communicate using *avatars* (online images or characters), without revealing their true identity. Many people on the Internet choose to remain anonymous or use a false name.

On the other hand, some people post significant amounts of personal information about themselves online. Search engines, social networks, and other technologies make it easy to find such information. Even when people use false names, ISP's can typically trace their online activity to a home address.

Search engines, online stores, and other websites also collect information about their users. *Spyware* is special software that gathers information about people's Internet habits. Some spyware is illegally secreted onto people's computers. Other kinds of spyware are legally installed without the user's knowledge.

Internet crime. Ideas and information are not the only things that spread quickly over the Internet. *Malware*—harmful software programs—can quickly infect thousands of connected computers. Such harmful programs include computer programs called *viruses* and *worms.* Some malware can access a person's e-mail and social networking accounts. They can thus send copies of themselves to the victim's friends and contacts.

Under certain circumstances, criminals can remotely control computers infected by malware. Wrongdoers sometimes hijack entire networks of infected computers, called *botnets,* for criminal purposes. Botnets can send out countless unsolicited *spam* e-mails advertising questionable products or linking to malware.

Filters and antivirus software can protect against malware to some extent. Modern web browsers have built-in security settings as well. People can also protect their computers by not opening or downloading suspicious-looking files.

Phishing is a criminal technique used to gain personal information about Internet users. Phishers "fish" for such information as passwords, social security numbers, and bank account numbers. Often, they pose as a bank or other legitimate institution requesting such information from customers. Criminals can use this information to assume the victim's identity for illegal purposes. This crime is called *identity theft.*

People can protect their online privacy to some extent by managing privacy settings in their web browsers. Social networks also typically enable people to control how much information is made publicly available.

The Internet and politics. National governments and political campaigns often have sophisticated websites and presences on social networking sites. People have also used such social networks as Facebook and Twitter as staging grounds for political revolutions. In 2011, for example, young people in Egypt and Tunisia used social networks to organize mass demonstrations against their countries' governments. Both governments eventually fell.

Censorship. Some governments, fearing such disruption, force ISP's to block access to social networks and other Internet services. In China, for example, the government blocks access to websites that it considers dangerous or inappropriate.

In the United States, information on the Internet is not typically censored. But nearly every government regulates the Internet to some degree. For example, many countries prohibit access to child pornography or terrorism sites.

Net neutrality is the idea that all pieces of data that move through the Internet should be treated equally. Most people access the Internet through a telecommunications company. Such companies may charge a flat rate for Internet access. But they can potentially increase their profits by controlling the amount of data they allow people to download.

Supporters of net neutrality worry that telecommunications companies will also seek to control the type of data people can access. For example, an ISP might limit access to data from a rival company. Or, it might limit data from a source critical of the ISP. Supporters argue that net neutrality is needed to safeguard the Internet's unique position as an open communications medium. Opponents of net neutrality charge that upholding the

CERN

Tim Berners-Lee, a British computer scientist working at CERN, a European scientific research center, developed the World Wide Web. The Web opened the Internet to multimedia.

idea would require intrusive government regulation and hamper technological innovation.

History

The Internet's history began during the Cold War, a period of intense rivalry between the United States and the Soviet Union following World War II (1939-1945). The Internet was originally designed for military and academic use. It rapidly expanded as personal computers became widespread. The Internet's capabilities evolved alongside those of the personal computer and, in the early 2000's, those of the mobile phone.

The early Internet. The Internet's development began in the United States during the 1960's. The U.S. Department of Defense worried that a Soviet attack or a nuclear war could cripple the country's communication network. The department's Advanced Research Projects Agency (ARPA) began working with computer science departments in research universities. They sought to create a system that could transmit information from one place to another through multiple paths, if necessary. The Internet's packet switching protocol resulted from this research. Throughout the 1970's, the system—called ARPANet—tested a number of improvements in computer interaction.

By 1981, over 200 computers were linked to ARPANet. Then the U.S. military split the network into two parts. One part was dedicated for military use. The National Science Foundation (NSF), an independent agency of the U.S. government, absorbed the other part. The NSF incorporated its part of ARPANet into a network called the National Science Foundation Network (NSFNET). The NSF's system eventually became known as the Internet.

The Web forms. In 1991, the British computer scientist Tim Berners-Lee developed the two fundamental technological components of the Web—HTML and HTTP. At the time, Berners-Lee was working at the European Organization for Nuclear Research in Switzerland (CERN). By 1993, web browsers became widely available on personal computers. Before this time, the Internet

was so difficult to use that most of its users were computer experts. The development of the World Wide Web and web browsers enabled the average person to easily use the Internet.

Throughout the 1980's and 1990's, personal computers became cheaper and more powerful. Businesses, schools, and other institutions increasingly relied on the machines. In addition, many people purchased computers for their homes. Businesses recognized that they could reach many customers through Internet-connected home computers. Three especially successful websites launched in 1995: Amazon, Craigslist, and eBay. These sites helped establish online consumption as an alternative to purchasing products in physical stores.

Other websites sought to organize the sprawling information on the Web. Yahoo!, a popular online portal, launched in 1994. Google launched its search engine in 1998. Google featured a clean design, high-quality search results, and money-making ads displayed alongside the list of results. Both Yahoo! and Google later offered other services, such as e-mail and instant messaging accounts and online maps.

The number of businesses active on the Internet skyrocketed during the late 1990's. Many Internet businesses drew much attention and economic investment. But few actually made profits. This rapid expansion of Internet businesses, unsupported by profits, came to be known as the "dot-com bubble." By 2000, the bubble had burst, and many businesses failed.

The evolving Internet. During the first decade of the 2000's, broadband connections became more widespread in a number of countries. Internet connectivity gradually shifted from a luxury to a near necessity, like electric power. New video game consoles enabled users to play together over the Internet. Laptop computers gained popularity, rivaling larger desktop computers in power and usability. Many coffee shops, libraries, and other public places began offering Wi-Fi (short-range wireless Internet) connections for laptop computers. Computerlike phones, called *smartphones*, also became popular. Mobile phone companies developed wireless technologies to bring mobile phones online at faster and faster rates.

The Internet's hardware evolution coincided with a virtual reinvention of the Web. During the 1990's, websites functioned largely as storage places for information. It was easy for people to access such sites. But it was technically difficult to create them. During the early 2000's, more sites enabled ordinary people to easily create and post content. This model of increased interactivity became known as Web 2.0.

Blogs were a prominent feature of Web 2.0. Two popular blogging services, Blogger and LiveJournal, launched in 1999. *Wikis* also helped ordinary people contribute to the Web. Wikis are websites that enable multiple people to quickly and easily edit their content. Wikipedia, a wiki-based encyclopedia, started in 2001. It quickly became one of the Internet's most popular sites.

New social networking websites made it especially easy to create and share content. They included Friendster (launched in 2003), MySpace (2003), and Facebook (2004). At first, Facebook was only available to students at Harvard University. But Facebook soon opened itself to people around the world and became the most popular social network. Twitter, which streamlined the social networking experience to transmit only short messages called *tweets*, launched in 2006.

With faster connections, the diversity of the Web's content blossomed. But so did the file sizes. People posted increasingly large photo collections on special photo-sharing sites and social networks. *Streaming* technology enabled people to listen to music or watch videos on their web browsers as the files downloaded, rather than waiting to receive whole files. The video-sharing website YouTube launched in 2005. YouTube expanded to become a central location distributing videos on the Web. Television and film companies also began offering streaming videos of their content on sites. In addition, Google and a number of other companies began offering cloud computing applications. These applications included online word processors, spreadsheets, and digital storage spaces.

Ongoing controversies. By 2010, the Internet had connected nearly a third of the world's population. As the technology's reach extended to nearly every aspect of modern life, many people welcomed the flood of freely available information. But controversies emerged over the Internet's erosion of privacy. For example, such companies as Google and Facebook often employed *opt-out* privacy policies. Such policies meant that unless people specified that their information be kept private, the companies made it public. Google also published photographs of people's houses and streets on its Google Maps service. Such policies prompted government oversight and fines in some countries.

Along with individuals, government agencies also saw their privacy threatened by the Internet. In 2010, an organization called WikiLeaks began publishing hundreds of thousands of secret documents from the U.S. military and the Department of State. It was by far the largest leak of secret material in history. WikiLeaks disclosed day-to-day communications from the Iraq and Afghanistan wars along with sensitive diplomatic messages. Supporters of WikiLeaks argued that the published documents would help hold the U.S. government accountable. But the U.S. government, along with other opponents of WikiLeaks, charged that government services were also entitled to privacy. It also claimed that the information leaked endangered the lives of soldiers, government officials, and others.   Jarice Hanson

King penguin is second only to the emperor penguin in size. The king penguin typically reaches about 2 ¾ feet (85 centimeters) tall. By comparison, the emperor penguin usually reaches about 3 feet (90 centimeters) tall.

The king penguin is bluish-black on its back and flippers, with a pale underside. The head is black except for bright orange-yellow ear patches. The upper chest also has an intense golden color. The weight of adults varies during the year from about 22 to 35 pounds (10 to 16 kilograms). Like other penguins, the king penguin does not fly. Instead, it swims by beating its flippers.

King penguins live on islands throughout the Southern Ocean. They live together in large communities called *colonies.* In the winter, king penguins swim toward the Antarctic pack ice to feed. They can travel hundreds of miles or kilometers in search of food.

The king penguin feeds on small fish and squid. It es-

pecially prefers lantern fish. It dives to depths of 400 to 800 feet (120 to 240 meters) to find food. Scientists have observed dives as deep as nearly 1,000 feet (300 meters).

King penguins are hunted by killer whales and leopard seals. These animals patrol the edge of the colonies. They catch penguins going out to sea. In addition, skuas eat king penguin eggs. Giant petrels can eat chicks.

The king penguin lays only one egg. It carries this egg on its feet, tucking it under the belly for warmth. Chicks hatch after about 55 days. King penguins can live for more than 30 years.   Barbara Wienecke

Scientific classification. The scientific name of the king penguin is *Aptenodytes patagonicus.*

Leopard seal is a large *earless seal* of the Antarctic that has gray spots on the throat and sides. Earless seals lack visible earflaps, but they do have ears and excellent hearing. The leopard seal has a streamlined body with a large head and a slender neck. It has gaping jaws with long canine teeth. The leopard seal is dark gray on the back and silvery pale on the belly.

Female leopard seals grow larger than males. Females reach nearly 12 feet (3.7 meters) long. They can weigh more than 1,100 pounds (500 kilograms). Males reach nearly 10 feet (3 meters) long. They can weigh more than 650 pounds (295 kilograms).

Leopard seals spend most of the year on and around the Antarctic sea ice. In winter months, young animals move north to islands in the Southern Ocean. They also may travel to beaches in Australia, South Africa, and South America.

The leopard seal is a strong hunter. It is a top *predator* (hunting animal) in the food chain. In spring and summer, the leopard seal feeds mostly on other seals and penguins. It typically seizes such prey from beneath the water and thrashes violently to rip away chunks of flesh. During winter, the leopard seal feeds mostly on fish and *krill* (shrimplike animals). It captures krill by straining water through its *molar* (back) teeth. Leopard seals are sometimes killed and eaten by killer whales.

Leopard seals are solitary except when they breed. Both males and females use a variety of calls to attract mates. Females "sing" for only a few days. Males sing throughout the breeding season. Females give birth to a single pup between October and December. Pups nurse for only a few weeks.   Tracey Rogers

Scientific classification. The scientific name of the leopard seal is *Hydrurga leptonyx.*

© Visuals Unlimited/Masterfile

The leopard seal is a hunting animal of the Antarctic.

© Minden Pictures/Masterfile

Snakes have inspired more awe and fear in people than many other kinds of animal. But most snakes are harmless to people, and snakes are an important part of the balance of nature in most areas. This Asian whip snake from the rain forests of Borneo feeds mainly on frogs and lizards.

Snake

Snake is an animal with a long, legless body covered in dry scales. To move about on land, a snake usually slides on its belly. Clear scales—instead of movable eyelids—cover the snake's eyes. As a result, the eyes never truly close. Snakes have a narrow, forked tongue, which they repeatedly flick in and out. The tongue carries odors to a special sense organ inside their mouth.

Snakes are closely related to lizards. Together, snakes and lizards belong to a class of animals called reptiles. Like other reptiles, snakes are *cold-blooded,* or *ectothermic.* The body of a cold-blooded animal stays about the same temperature as its surroundings. Snakes regulate their body temperature through their behavior. For example, they raise their body temperature by lying in the sun. They lower it by crawling into the shade or into cool water. In contrast, mammals and birds are *warm-blooded,* or *endothermic.* The body of a warm-blooded animal stays around the same temperature regardless of its surroundings.

Snakes live on every continent except Antarctica. They inhabit deserts, forests, oceans, streams, and lakes.

Many snakes live on the ground. Some make their homes underground. Others live in trees. Still others spend most of their time in water. Only a few areas in the world have no snakes. Snakes cannot survive where the ground stays frozen the year around. Thus, no snakes live in the polar regions or at extremely high elevations in mountains. In addition, some islands, including Ireland and New Zealand, have no native snakes.

There are thousands of *species* (kinds) of snakes. The greatest variety live in the tropics. The largest snakes are the green anaconda of South America, the reticulated python of Southeast Asia, and the African rock python. All three can reach nearly 30 feet (9 meters) long. Among the smallest snakes is the Barbados thread snake. This Caribbean snake grows only 4 inches (10 centimeters) long. When coiled, it can fit onto a small coin.

Some snakes can inject *venom* (poison) through their fangs when they bite. About 15 percent of all snake species have venom that is harmful or fatal to human beings. About 25 species cause most of the deaths from snakebites. These include the Indian cobra of Asia, the black mamba and the saw-scaled viper of Africa, and the tiger snake of Australia.

Some people fear and dislike snakes, partly because some species are venomous. But snakes are mostly harmless to people. Many myths and superstitions may have inspired people to fear snakes. But snakes are an important part of the balance of nature. Snakes also help control the numbers of rats and other pests.

The bodies of snakes

Body shape. Snakes vary in body shape. Some snakes, such as the Gaboon viper of Africa, have a thick, stout body. Certain tree snakes have a thin, long, light-weight body. Such a snake might resemble a vine or a branch. Sea snakes have a body that makes them good swimmers. Their body is flattened vertically, and their tail resembles a paddle. In most species of snakes, the males and females look alike.

Scales and color. Dry scales cover the body of a snake. The scales may be smooth or ridged. Most snakes have overlapping scales that stretch apart. The belly scales, called *ventral scutes,* consist of one row of enlarged scales extending from the neck to the tail among most species. The belly scales may help the snake move. The side and back scales vary in size and shape among different species.

The scaly skin of a snake has two layers. The inner layer consists of cells that grow and divide. The cells die as they are pushed upward by new cells. The dead cells form the outer layer of skin. From time to time, a snake sheds the outer layer of skin because it is worn or because the snake has grown.

The skin-shedding process is called *molting* or *ecdysis.* For a short time before molting, a snake is less active than usual. The animal's scales, including its eye scales, become clouded. About one day before molting, the snake's skin appears bright, as if the snake had already molted. A short time later, however, the snake begins to loosen its dead skin. It starts around the mouth and head by rubbing its nose, catching the skin on a rough surface. The snake then crawls out of the old skin, turning it inside out in the process.

How often a snake molts depends on its age, growth, activity, and health. Young snakes shed more often than older ones. Snakes in warm climates are active for longer periods than those in cooler climates. As a result, they molt more often. Some pythons of the tropics shed six or more times a year. In contrast, some North American rattlesnakes average two or three molts a year. They may add a new section to their tail rattle each time they molt. Snakes with skin injuries also molt more often.

A snake's color pattern comes chiefly from special pigment cells deep in the skin. Snakes have many different colors, including black, blue, brown, green, orange, red, and yellow. Some blue or purple coloration may be due to the way light is reflected from the surface of the scales. The color seems to change as the snake moves, an effect called *iridescence.*

Skeleton. The main parts of a snake's skeleton are the skull, vertebrae, and ribs. A few snakes, such as blind snakes, boas, and pythons, have *vestiges* of hind legs or hipbones. A vestige is a remaining trace of a body part that a group of animals has lost through *evolution*

(change over time). Snakes that have such vestiges show their close relationship to lizards.

Skull. Most of the bones of a snake's skull are loosely connected. Bone completely encases the brain, however. In most snakes, the lower jaw has two bones connected at the chin by an elastic tissue, or *ligament.* This structure enables the bones to stretch wide apart. The lower jaw is loosely attached to the upper jaw. Several bones of the upper jaw and roof of the mouth also are loosely joined to one another and to the rest of the skull. The two sides of the jaws can move separately.

The flexible structure of the jaws enables most snakes to open their mouth wide enough to swallow animals that are larger than their own head. To swallow an animal, a snake moves first one side of its jaws forward and then the other side. Some bones of the lower and upper jaws have pointed teeth that curve back toward the throat. These teeth are not for chewing. Instead, they stick into prey and prevent it from escaping as it is swallowed whole. As the snake alternately draws each side of its jaws forward, it pulls the animal toward the throat. Saliva in the snake's mouth and throat eases the passage of the prey. The snake's saliva may also begin digesting the prey before it reaches the stomach.

In some cases, a snake may take more than an hour to swallow an animal. A special feature prevents the *trachea* (windpipe) from being blocked while the snake's mouth and throat are full. The trachea moves forward over the tongue so that the snake can breathe while swallowing.

Vertebrae. The backbone of snakes consists of an unusually large number of vertebrae. Snakes have from about 150 to more than 430 vertebrae, depending on the species. Strong, flexible joints connect the vertebrae. These joints enable the body to make a wide range of movements, including coiling into a ball.

Ribs. A pair of ribs is attached to the sides of each

Interesting facts about snakes

One of the smallest snakes is the Barbados thread snake. This snake grows to only 4 inches (10 centimeters) long. It feeds on the young of ants and termites.

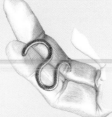

Barbados thread snake

An African Gaboon viper in a zoo once fasted for more than 2 years. Large snakes may eat a big meal and then go without another meal for months.

African Gaboon viper

The fastest snake is probably the black mamba of Africa. It was timed moving at the speed of 7 miles (11 kilometers) per hour over a short distance.

Black mamba

The African ball python protects itself from predators by coiling into a ball with its head in the middle. Many other snakes also use this method of defense.

African ball python

The Madagascar leaf-nosed snake is unusual because males and females differ markedly in appearance. The male, *top,* has a tapering snout. The female has a leaf-shaped snout.

Madagascar leaf-nosed snakes

The spitting cobra of Africa can squirt venom 6 to 8 feet (1.8 to 2.4 meters). The snake aims for the eyes of a threatening animal. The venom causes a burning sensation and can produce blindness.

Spitting cobra

The North American hognose snake sometimes plays dead when threatened. The illustration shows the hognose in a natural position, *near right.* When threatened, it may jerk violently until it rests upside down with its mouth open and tongue out, *far right.*

One of the largest snakes is the green anaconda of South America. It has a stout body and may grow up to 30 feet (9 meters) long.

WORLD BOOK illustrations by Alex Ebel and Adam Weiskind

vertebra in front of the tail. The rib tips are not joined to-gether along the belly and so can be extended outward. After a snake has swallowed a bulky meal, the ribs spread out as the animal's stomach expands.

Muscles. As many as 24 small muscles are attached to each vertebra and rib in a snake's body. These muscles connect one vertebra to another and the vertebrae to the ribs. Snakes use most of these muscles to move.

Internal organs. The lung, liver, and other major in-ternal organs of snakes are long and slender. Most snakes have only one lung, though some have a vestige of a second lung. Snakes have a pair of kidneys and a pair of sex organs—*ovaries* in a female and *testes* in a male. The paired organs lie one on each side of the body. But each pair is staggered from front to back. In most other animals, paired organs lie across from each other.

In most snakes, the stomach and intestines are spe-cially suited for handling bulky food. Both have a thick lining that can expand greatly. The stomach and in-testines produce substances called *enzymes.* The en-zymes break down food into smaller particles that can be absorbed. Snakes can digest the entire body of their prey, except for hair or feathers. Bone may be complete-ly digested within 72 hours. Waste products pass out of a snake's body through an opening called the *cloaca* or *vent.* The vent marks the end of the snake's trunk and the beginning of its tail. In female snakes, the cloaca is also the cavity into which the *oviducts* (tubes from the ovaries) empty.

Snakes that eat large meals use a great deal of energy

© Minden Pictures/Masterfile

A snake sheds its skin beginning with the head. First, it rubs its nose on a hard surface, loosening the skin there. It then crawls out of the skin. This photograph shows a steppes rat snake.

digesting food. Between meals, their intestines, liver, and other internal organs may shrink. The snakes' bod-ies must restore these organs to their full size before they can digest new food.

Sense organs. Snakes can hear sounds and feel vi-brations. Some snakes have excellent eyesight. Most can see movement. But snakes rely mainly on special sense organs to provide information about their surroundings.

The anatomy of a snake

This drawing of a male water moccasin shows the skeleton and internal organs. A snake's skeleton consists of a skull and many vertebrae and ribs. Most of the animal's internal organs are long and thin. Only venomous snakes have fangs and venom glands.

WORLD BOOK diagram by James Teason

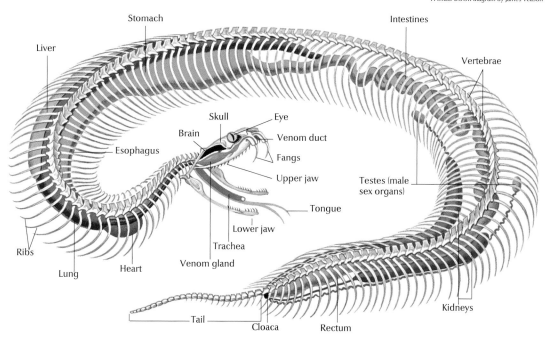

Stomach

Intestines

Liver

Vertebrae

Skull

Eye

Brain

Venom duct

Esophagus

Fangs

Upper jaw

Testes (male sex organs)

Tongue

Lower jaw

Ribs

Trachea

Lung

Heart

Venom gland

Kidneys

Tail

Cloaca

Rectum

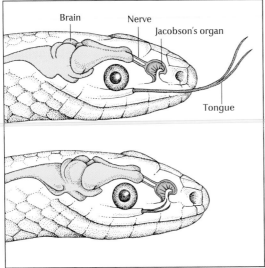

WORLD BOOK diagram by Patricia J. Wynne

The Jacobson's organ in snakes is used with the tongue to detect odors. The snake flicks out its tongue and picks up scent particles. When the snake pulls in its tongue, the particles are transferred to the odor-sensitive Jacobson's organ.

Snakes have an eye on each side of the head, which gives them a wide field of view. A clear scale called a *brille* covers each eye. The snake sheds these scales and replaces them each time it molts.

Snakes lack outer ear openings. However, they have inner ears and can hear a limited range of sounds carried in the air or through the ground. Certain bones in a snake's head transmit sound waves to the inner ear.

An organ of smell called the *Jacobson's organ* enables snakes to detect odors. The Jacobson's organ consists of two hollow sacs in the roof of a snake's mouth. The sacs have many nerve endings that are sensitive to odors. A snake sticks out its tongue to pick up scent particles in the air or on the ground. When the snake pulls its tongue back into the mouth, these particles enter the Jacobson's organ. The organ enables a snake to recognize and follow the scent trail of its prey. In addition, a snake can recognize a member of its own species and detect whether the individual is male or female.

Certain snakes have special heat-sensitive *pit organs*. Pit vipers have two pit organs, one on each side of the head, between the eye and nostril. Boas and pythons have many pits along the lip of the upper jaw. Pit organs enable a snake to detect the exact location of a warm-blooded animal by its body heat. Thus, the snake can accurately direct its strike at warm-blooded prey even in the dark. A snake with pit organs can sense a change in temperature of less than 1 °F (0.5 °C) near its head.

Fangs and venom glands. Only venomous snakes have fangs and venom glands. Venom glands developed from *salivary glands* (glands that produce saliva). Venomous snakes bite a victim with their fangs and inject venom into the wound. Several kinds of snakes can also spit venom.

Most venomous snakes have fangs in the front of the mouth. The two foremost teeth in the upper jaw form hollow fangs, which act somewhat like hypodermic nee-

dles. A tube connects each fang to a venom gland on each side of the upper jaw. The snake may shed and replace the fangs several times a year.

There are two main groups of venomous snakes—*vipers* and *elapids,* pronounced *EHL uh pihdz.* The two groups have different fangs. Vipers, which include cottonmouths and rattlesnakes, have long, movable front fangs. When not in use, the fangs fold back into a sheath on the roof of the mouth. When the snake strikes, the fangs swing forward. Elapids, which include cobras, coral snakes, and sea snakes, have short front fangs that are fixed in place.

A third group of venomous snakes is the *colubrids,* pronounced *KAHL yuh brihdz.* Some colubrids have short rear fangs that are fixed. They must chew on their prey to release the venom. Most colubrids are harmless to people, but some have injured or even killed people.

A snake uses its fangs and venom chiefly to slow or kill prey. Venom glands produce a number of enzymes and other substances that can cause death. After a snake bites its prey, some of these enzymes begin the process of digestion even before the snake starts to swallow the animal. However, the snake usually waits for the venom to cause unconsciousness or death before swallowing.

In addition to enzymes, most snake venoms include *neurotoxins* and *hemotoxins.* Neurotoxins affect the nervous system. They cause difficulties in breathing, swallowing, and heart function. Hemotoxins damage blood vessels and body tissues. Sea snakes have an unusual type of venom that directly affects muscles.

The life of snakes

Snakes are difficult to observe in their natural surroundings because they stay hidden much of the time. Little is known about ways of life among many species. Scientists who study snakes and other reptiles and amphibians are called *herpetologists.* They have detailed information about the behavior of relatively few species.

In general, the life of a snake consists mainly of moving about alone in search of food, shelter, or a mate. Many snakes are active during the day. Others move about at night. During certain times of the year, a shift in

© Marc Chamberlain, Alamy Images

A viper's fangs swing forward during a strike, delivering venom into a bite wound. The fangs fold back into the roof of the mouth when not in use. This snake is a neotropical rattlesnake.

Lateral undulation is the most common way in which snakes move. In lateral undulation, the snake flexes its muscles, first on one side of the body, then on the other. This causes its body to push against the ground or water. This banded sea snake uses lateral undulation to swim.

© Visuals Unlimited/Masterfile

activity can occur. Snakes sometimes become inactive for long periods because of cold or hot weather, or because of scarce water or food.

Some snakes stay within a limited area. For example, a study of prairie rattlesnakes showed that the males roamed an area about ¾ mile (1.2 kilometers) in diameter. The females kept to an area about ⅙ mile (0.3 kilometer) in diameter.

How snakes move. Snakes often seem to slither swiftly. But they actually move slowly compared with other animals. Garter snakes and pythons, for example, crawl less than 3 miles (5 kilometers) per hour. The fastest snake may be the African black mamba. It can move at speeds of 7 miles (11 kilometers) per hour over a short distance. In comparison, people can sprint 10 to 15 miles (16 to 24 kilometers) per hour.

Snakes have four main ways of moving. They are (1) lateral undulation, (2) rectilinear movement, (3) concertina movement, and (4) sidewinding. Some snakes also move in other, unusual ways.

Lateral undulation is the most common way in which snakes move. The snake flexes its muscles, first on one side of its body, then on the other. The loops of its body push against the ground. In this manner, the snake's body moves forward. Snakes also use lateral undulation to propel themselves through water.

Rectilinear movement is also known as creeping. Snakes often use this method to climb trees or pass through narrow burrows. Many thick-bodied snakes, such as puff adders and pythons, may use rectilinear movement when crawling on the ground.

In rectilinear movement, the snake contracts muscles that pull its belly scales forward. The back edges of the scales catch on a rough surface. The snake then contracts other muscles, which push the scales against the surface. Pushing moves the body forward.

Rat snakes and many other snakes have belly scales especially suited to climbing. The edges of the scales are squared. They readily catch on any rough surface that the snake climbs, such as tree bark.

Concertina movement is often used by snakes to crawl through trees or advance over smooth surfaces. The front part of the snake's body moves forward and coils slightly, pressing against the surface to anchor itself. The snake then pulls its back end forward, coils that part, and presses it down. The back end grips the sur-

face, enabling the front part to move forward again.

Sidewinding is used chiefly by certain snakes that live in areas with loose soil or sand. These snakes include the sidewinder of North America and the carpet viper and horned viper of Africa. In sidewinding, the snake's head and tail serve as supports. The snake lifts the middle of its body off the ground and moves it sideways. The snake then moves its head and tail into position with the rest of its body. It then repeats the sequence.

Unusual ways of moving. Many small species of snakes seem to jump when trying to escape from danger. They hurl their body forward or to the side by rapidly straightening from a coiled position. Certain snakes of southern Asia can glide from a high tree limb to a lower one. They leap from a branch and spread their ribs, which flattens the body and helps slow the

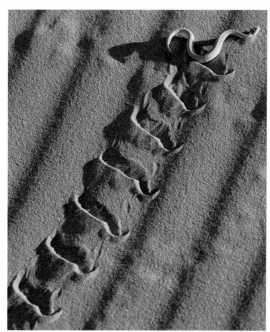

© age fotostock/SuperStock

Sidewinding is a method of travel used in areas of loose soil or sand. Supported by its head and tail, the snake lifts its trunk sideways. This sidewinder leaves distinctive tracks in the desert sand.

© Minden Pictures/Masterfile

Snakes hatch from eggs, slicing open the leathery shell with a growth called an *egg tooth*. Most snake species hatch outside the mother's body, like these South American bushmasters.

fall. Scientists have observed these snakes gliding up to about 330 feet (100 meters).

Reproduction. Snakes ordinarily reproduce sexually. In sexual reproduction, a *sperm* (male sex cell) unites with an *egg* (female sex cell), forming a fertilized egg. The fertilized egg develops into a new individual.

Male snakes have a pair of sex organs called *hemipenes*. These organs lie inside the base of the tail and can be pushed out through the cloaca. During mating, the male curls his tail under the female's, inserts a hemipenis into her cloaca, and deposits sperm. Among some species, the sperm can live within the female's body for several months or even longer. Thus, the eggs may become fertilized long after mating occurs. Male and female snakes do not stay together after mating.

In regions with warm summers and cold winters, most snakes mate in the spring or fall. In the tropics, snakes may mate at any time of the year.

Most snakes lay eggs. The females generally lay eggs in shallow holes, rotten logs, tree stumps, or similar places. The number of eggs laid at one time varies among different species. In many species, the female lays 6 to 30 eggs at a time. Large pythons usually lay about 50 eggs, but they can produce up to 100.

Most female snakes leave their eggs after laying them. But among a few species, including Indian pythons and king cobras, the females may coil on top of their eggs and guard them. Some pythons may also *incubate* their eggs—that is, keep the eggs warm to help the young develop quickly. A female python curls her body around the eggs and contracts her muscles to produce heat if the temperature is cool. In this way, she keeps her eggs as warm as 85 °F (29 °C), which aids in hatching.

The shells of snake eggs are leathery. The eggs expand as the young grow inside. The young snakes typically hatch in about 8 to 10 weeks, depending on the temperature. Females of some species carry their eggs within their body several weeks before laying them. As a result, the eggs are well developed by the time they are laid. They hatch within two to six weeks. When young snakes are ready to hatch, they slash their shells with a special growth on the upper jaw called the *egg tooth*. The little snakes shed that tooth shortly after tearing through their shells.

About a fifth of all species of snakes bear live young. Pregnancy among most of these species lasts about two or three months. Some species have more than 100 young at a time, but most bear far fewer.

Newly hatched or newborn snakes live entirely on their own. They must find their own food and shelter. They grow rapidly. The young of some species reach maturity—that is, become able to reproduce—in one year. Among other species, the young mature in two to four years. Snakes continue to grow after maturity.

Regulation of body temperature. The body temperature of snakes varies with changes in the temperature of their surroundings. However, a snake must keep its body temperature within a certain range to survive. Most snakes can be fully active only if their temperature measures between 68 and 95 °F (20 and 35 °C). They cannot move if their temperature drops below about 39 °F (4 °C). On the other hand, most snakes will die if exposed to temperatures above 104 °F (40 °C).

Snakes maintain their body temperature within the necessary range by moving to warmer or cooler places. They typically raise their body temperature by lying in the sun. After sunset, they may stretch out on a warm surface. Snakes that live underground move to warmer areas in the soil. Snakes avoid excess heat by seeking shelter under bushes, logs, or rocks, or in water. Some snakes that live in the tropics spend the hottest part of the year in a state of reduced activity called *estivation*.

Snakes that live in regions with cold winters hibernate. They spend the winter in caves, burrows, or other frost-free places where the temperature is constant. In most areas of the world, a snake sheltered 3 feet (90 centimeters) below the surface of the ground is protected from freezing. During hibernation, a snake's body temperature may measure from about 39 to 41 °F (4 to 5 °C).

If suitable sites for hibernation are scarce, hundreds of snakes of different species may spend the winter in the same place. Such a shared shelter is called a *hibernaculum*. In the fall and spring, the snakes may be seen near the hibernaculum warming themselves in the sun.

Feeding habits. Most snakes eat birds, fish, frogs, lizards, and such small mammals as rabbits and rats. Some snakes, such as Asian king cobras and North American kingsnakes, eat other snakes. Large constrictors sometimes eat animals that weigh more than 100 pounds (45 kilograms), such as antelopes and hogs.

Numerous snakes have specialized feeding habits. For example, some species eat chiefly snails. The teeth and lower jaw of some snail-eating snakes are specially adapted for pulling the snails out of their shells. Snakes that eat mainly termites have tiny mouths. They suck the insides of a termite's abdomen from its body, leaving the less digestible parts. Certain snakes that eat eggs have long spines inside the throat. After the snake swallows an egg, these spines pierce the shell. Then the snake's muscle contractions crush the egg. The contents of the egg pass through the throat, but the spines prevent passage of the shell. The snake spits out the shell.

Snakes capture prey in various ways. They may wait in ambush, stalk an animal, or pursue it. When a snake strikes, it lunges forward with its mouth wide open. A snake usually can strike effectively only at a distance equal to one-half to two-thirds of its body length.

Most snakes swallow their prey while it is unconscious but still alive. However, venomous snakes generally wait for their venom to kill an animal before they devour it. Constrictors, including boas, bull snakes, kingsnakes, pythons, and rat snakes, squeeze prey until it is unconscious before eating it. A constrictor wraps two or more loops of its body around its catch and then contracts its muscles. The snake squeezes the animal tighter with every breath until it falls unconscious. Some people think constrictors kill by crushing their victims. Actually, constrictors kill by suffocating their prey.

After feeding, a snake may lie in the sun. The warmth raises its body temperature, which speeds digestion. A meal may last a snake a long time. Large snakes, such as boas and pythons, may eat a big meal and then go without another for months. Occasionally, some large snakes fast for more than a year.

Snakes can survive a long time without food for several reasons. Unlike warm-blooded animals, snakes need little energy to maintain their body temperature. Snakes also may remain inactive for extended periods. In addition, snakes store a great deal of fat in their body. During long fasts, they live off this fat.

Protection against predators. Many kinds of *predators* (hunting animals) feed on snakes. These predators include large birds, such as eagles and herons. Certain mammals, such as mongooses and hogs, prey on snakes. King cobras and kingsnakes are among the snakes that hunt other snakes.

Snakes have a wide variety of defenses against predators. Many species have color patterns that match their surroundings, which helps to conceal them. For example, the North American copperhead has brown bands that blend with the dead leaves on the forest floor, where it lives. The North American smooth green snake has a thin body with a green back. The snake blends in with green vines and other vegetation.

Some snakes have bright colors. For example, the coral snakes of North America have bands of black, red, and yellow. These colors may serve as *warning coloration,* cautioning potential predators to avoid venomous snakes.

Some harmless snakes may gain protection from their resemblance to venomous snakes. For example, the harmless scarlet kingsnake has a color pattern that resembles that of the venomous coral snake. Predators may avoid the kingsnake, confusing it with the coral snake. This type of protection is called *Batesian mimicry.*

Snake behaviors also help to defend them against predators. If threatened, a snake may escape by fleeing into a burrow, the water, or some other place where the predator cannot follow. Some shield-tailed snakes of southern Asia can block the entrance to their burrow with their short, blunt tail.

Many snakes make threatening noises when a predator approaches. Some hiss loudly. Most snakes shake their tail when threatened. Rattlesnakes make a distinctive buzzing sound by shaking the rattle, a loose, horny structure on the tail. The African saw-scaled viper makes a rasping sound by rubbing its side scales together.

Some snakes adopt a threatening posture that may frighten away predators. For example, the cobra lifts its neck and spreads its ribs, forming a broad hood. North American hognose snakes and other species may spread their neck ribs and inflate their lung. These actions make them look larger and fiercer. This type of behavior is called a *threat display.*

Some kinds of harmless snakes mimic the behavior of venomous snakes. For example, kingsnakes and rat snakes vibrate their tail among dry leaves. This action produces a sound like that made by rattlesnakes. Some harmless snakes of Africa mimic the rasping sound of the saw-scaled viper. Certain harmless Asian snakes and the Madagascar leaf-nosed snake spread their ribs and form a hood similar to that of the cobra.

Some animals that prey on snakes have no interest in dead snakes. Thus, certain snakes defend themselves by playing dead. The North American hognose snake is especially well known for this behavior. When threatened, it may twitch violently until it rests upside down with its mouth open and tongue out. After the threat has passed, the snake rights itself and crawls away to safety. The African ball python coils into a tight ball with its head in the middle. This position makes it difficult for predators to reach vulnerable parts of the snake's body. This defense also is used by North American ground snakes, rubber boas, and other species.

A snake's flexible jaws enable it to swallow food that is larger than its head, such as this egg. The snake shown in this photograph is the common egg-eater of Africa.

© Minden Pictures/Masterfile

The ribs of a snake can spread out to accommodate a bulky meal. A snake swallows its food whole, as this common egg-eater has done with an egg.

If other defenses fail, a snake may attack. The bite of a venomous snake is a powerful weapon. But the snake could be clawed or bitten before its venom takes effect. The African "spitting" cobra has added protection. It can squirt venom into the eyes of a predator 6 to 8 feet (1.8 to 2.4 meters) away. The venom produces an immediate burning sensation and can cause blindness. Large constrictors are also a powerful match for most predators. They can quickly coil around an animal and suffocate it, just as they do to their prey.

Battles among male snakes. Among some snake species, adult males sometimes fight each other. In a typical battle, two snakes rear up and twist their bodies together. They try to push each other downward until one snake retreats. These encounters, called *combat rituals,* usually occur during the mating season. The victor wins the right to mate with a nearby female. Such battles are especially common among vipers. But they also occur among such small, harmless snakes as North American kingsnakes and European smooth snakes.

Life span. Scientists do not know how long most snake species live in the wild. Few snakes in zoos survive longer than 15 years.

Snakes and the environment

Snakes and ecosystems. Snakes are a vital part of many *ecosystems.* An ecosystem consists of the living and nonliving things in a particular place. Each species of animal in an ecosystem depends on other organisms for food. The feeding relationships among all the animals in an area can help prevent any one species from becoming too numerous. Snakes can help to preserve this balance of nature. See **Balance of nature.**

In many ecosystems, snakes feed on small animals that grow and reproduce quickly. For example, imagine an ecosystem in which snakes feed on mice. If snakes were removed, the number of mice would grow rapidly. The mice would harm many plants by eating their leaves, stems, and roots. In addition, the mice would soon consume much of the food needed by other animals. Birds and other animals also feed upon snakes. These animals might not be able to find enough food without snakes. In this way, removing snakes from an ecosystem would result in much destruction.

Snakes as invasive species. People have introduced snakes into ecosystems where they do not live naturally. These snakes can become an *invasive species*—that is, an introduced species that spreads quickly and harms native wildlife.

Snakes have colonized a number of islands. For example, in the late 1940's or early 1950's, brown tree snakes came to the island of Guam. The snakes are native to Australia and Papua New Guinea. They may have reached Guam by traveling with military cargo. The brown tree snake is a fierce predator of small animals, including birds and lizards. Animals native to Guam had no experience of tree snakes. Nor were there predators to control the snake's numbers. The snake soon spread throughout most of the island. It destroyed native bats, birds, and other animals. Most of the island's native bird species became extinct.

Invasive snake species also threaten native wildlife in North America. Burmese pythons, traditionally considered a subspecies of Indian pythons, have colonized the Florida Everglades. These snakes are large constrictors that are native to Southeast Asia. They can reach about 20 feet (6 meters) long. Researchers estimate that many thousands of Burmese pythons now reproduce in the wild in Florida. They feed on native species, including endangered birds and mammals. They also compete with native snakes. Scientists worry that the pythons may spread to similar areas elsewhere in North America. Boa constrictors also have become established in southern Florida. Scientists think that another python, the African python, probably has become established as well.

Snake conservation. Many species of snakes are abundant and face few threats to their survival. But humans have caused a decline in the numbers of many other snake species. Scientists are not certain how many snake species are in decline. That is partly because scientists have not studied wild snakes as much as they have many other animals. Also, snakes can be difficult to survey because they may remain hidden most of the time. However, many scientists consider it likely that at least 1 in 4 snake species are threatened.

Species that are in danger of becoming extinct include the broad-headed snake, the Jamaican boa, and the giant garter snake. People have already caused the extinction of several snake species, including the Round Island burrowing boa and the Saint Croix racer.

The single largest threat to snakes is habitat destruction. People destroy the places where snakes live by clearing land for farms, cities, or other uses. Some snakes are threatened because people have captured so many for the pet trade. Snakes also are threatened because people kill them for their skin. For example, Burmese pythons are invasive in Florida, but they have become threatened in their native Asia because so many have been taken for pets and skins. People also kill many snakes needlessly, out of fear or misunderstanding.

Snakes and people

The uses of snakes. Snakes provide many benefits to human beings. They can aid farmers by preying on pests, such as mice and rats. Because these pests may carry disease, snakes can help to protect human health. In some countries, such as China, people eat the meat of snakes. The skin of many kinds of snakes is used to make such items as belts, boots, and handbags. However, this use of snakeskin has threatened the survival of some species.

Snake venom has several uses in medicine and biological research. *Antivenin,* which is used to treat snakebite, is prepared from the blood of animals that have been injected with venom. Certain painkilling drugs are prepared from neurotoxins in venom. Researchers use the powerful enzymes in venom to break down complex proteins for biochemical studies.

Snakes as pets. Some people keep snakes as pets. However, many snake species do not make good pets. Some snakes move around little and stay hidden most of the time. Snakes may have unusual feeding habits, which makes it difficult to give them an adequate diet. Venomous snakes make especially poor pets. In addition, some snakes may be easy to care for when young, but they soon grow huge. Unfortunately, people who feel they can no longer care for the animals sometimes release them into the wild. For example, pet owners likely released the Burmese pythons that colonized the Everglades. Pets should never be released into the wild, and releasing them is illegal in many places.

People who would like to keep a snake as a pet must commit to feeding and caring for the animal. They should carefully consider whether a particular species would make a good pet. Most people cannot properly care for large constrictors, such as Burmese pythons. Because some snake species have become threatened in the wild, it is better to buy a snake that was bred in captivity rather than captured.

Snakebites. Snakes rarely bite people, and most snakebites cause only minor injuries. The majority of snakes lack venom. Even venomous snakes often inflict *dry bites.* A dry bite occurs when a venomous snake pierces the skin with its fangs but does not inject venom. Some researchers think that venomous snakes can control how much venom they inject into a bite wound.

Dangerous snakebites are rare in most of the world. Even in Australia, which has a variety of venomous snakes, few people suffer dangerous bites. Lightning strikes cause more deaths in Australia than snakebites do. However, snakes do kill thousands of people per year in certain rural, tropical areas of Africa and Asia. Venomous snakes are more common in these areas, and people may have limited access to medical care.

Some nonvenomous snakes of the world

WORLD BOOK illustrations by James Teason

Common garter snake
Thamnophis sirtalis
18 to 26 inches (0.46 to 0.66 meter) long
North America

Coachwhip
Masticophis flagellum
3 ½ to 5 feet (1 to 1.5 meters) long
North America

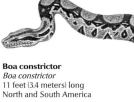

Ringneck snake
Diadophis punctatus
10 to 14 inches (0.25 to 0.36 meter) long
North America

Sonoran mountain kingsnake
Lampropeltis pyromelana
18 to 41 inches (0.46 to 1.04 meters) long
North America

Boa constrictor
Boa constrictor
11 feet (3.4 meters) long
North and South America

Rough green snake
Opheodrys aestivus
22 to 32 inches (0.56 to 0.81 meter) long
North America

Carpet python, or diamond python
Morelia spilota
6 ½ to 13 feet (2 to 4 meters) long
Australasia

Milk snake
Lampropeltis triangulum
21 to 28 inches (0.53 to 0.71 meter) long
North America

Paradise tree snake
Chrysopelea paradisi
3 to 4 feet (0.9 to 1.2 meters) long
Asia

Northern water snake
Nerodia sipedon
24 to 42 inches (0.61 to 1.07 meters) long
North America

Eastern racer
Coluber constrictor
30 to 50 inches (0.76 to 1.27 meters) long
North America

A person bitten by a venomous snake should seek medical help immediately. In most areas with venomous snakes, antivenin is available to treat snakebite victims. Nearly all people who receive treatment with antivenin survive. However, some people have allergic reactions to antivenin, so it must be given under proper medical supervision. For information on the treatment of snakebites, see **Snakebite.**

People are sometimes bitten when they accidentally step on a venomous snake. But most bites result from people trying to harm snakes. People should keep a safe distance from dangerous or unfamiliar snakes. Generally, snakes attack people only if they feel threatened.

The evolution of snakes

The earliest known snake fossils date from about 100 million years ago, during the time of the dinosaurs. However, the first snakes probably evolved millions of years earlier, possibly as early as 150 million years ago. Snake skeletons are delicate, and their fossils are difficult for scientists to discover and fully understand.

Snakes evolved from lizards. Many scientists think that snakes evolved from burrowing lizards that tunneled through the soil in search of food. The first snakes may have resembled such small, wormlike snakes as blind snakes. According to this theory, certain groups of snakes that evolved from these burrowing snakes later

Some venomous snakes of the world

WORLD BOOK illustrations by James Teason

Copperhead
Agkistrodon contortrix
22 to 30 inches (0.56 to 0.76 meter) long
North America

Banded krait
Bungarus fasciatus
4 to 7 feet (1.2 to 2.1 meters) long
Asia

King cobra
Ophiophagus hannah
12 to 18 feet (3.7 to 5.5 meters) long
Asia

Eastern coral snake
Micrurus fulvius
20 to 30 inches (0.51 to 0.76 meter) long
North America

Eastern diamondback rattlesnake
Crotalus adamanteus
33 to 72 inches (0.84 to 1.83 meters) long
North America

Asp viper, or European asp
Vipera aspis
1½ to 2½ feet (0.46 to 0.76 meter) long
Europe

Massasauga
Sistrurus catenatus
20 to 30 inches (0.51 to 0.76 meter) long
North America

Saw-scaled viper
Echis carinatus
16 to 28 inches (0.41 to 0.71 meter) long
Asia

Water moccasin, or cottonmouth
Agkistrodon piscivorus
30 to 48 inches (0.76 to 1.22 meters) long
North America

Taipan
Oxyuranus scutellatus
10 to 13 feet (3 to 4 meters) long
Australia

Boomslang
Dispholidus typus
4½ to 6 feet (1.4 to 1.8 meters) long
Africa

adapted to life above ground and in the water.

However, other scientists argue that snakes evolved from *aquatic* (water-dwelling) lizards. According to this theory, certain groups of snakes that evolved from aquatic snakes later adapted to life on land. Snake researchers must find additional and better-preserved fossils to fully determine the evolutionary history of snakes.

By the time the dinosaurs went extinct, about 65 million years ago, blind snakes, boas, pipe snakes, and other groups had become widespread. Many snake species went extinct during the Eocene Epoch, which ended about 34 million years ago. During the Oligocene Epoch, which lasted from about 34 million to 23 million years ago, a new group of snakes called *colubrids* evolved. The colubrids ultimately gave rise to hundreds of new species. In fact, more than half of modern snake species descend from colubrids.

Snakes, especially colubrids, became much more diverse during the Miocene Epoch, which began about 23 million years ago. In fact, some scientists refer to the Miocene as the *Age of Snakes*. The spread of small birds and mammals may have encouraged the evolution of snakes during this time. Such diversifying species would have provided many new sources of food for snakes, causing snakes in turn to diversify. Many venomous species evolved during this time, which provided new opportunities for snakes. Also, many snake species feed on other snakes, which might have contributed to diversification in both the predatory snake species and the hunted ones. Most modern snake groups had developed by the start of the Pliocene Epoch, about 5.3 million years ago.

Classification of snakes

There are thousands of snake species. They are classified into various families, based on how closely related they are. Not all scientists agree on the number and arrangement of snake families. Scientists continue to uncover new evidence that affects how snakes should be classified, and not all researchers agree on how to interpret this evidence. This section describes families that include most familiar snakes. It does not list all snake families. The scientific name of each family is given in parentheses after the common name.

Blind snakes (Typhlopidae) burrow underground and eat mainly ants and termites. Blind snakes look much like earthworms, though some species may grow to more than 2 feet (60 centimeters) long. Their eyes are covered by head scales. Most live in tropical and subtropical regions. There are hundreds of species.

Boas (Boidae) typically have large, stout bodies. The green anaconda can reach about 30 feet (9 meters) long. However, some boa species may grow less than 3 feet (90 centimeters) long. Most boas have external vestiges of hind legs, called *spurs*. Most boas live in tropical and subtropical regions. The different species may live on land, in trees, or in water. There are dozens of species.

Colubrids (Colubridae) make up more than half of all species of snakes. The different species vary greatly in appearance and ways of life. The family includes most of the common harmless snakes, such as the North American garter snakes and rat snakes. It also includes many species of venomous, rear-fanged snakes. However,

only a few rear-fanged snakes, such as the African bird snakes and boomslangs, are dangerous. Colubrids live throughout most of the world. They make their homes on land, in trees, in water, or underground.

Early blind snakes (Anomalepididae, or Anomalepidae), also called *primitive blind snakes,* are small worm-like snakes that burrow on the floor of rain forests in Central and South America. They eat small *invertebrates* (animals without backbones). There are more than a dozen species.

Elapids (Elapidae) are venomous snakes with short, fixed front fangs. Elapids are most diverse in Australia and nearby islands. Australian species include the black snakes, death adders, taipans, and tiger snakes. The cobras of Africa and Asia, the kraits of southern Asia, the mambas of Africa, and sea snakes are also elapids. There are dozens of species.

Homalopsids (Homalopsidae), sometimes called *rear-fanged water snakes,* are aquatic snakes that live in Southeast Asia and Australia. They are venomous but are considered to pose little threat to humans. Traditionally, this group was placed in the colubrid family. There are dozens of species.

Pythons (Pythonidae) are a group of mostly large snakes from Africa, Asia, and Australia. They inhabit a wide variety of habitats, from rain forests to dry scrub. Most species live on the ground, though some dwell in trees or in water. Pythons eat a variety of *vertebrates* (animals with backbones), often including warm-blooded animals. Most species have heat-sensitive pits on their faces to locate prey. Some researchers place pythons in the boa family. There are dozens of species.

Shield-tailed snakes (Uropeltidae) are burrowing snakes that live in Sri Lanka and southern India. They have a pointed or wedge-shaped snout; a short, blunt tail; and smooth scales. Most species live in the soils of humid mountain areas. There are dozens of species.

Slender blind snakes (Leptotyphlopidae), also called *worm snakes* or *thread snakes,* resemble other families of blind snakes and have similar ways of life. Slender blind snakes live in Africa, southern Asia, and warm areas of North America and South America. There are dozens of species.

Vipers (Viperidae) have hinged fangs attached to the front of the upper jaw. The fangs, which may be long, can move forward and backward. The Gaboon viper, or *Gaboon adder,* has perhaps the longest fangs of any snake. Its fangs can grow to about 2 inches (5 centimeters) long. There are hundreds of viper species.

The two largest groups of vipers are *pit vipers* and *true vipers.* Pit vipers have pit organs between their eyes and nostrils. They inhabit the Americas, Asia, and Europe. Pit vipers include rattlesnakes and moccasins. True vipers lack pit organs. They live in Africa, Asia, and Europe. True vipers include the Gaboon viper and carpet vipers, also called *saw-scaled vipers.*

Other snake families. There are a number of other snake families with relatively few members. For example, *Asian pipe snakes* (Cylindrophiidae) are small to medium-sized burrowing snakes. *File snakes* (Acrochordidae) are aquatic snakes with a stout body and wrinkled skin. The *pipe snake* (Aniliidae), sometimes called the *false coral snake,* is a burrowing snake.   Kenneth L. Krysko

Seasonal affective disorder, abbreviated SAD, is a disturbance of mood that occurs with a change in season. It usually occurs during the fall or winter. For this reason, it is sometimes called *winter depression.* The most common symptoms include sadness, irritability, sleeping and eating much more than usual, poor concentration, fatigue, aches and pains, and severe anxiety. The symptoms typically go away in the spring. Doctors make a diagnosis of SAD only when symptoms occur in three different years or at least two years in a row.

SAD results from the shortening of the period of daylight during fall and winter. In the Northern Hemisphere, SAD is usually more common among people who live farther north, where winter daylight is shorter.

Most victims of SAD suffer their first episode as teenagers or young adults. For some, SAD may begin during childhood. Students with SAD may do well at the beginning and end of the school year, but they may perform poorly in winter months. Teachers and parents may mistake SAD symptoms for misbehavior. Similarly, adults with SAD may have poor job performance during the fall and winter months.

SAD may be treated with high-intensity artificial light or with medication. Treatment with bright light requires special fluorescent tubes that emit light similar to sunlight. SAD patients receive the light treatment for a half an hour to one hour each day. Improvements in the patient's condition generally occur after a few days to two weeks. SAD also can be treated with antidepressant drugs.   Brett C. Plyler

Tetrapod is an animal with a backbone and usually with four limbs. All living and extinct amphibians, birds, mammals, and reptiles—including snakes—are tetrapods. Early forms of tetrapods were the first *vertebrates* (animals with backbones) to live on land. Many of these early tetrapods left no modern descendants.

Early tetrapods. The oldest known tetrapod fossils come from rocks that are about 370 million years old. But trace fossil footprints suggest that these animals may have developed by about 395 million years ago.

Tetrapods *evolved* (changed over many generations) from lobe-finned fishes. Some of these fish developed a unique set of features that helped them to thrive in shallow waters and wetlands. Their fleshy fins became supported mostly by a bony skeleton rather than by *fin rays* (long, narrow rods in the skin). These limblike fins were useful for moving in shallow water.

The creatures had lunglike organs and a snout with a nasal passage. These features likely helped them gulp air from above the surface of waters with relatively low levels of oxygen. The animals also developed relatively flat skulls with a solid roof and eyes on the top.

The evolution of tetrapods from lobe-finned fishes took place over millions of years. Scientists classify an animal as a tetrapod only if it has limbs with *digits* (fingers or toes) and no fin rays. The earliest tetrapods apparently continued to live in water. Some may have developed a way of life similar to that of modern amphibians, especially in their need to lay eggs in water. After many millions of years, some evolved features that enabled them to spend much of their lives on land. Such features include more powerful limbs for walking and changes that helped the shoulders, hips, and back to support the body.

Modern tetrapods. Most early tetrapods left no modern descendants. However, some early tetrapods gave rise to amphibians and *amniotes.* Amniotes produce eggs protected by a shell that prevent them from drying out. That enabled amniotes to live entirely on land. Amniotes had evolved by about 320 million years ago. Early amniotes were the ancestors of all mammals and reptiles. Early reptiles gave rise to dinosaurs and other groups. Dinosaurs gave rise to birds.

The word *tetrapod* means *four-footed,* but not all tetrapods have limbs with feet. The limbs of sea turtles and whales became paddlelike as their ancestors returned to water. The forelimbs of bats and birds became wings. Snakes appear to have no limbs. But snakes descended from limbed reptiles, and some still have traces of hind limbs or hip bones. These animals are all tetrapods because they all descended from four-footed ancestors that lived millions of years ago.   Ted Daeschler

Tiktaalik, *tihk TAH lihk,* was a lobe-finned fish that was closely related to the first animals with legs. The first animals with legs are called *early tetrapods* (see **Tetrapod**). Some early tetrapods became the first *vertebrates* (animals with backbones) to live on land. Thus, all amphibians, birds, mammals, and reptiles descend from

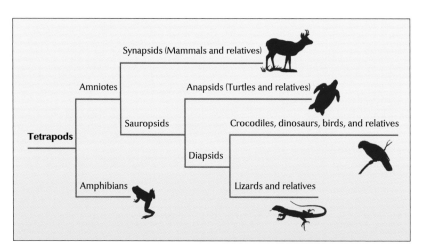

Tetrapods were the first *vertebrates* (animals with backbones) to live on land. Over millions of years, different groups of tetrapods evolved. This diagram shows the evolutionary relationships among living groups of tetrapods. For example, all living tetrapods except for amphibians are amniotes. This diagram does not include many groups of prehistoric animals that left no modern descendants.

WORLD BOOK illustration by Precision Graphics

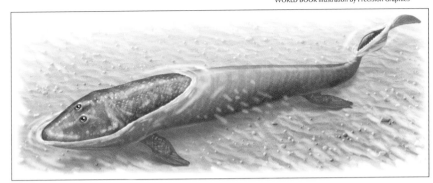

Tiktaalik was a lobe-finned fish that lived about 375 million to 385 million years ago. Close relatives of *Tiktaalik* developed legs. Some of them became the first animals with backbones to live on land.

lobe-finned fish that were similar to *Tiktaalik. Tiktaalik* lived during the late part of the Devonian Period, about 375 million to 380 million years ago.

Tiktaalik had a body that was mostly covered in scales. It had a wide head with a flattened snout. Two rows of teeth—including several large fangs—lined the mouth. These teeth and other features indicate that *Tiktaalik* was a *predator* (hunting animal). The known fossils of *Tiktaalik* suggest it could reach about 9 feet (2.7 meters) long.

Tiktaalik is one of a series of fossils that show how certain lobe-finned fish developed features that would enable their descendants to live on land. These features were originally adaptations to life in shallow waters. Tiktaalik's head and body were flattened, with eyes on the top of its skull. This arrangement is similar to that of crocodiles, likewise adapted to live in shallow water. Also, the bones of *Tiktaalik's* front fins were arranged like limb bones. These fins were farther under the body than are the fins of most fish. Such limblike fins would have been useful for moving in shallow water. Also, *Tiktaalik* could probably use these fins to prop its upper body out of the water. That posture may have helped *Tiktaalik* to gulp air from the surface.   Ted Daeschler

Triangulum Galaxy, also known as M33 or NGC 598, is ranked as the second closest large galaxy to our home galaxy, the Milky Way. Only the Andromeda Galaxy is nearer. The Triangulum Galaxy lies about 3 million *light-years* from Earth. A light-year is the distance that light travels in a vacuum in one year—about 5.88 trillion miles (9.46 trillion kilometers). The Triangulum Galaxy can be seen on fall and winter nights in the Northern Hemisphere. It appears north of the constellation Pisces, the Fishes, in the constellation Triangulum, the Triangle. It is barely visible to the unaided eye but can easily be seen with binoculars.

The Triangulum Galaxy, like the Andromeda Galaxy and the Milky Way, is a *spiral galaxy,* with sweeping arms of stars wrapped about its center. Unlike the other two galaxies, however, the Triangulum Galaxy does not have a bright central bulge. Instead, it consists almost entirely of a thin spiral disk. The disk faces Earth, clearly showing the galaxy's spiral shape. For this reason, the Triangulum Galaxy is also called the Pinwheel Galaxy in Triangulum. The galaxy also lacks a well-defined *halo* of old stars extending far beyond the visible disk, as seen in the Andromeda and Milky Way galaxies.

The Triangulum Galaxy has no known *satellite galaxies,* smaller galaxies that revolve around a larger one. In fact, some evidence suggests that the Triangulum Galaxy may be a remote, massive satellite of the Andromeda Galaxy. The Triangulum Galaxy lies about 1 million light-years from the Andromeda Galaxy.

The Triangulum Galaxy ranks as the third largest member of the *Local Group* of galaxies, the group of galaxies that includes our own (see **Local Group**). Only the Andromeda Galaxy and the Milky Way are bigger. By studying the Triangulum Galaxy's rotation, astronomers have determined its *mass* (amount of matter). It measures about 10 percent as massive as the Andromeda Galaxy or the Milky Way. The Triangulum Galaxy contains about 50 billion times the mass of the sun.

Because the Triangulum Galaxy is relatively near to Earth, astronomers can study its spiral arms in great detail. Their observations provide clear evidence for the theory that such arms result from waves in the density of matter in the disk (see **Galaxy** [Spiral galaxies]). According to this model, as the waves travel, they compress cold gas. The compression causes the formation of stars, which heat the gas. The hottest stars die quickly, leaving behind cooler, longer-lasting stars. The Triangulum Galaxy's spiral arms contain regions where cold gas, young stars in hot gas, and old stars are arranged just as the model predicts.   Mario Mateo

NOAO/AURA/NSF/T. A. Rector

The Triangulum Galaxy consists of a thin disk marked by spiral "arms" of stars. It is the second closest major galaxy to our own galaxy, the Milky Way. Only the Andromeda Galaxy is closer.

AP Photo

A zoo gives people a chance to see many kinds of animals they might never see otherwise. Many zoos keep their animals in spacious outdoor and indoor exhibits. This photograph shows an Asian sun bear at the Henry Doorly Zoo in Omaha, Nebraska. A zookeeper has thrown the bear an apple.

Zoo

Zoo is a place where people keep and display animals. Visiting zoos is a popular recreational and educational activity throughout the world. Almost every large city has at least one zoo, and many smaller communities also have one. Many zoos have beautiful gardens and tree-lined paths leading from one animal display to another. The word *zoo* is short for *zoological garden.*

Zoos vary in the type of animals they keep. Many large zoos keep mammals, birds, reptiles, and fish from all over the world. Some even have collections of interesting insects. Smaller zoos may have animals from just one part of the world, or just one type of animal. Zoos that have only fish and aquatic mammals, which live in water, are called aquariums. Some zoos display only animals from the region where the zoo is.

Zoos range in size from hundreds of acres or hectares to only a few. But size alone does not determine the quality or importance of a zoo. The best zoos are those that have healthy, well-tended animals and displays that help visitors learn about each animal's natural behavior and its role in the environment.

Modern zoos have become refuges for some *species* (types) of animals that are in danger of *extinction* (dying out) in the wild. Many human activities threaten the survival of wild species, especially the destruction of *habitats* (natural environments). Most animals are specially suited to live in a certain environment and cannot survive when their habitat is destroyed. Zoos are becoming increasingly active in the struggle to save the world's vanishing wildlife.

The importance of zoos

Zoos are important centers for (1) recreation and education, (2) wildlife conservation, and (3) scientific studies.

Recreation and education. People of all ages enjoy

viewing animals they would probably never see otherwise. In the United States and Canada, zoos attract millions of visitors every year. Zoos also help people understand how animals live. In addition, zoos teach people about the problems facing wildlife and about conservation.

In many zoos, trained workers give visitors brief talks and provide guided tours. Many zoos have education departments that conduct lectures, classes, and group programs for children and adults. Some zoos offer summer day camps and junior zookeeper programs that give youngsters opportunities to help care for the animals. In addition, zoos publish magazines, pamphlets, and other materials that describe their activities. Some zoos even produce television programs.

Wildlife conservation has become one of the most important jobs of zoos. Zoos breed many endangered species to increase their numbers. Such captive breeding in zoos has helped save several species from extinction, including the European bison; the *nene,* also known as the Hawaiian goose; and the Arabian *oryx,* a type of antelope.

Zoos throughout the world trade and lend animals to one another to avoid *inbreeding* (breeding animals that are closely related to each other). Inbreeding can produce birth defects and can eventually weaken an entire population. A number of zoo associations share breeding information through the International Species Information System (ISIS), a computerized inventory of hundreds of thousands of animals cared for by zoos throughout the world. ISIS also maintains records on the ancestors of the animals to more accurately track the genetic background of the living animals.

The Association of Zoos and Aquariums sponsors the Species Survival Plan (SSP), a long-term plan to save some of the most seriously endangered species. Many major zoos in the United States and other countries par-

© Justin Sullivan, Getty Images

Children can approach zoo animals and even touch some animals at many zoos. These children encounter Magellanic penguin chicks exploring their new home at the San Francisco Zoo.

ticipate in the SSP. There are dozens of SSP programs, each focusing on a different species or group of species. Participating zoos keep careful records of each animal's family lines and physical characteristics. Zoos use this information to determine which males and females to breed together. The goal is to develop healthy populations of animals that can someday be returned to the wild.

Zoos also participate in conservation projects outside their walls. For example, many zoos sponsor efforts to preserve the natural habitats of threatened species, such as the Asian bamboo forests of the giant panda and the

WORLD BOOK photo

Tigers and deer at the Milwaukee County Zoo live in areas that are side by side. A deep moat, which visitors cannot see, prevents the tigers from attacking the deer.

Interesting facts about zoo animals

A polar bear's coat sometimes looks green instead of white. Each hair of a polar bear's coat is hollow. The air in the middle of each hair helps keep the bear warm. Sometimes, green *algae* (simple plantlike organisms) grow in the hollows and the green color shows through.

A giraffe's tongue is up to 21 inches (53 centimeters) long. A giraffe uses its tongue to reach high into trees for leaves and tender branches. The outer part of the tongue is purplish-blue. The dark pigment may help protect the tongue from sunburn.

WORLD BOOK illustration by Colin Newman, Bernard Thornton Artists

The fierce-looking gorilla is actually a gentle, peaceful animal. A gorilla will not hurt a human being unless the gorilla or its family is threatened or attacked. The animal's ferocious "King-Kong" reputation is just a movie myth.

An elephant uses its trunk as a human being uses hands and arms. An elephant's trunk has about 40,000 muscles. It is strong enough to lift a 600-pound (270-kilogram) log. Yet the tip of the trunk has enough flexibility to grasp a single peanut.

Snakes in zoos sometimes eat only once a month. Their meals last a long time because snakes, which are cold-blooded, do not use much food energy to maintain a steady body temperature. The bodies of cold-blooded animals are warm when their surroundings are warm, and cool when their surroundings are cool. Also, snakes use little energy because they stay inactive for long periods and live off their body fat.

Flamingos need a special diet to maintain the bright pink and red colors of their feathers. In zoos, these birds may receive reddish foods such as shrimp and sometimes even liquid red dye.

WORLD BOOK illustration by Colin Newman, Bernard Thornton Artists

When a dolphin dives, its lungs collapse and its heart beats slower. These actions allow the animal's body to adjust to the increasing pressure of the water as the dolphin dives deeper.

South American tropical rain forests of the *lion tamarin,* a species of small monkey.

Scientific studies. Zoos provide scientists with living laboratories in which to study animals. By treating diseased animals and by studying animals that have died, zoo veterinarians and other scientists have developed and improved medical equipment, drugs, and surgical techniques for animals.

Scientists called *zoologists* study animals in zoos, as well as in the wild, to learn about animal behavior, such as hunting, eating, breeding, and caring for the young. Such research helps zoos know how to better care for

their animals and how to make their exhibits as natural as possible. This knowledge is especially important for breeding because many animals will only reproduce if they are healthy and living in natural surroundings.

Scientific progress in breeding techniques has greatly reduced the need to move animals from zoo to zoo for mating. Researchers can freeze the sperm and embryos of various species. The frozen material can be shipped to another zoo for use in *artificial insemination, embryo transfer,* and other breeding techniques (see **Breeding** [Animal breeding]).

Displaying animals

In the past, zoos kept their animals in rows of mostly bare cages made of concrete and steel bars. Often, the cages were arranged in no particular order.

Today, animal displays are far different. Zoos have replaced most old-fashioned cages with natural-looking enclosures that give animals greater liberty to lead normal lives. Both the layout of the zoo and the design of the exhibits teach visitors about animals.

Layout of a zoo. Many zoos group their animals mostly by type. For example, lions, tigers, and other large cats may be kept in the same building or in nearby outdoor exhibits. Animals from similar climates, such as warm tropical areas or chilly polar regions, are often housed together. Zoos also group animals by the continent where they naturally live, such as Africa or Asia.

Another grouping method is by the animals' natural habitat, such as the East African *savanna* (grassland with scattered trees) or the Australian desert. In habitat groupings, many animals appear to be living together. However, animals that would attack each other are kept apart by empty *moats* (deep, wide pits) or by hidden fences.

Many zoos have a *children's zoo,* where boys and girls can pet and even feed tame animals. Some children's zoos give city youngsters an opportunity to see farm animals. Many children's zoos feature baby animals.

Exhibits. Most modern exhibits, both indoors and outdoors, are *naturalistic*—that is, they resemble the animal's natural habitat. Such exhibits contain rock formations, pools, grass, trees, shrubs, and places for the animals to take shelter or hide. Heating coils may be concealed in artificial rocks or trees to attract the animals to locations where they can be seen by visitors.

Many animals become bored if they have nothing to do. To combat boredom, exhibits may provide climbing structures and toys that encourage active behavior. Giant ice cubes keep polar bears occupied. Rhinoceroses and elephants seem to enjoy rolling in shallow pools of mud. In addition, keepers often hide meals in shrubs, trees, and other places so that the animals must search for the food just as they would in the wild. A stimulating environment is especially important to apes, elephants, and other intelligent species. In some zoos, chimpanzees may keep busy for hours probing artificial termite mounds filled with honey, cereal, or other treats.

Barriers. Zoos use a variety of barriers to keep animals in their exhibits. One widely used naturalistic barrier is a moat surrounding the display area. Moats enable zoos to safely keep bears, lions, tigers, and other large animals in spacious outdoor settings.

Zoos also use barriers that are almost invisible, such as glass or a net of thin wire. Through underwater viewing windows, visitors can watch such animals as polar bears and hippopotamuses swimming or observe beavers building a dam. A zoo may cover a huge bird shelter, complete with trees and plants, with a wire net.

Controlled environments. Indoor exhibits enable zoos to reproduce the environmental conditions that some animals need to stay healthy. For example, penguins from the Antarctic need cold air. Other creatures may require moist air, dry air, or regular rain showers.

One special indoor exhibit is for *nocturnal* animals, which are active at night. Zoos display such nocturnal animals as owls, bats, and raccoons under a blue light or other dim light, which seems like darkness to the animals. But visitors can clearly see the animals going about their normal nighttime activities. At night, a bright light causes the animals to sleep as if it were day.

With modern technology, a number of zoos have created vast enclosures that imitate scorching deserts, frigid polar regions, and other natural habitats. Such exhibits house a variety of mammals, fish, birds, reptiles, and insects that would naturally live in the environment. A number of zoos, for example, have large indoor exhibits that reproduce steamy tropical rain forests. These exhibits house trees, cliffs, and waterfalls in structures several stories tall. Machines produce a foglike mist. Elevated walkways allow zoogoers to stroll among the treetops and view several types of primates, birds, and other animals that live in the trees.

Cageless zoos. Drive-through zoos keep their animals in outdoor settings without cages, though predators and prey are kept apart. Visitors view the animals while riding through the zoo in their automobile or aboard a bus or a train.

Wild-animal parks resemble drive-through zoos because the animals are not caged. But these parks are larger than most drive-through zoos and are more interested in breeding animals, especially endangered species, than in exhibiting them. Such parks provide the natural surroundings many animals need to mate successfully and raise offspring. The San Diego Wild Animal Park (now the San Diego Zoo Safari Park), the first such establishment in the United States, opened in 1972. In this enormous zoo, which covers about 2,200 acres (900 hectares), groups of rhinoceroses, giraffes, deer, antelope, zebras, and many other species roam over large areas under the close watch of zoo workers. Visitors ride a special train that travels through the park. The train's route skirts the areas where animals live, thus disturbing the herds as little as possible.

Caring for zoo animals

Zoo animals receive daily care, special diets, and regular medical attention.

Daily care. Trained workers called *keepers* take care of the animals' daily needs. In large zoos, each keeper usually looks after just one type of animal. The keepers clean the animals' enclosures. They feed the animals and watch for changes in behavior, eating habits, and overall appearance that may be signs that an animal is sick or injured. Keepers also provide companionship for the

© Rodger Tamblyn, Alamy Images

An underwater viewing exhibit enables zoo visitors to observe the graceful movements of animals beneath water level. At the left, a woman meets a sea lion close up in a viewing tunnel at the Colchester Zoo in the United Kingdom.

animals. Many types of animals, including monkeys and apes, become fond of their keepers and develop special relationships with them.

Diet. An appropriate diet is vital in keeping zoo animals healthy. The kinds and amounts of food different creatures require vary greatly.

Zoo kitchens stock a wide assortment of basic foods, including cereals, dairy products, fish, fruits, grains, hay, meat, seeds, and vegetables. They also have such unusual items as brine shrimp, crickets, mice, rats, snakes, and worms. Many animals enjoy grazing on the leaves of freshly cut branches. In addition, zoos use large quantities of prepared pellets, seed mixes, and other foods made especially for animals. Zoos also use vitamins and mineral supplements to ensure a nutritious diet for each animal.

Some animals require exactly the type of food they would eat in the wild. For example, koalas will eat only certain kinds of eucalyptus leaves. Giant pandas must

© Attila Kisbenedek, AFP/Getty Images

Zoos provide refuge for animals that are threatened in the wild. In this photo, a zookeeper feeds ring-tailed lemurs at the Nyíregyháza Zoo in Hungary. Ring-tailed lemurs are threatened by hunting and habitat destruction in their native Madagascar.

have bamboo. Zoos ship in these foods from wherever they are grown or grow the foods themselves.

In zoo kitchens, keepers, nutritionists, and other trained workers prepare balanced meals for each animal in whatever form the animal will eat. Some animals eat their food just as it comes. But for many animals, zoo workers must peel, chop, combine, and even cook foods. Some animals, including certain birds and small mammals, eat several meals each day. Other animals, such as some species of snakes, eat only once every few weeks.

A zoo animal's diet varies under certain circumstances. For example, pregnant females and mothers nursing their young require special food. Animals may also need special diets for gaining or losing weight, for breeding, or for health problems.

Some zoos sell food pellets that visitors may distribute to certain animals. The zoo controls the amount of food provided so the animals are not overfed. Except for such pellets, visitors should not feed zoo animals. Candy, popcorn, and similar foods can make an animal sick. Thoughtless visitors often throw wrappers or other trash to the animals. If an animal swallows this trash, it could become ill and might even die.

Medical care. Most large zoos employ one or more full-time veterinarians. Smaller zoos often have part-time veterinarians. The doctor visits regularly and treats sick or injured creatures. Many animals receive routine vaccinations to protect them from diseases.

Before examining or treating an animal, the doctor may inject the animal with tranquilizers or drugs that temporarily paralyze the patient. After the drugs take effect, the doctor can examine and treat the animal without danger of injury to either the doctor or the animal.

Many large zoos have their own hospitals with operat-

© AWL Images/Masterfile

Zoos in cities enable many people to enjoy wildlife without having to travel the world. In this photograph, giraffes feed at the Taronga Zoo in Australia. The skyscrapers and Opera House of Sydney are visible on the far side of the harbor.

ing rooms, X-ray machines, and laboratories. Some zoos have *quarantine* areas where newly acquired animals or those with contagious diseases are kept apart from the other animals to prevent the spread of disease.

How zoos operate

Many zoos are owned and operated by local governments. Some zoos are owned by individuals or nonprofit corporations. In the United States, zoos must be licensed by the U.S. Department of Agriculture.

In the United States and Canada, a number of zoos are members of the Association of Zoos and Aquariums. The association requires its members to maintain high standards of animal care and management. All member institutions must pass an inspection every five years.

Funding. Zoos obtain funding for their operations from a number of sources. Many zoos receive funds from local governments. Most zoos charge admission fees. Other money comes from food and gift shop sales, fund-raising events, donations, "adopt-an-animal" programs, membership fees, and grants from foundations and corporations.

Zoo workers. A zoo is similar to a small town and needs many types of workers to operate smoothly. A *director* is the head of the zoo. A *curator* manages the care of zoo animals and supervises the people who work with the animals. Large zoos may have more than one curator, each overseeing a particular group of animals. Keepers take care of the animals, and veterinarians provide medical care. Zoo scientists study the animals and do research.

Most zoo jobs that involve working with animals require a college degree. Keepers and curators often study biology or zoology. Zoo scientists usually have training in such fields as animal behavior, anthropology, genetics, nutrition, reproductive science, or veterinary technology. Some veterinary schools offer training in wild-animal medicine. Some zoos provide internships for students at the graduate and undergraduate levels.

Many people who have jobs at zoos do not work directly with the animals. Large numbers of employees are involved in administration, office work, fund-raising, security, and maintaining the grounds and buildings. In addition, zoos may rely on volunteer workers to sweep sidewalks, help keepers watch animals, guide tours, and perform many other important jobs.

Obtaining animals. Most zoo animals are born in captivity. A smaller and smaller number of zoo animals are captured in the wild by hunters.

A zoo's director and curators usually decide which animals the zoo needs. Zoos often get animals to fill a gap in their collection, such as when an animal dies. To obtain animals, zoos deal directly with one another, buying, trading, or lending stock. Zoos also buy animals from professional animal dealers. The Association of Zoos and Aquariums and animal dealers circulate lists of what each zoo needs and what species are available.

The United States government severely restricts the importing of many animals, especially endangered species and those that may transmit diseases. Animals that enter the United States from zoos outside the country or from the wild must be *quarantined* (kept in isolation) for a time to be sure they are disease-free.

When an animal first comes to a zoo, it must adjust to its new keepers, its exhibit mates, and its surroundings. Keepers watch the newcomers carefully so that they do not hurt themselves or harm other animals.

History

Early zoos. People have put wild animals on display since ancient times. One of the earliest known zoos was established by Queen Hatshepsut of Egypt about 1500

Jim Tuten, Earth Scenes

Inside a zoo kitchen, trained workers peel, chop, combine, and even cook foods for the animals. Zoo kitchens stock a wide variety of fruits, vegetables, seeds, and many other types of foods. Each animal receives nutritionally balanced meals.

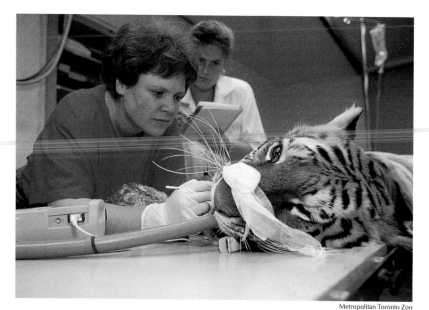

Regular medical treatment helps keep zoo animals healthy. In this photograph, a veterinarian gives a Siberian tiger a dental checkup. Before an examination, doctors often tranquilize the animal to eliminate the danger of injury to either the medical personnel or the animal.

Metropolitan Toronto Zoo

B.C. About 500 years later, the Chinese emperor Wen Wang founded the Garden of Intelligence, an enormous zoo that covered nearly 1,500 acres (610 hectares). Between 1000 and 400 B.C., rulers in northern Africa, India, and China established many small zoos that were designed to display their wealth and power.

In ancient Greece, rulers and nobles kept private zoos for their own enjoyment. Scholars visited such zoos to study the animals. The Romans also had many private zoos. In addition, the Romans kept a large collection of wild animals used in bloody fights in large outdoor theaters such as the Colosseum. During the Middle Ages, from about the A.D. 400's through the 1400's, many European rulers and nobles maintained private zoos.

By the end of the 1400's, global exploration and an increased interest in learning promoted the popularity of zoos in Europe. Explorers returned from the New World with strange creatures for European zoos. In 1519, Spanish explorers discovered a huge zoo built by the Aztec Indians in what is now Mexico.

During the next 250 years, several zoos were established in Europe. Some of them were merely small exhibits called *menageries*. These consisted of a few bears, lions, or tigers kept in small, gloomy cages or in pits. Only the nobility were allowed to visit most of these exhibits.

The first modern zoos. Over the years, menageries were replaced by larger collections of animals that received better care. These facilities not only displayed animals but also served as centers of research. They developed into the first modern zoos.

The oldest zoo still in existence is the Schönbrunn Zoo, which was founded in Vienna, Austria, in 1752. The Madrid Zoo in Spain was established in 1775. The Paris Zoo, the third oldest zoo in continuous operation, dates from 1793. The Berlin Zoo, which became a leader in research on animal behavior, opened in Germany in 1844.

The development of zoos in the United States began

with the chartering of the Philadelphia Zoological Society in 1859. But the American Civil War (1861-1865) delayed construction of the zoo, which did not open until 1874. In 1889, Congress established the National Zoological Park in Washington, D.C. This zoo is the only one that is operated by the United States government. In Canada, the first zoo opened in Halifax, Nova Scotia, in 1847.

The evolution of zoos. In 1907, Carl Hagenbeck, a German animal dealer and zoo owner, developed the moat technique of displaying animals. The idea gradually spread to zoos throughout the world, improving the life of zoo animals and the experiences of visitors. Zoos began replacing barred cages with larger, more natural enclosures. The first children's zoo in the United States opened at the Philadelphia Zoo in 1938.

By the 1940's, zoologists recognized that many species of animals faced extinction in the wild. Zoos realized they could help preserve some of these species and began developing the first breeding programs. Before this time, most zoos had tried to display at least one member of as many different species as possible. Few zoos owned more than one or two animals of a rare species. Today, many zoos keep family groups and breeding populations.

Current issues. Some animal welfare groups criticize the treatment of animals in zoos. Some people are especially opposed to keeping large sea mammals, such as whales and dolphins, in captivity. They claim that these creatures fare poorly even under the best zoo conditions. Some animal rights activists call for all zoos to be shut down. They believe people have no right to keep animals in captivity.

Zoo officials stress the importance of zoos in conservation and science. They agree that substandard zoos should improve their treatment of animals but point out that many zoos meet high standards of care.

Jack Hanna

INDEX

How to use the index
This index covers the contents of the 2011, 2012, and 2013 editions.

Each entry gives the edition year and the page number or page numbers – for example, **Boltzmann, Ludwig, 13:** 137. This means that information on this scientist may be found on page 137 in the 2013 edition.

A page number in italics means that there is an article on this topic on the page or pages indicated. For example, there is an Update article called **Books about science** on pages 136-140 of the 2013 edition.

When there are many references to a topic, they are grouped alphabetically by clue words under the main topic. For example, the clue words under **Brain** group some of the references to that topic under subtopics.

The "see" and "see also" cross-references refer the reader to other entries in the index. For example, additional information on **Brain** can be found under the entries indicated, and information on **British Petroleum** can be found under the entry **BP.**

The indications (il.) and (ils.) mean that the topic appears only in an illustration or illustrations and not in the main text of a page or the facing page. For example, there is an illustration of the **Burj Khalifa** on page 215 of the 2013 edition.

An entry followed by "reprint" refers to a new or revised article in the supplement section, as in **Carbon cycle.** This means that there is an article on pages 242 of the 2013 edition.

ACKNOWLEDGMENTS

The publishers gratefully acknowledge the courtesy of the following artists, photographers, publishers, institutions, agencies, and corporations for the illustrations in this volume. Credits are listed from top to bottom and from left to right on their respective pages. All entries marked with an asterisk (*) denote illustrations created exclusively for this yearbook. All maps, charts, and diagrams were staff-prepared unless otherwise noted.

8 Simbex; © AP Images
9 © John Raoux, AP Images
12 NASA/JPL-Caltech/Max-Planck Institute/
P. Appleton (SSC/Caltech)
14 NASA/JPL-Caltech/Max-Planck Institute/
P. Appleton (SSC/Caltech)
15 NASA, ESA, and The Hubble Heritage Team
(STScI/AURA)/A. Aloisi (STScI/ESA)
16 NASA
17 NASA, ESA, and Johan Richard (Caltech, USA)
18 NASA, ESA, and A. Evans (Stony Brook University,
New York, University of Virginia & National Radio
Astronomy Observatory, Charlottesville, USA)
19 NASA/JPL-Caltech/Vassar
20-21 © John Dubinski
22 ESA/Hubble & NASA; X-ray NASA/CXC/IfA/
D. Sanders et al.
23 ESO/IDA/Danish 1.5 m/R.Gendler and
J.E. Ovaldsen
24 European Southern Observatory
25 NASA, H. Ford (JHU), G. Illingworth (UCSC/LO),
M.Clampin (STScI), G. Hartig (STScI), the ACS
Science Team, and ESA
26 © Galaxy Zoo
27 NASA, ESA, CFHT, CXO, M.J. Jee (University of
California, Davis), and A. Mahdavi (San Francisco
State University)
28 © Getty Images
31 © National Geographic/Getty Images
32 WORLD BOOK Publishing
33 © National News/ZUMAPress
34 © Visuals Unlimited/Masterfile
36 © AP Images
38 © Dave Martin, AP Images
41 © Jim Young, Reuters/Landov
42 © KEENPRESS/Getty Images
44 © Shutterstock
46 NOAA, © Shutterstock
47 WORLD BOOK illustration by Matt Carrington
48 © Minden Pictures/Masterfile; © Shutterstock
49 © Bryan and Cherry Alexander, Photo Researchers
50 © Steven Kazlowski, Getty Images; © Shutterstock
51 © Peter Van Rhijn, Getty Images
52 Jeff Masek, Landsat/NASA; © Shutterstock
53 © Diana Haeckeer, AP Images
54 © Peter Essick, Getty Images; © AP Images,
© Shutterstock
55 © AlaskaStock/Masterfile
56 © Shutterstock
59 © B. O'Kane, Alamy Images; © Tom Evans

60 Lewis Hine, National Archives; © iStockphoto
61 WORLD BOOK illustration by Matt Carrington;
© Bettmann/Corbis
62 © Comstock/Thinkstock; WORLD BOOK
illustration by Matt Carrington
63 © Oote Boe Photography 1/Alamy Images;
© Hemera/Thinkstock
64 © Shutterstock; © Science Faction/SuperStock;
WORLD BOOK illustration by Francis Paola
66 WORLD BOOK illustration by Francis Paola
68 Adrian Smith + Gordon Gill
69 © Shutterstock; © Bettmann/Corbis
70 © Radius/SuperStock
71 WORLD BOOK illustration by Matt Carrington
74 WORLD BOOK illustration by Matt Carrington
75 © Scott Camazine, Phototake
76 WORLD BOOK illustration by Matt Carrington;
Boston University
78 Department of Veterans Affairs, Bedford VA
Medical Center
79 © Focus on Sport/Getty Images
80 Amy Virden, OAA Orthopaedic Specialists
81 The Center for Sports Concussion, Idaho State
University
82 Simbex; Dan Sears, University of North Carolina
at Chapel Hill
83 Simbex
84 © Dusko Almosa/Getty Images
86 Mietje Germonpre, Yaroslav Kuzmin, PLoS ONE
(2011), vol. 6, no. 7, e22821
87 © PoodlesRock/Corbis
88 Institute of Cytology and Genetics
90 © iStockphoto/Thinkstock
91 © iStockphoto/Thinkstock; © Ingram
Publishing/Thinkstock; © Hemera/Thinkstock;
© iStockphoto/Thinkstock; © MPI for Evolutionary
Anthropology
92 © Manuela Hartling, Reuters/Landov
94 © Ingram Publishing/Thinkstock
95 © Monika Graff, UPI/Landov; © Masterfile
96 © James Brunker, Alamy Images
97 © Shutterstock
98 WORLD BOOK illustration by Matt Carrington
100 © Bob Sacha, Corbis
101 © Richard Levine, Alamy Images
102 © James Brunker, Alamy Images
105 © Wildlife Conservation Society
107 © David Eggen, The New York Times/Redux
109 © Michael J. Raupp
110 © Brian Biggins

111 © Lake Fong, *Post-Gazette*
113 Max Planck Institute for Evolutionary Anthropology
115 © Chip Clark & Brian Ireley, Smithsonian Institution
116 © 2011 M. Klein/7reasons/Ludwig Boltzman Institute for Archaeological Prospection & Virtual Archaeology
117 INAH, Mexico
118 © Bogdan Zurawski
119 © Thinkstock; © Bridgeman Art Library
120 © Chuck Beckley, AP Images
121 © Lior Taylor
123 NASA/JPL/University of Arizona
124 Brittney Schmidt/Dead Pixel VFX/Univeristy of Texas Austin
126 NASA
127 © Wlady Altermann, University of Pretoria
128 WORLD BOOK illustration by Lucy Lesiak
130 NASA
131 Julia Molnar, Royal Veterinary College of London; © Thinkstock
132 Gerhard Schulz, Getty Images
133 © Barcroft Media/Landov
134 © Thomas Bunyar
143 © Yu-Chin Li, Texas A & M University
145 NASA/JPL-Caltech/University of Colorado
146 NOAA
148 © Minrui Yu
151 © Bloomberg/Getty Images
152 © Shutterstock
153 © Shutterstock
154 Long Now Foundation
155 © Josh Haner/*New York Times*/Redux Pictures
156 WWF/Green Renaissance
157 © Indraneil Das
158 © Howard Perlman, USGS & Jack Cook, WHOI
159 © AP Images; Salk Institute of Biological Studies
160 © AP Images
161 © AP Images; Fox Chase Cancer Center
162 UCIrvine
164 © Hywel Roberts, London School of Hygiene and Tropical Medicine
166 © R. J. Ripple
167 © Dan Callister, Rex USA
168 © Jemeema Carrigan, University of Florida
169 © Lori Oberhofer, NPS/Bugwood; WORLD BOOK illustration by Lucy Lesiak
171 USDA
173 Courtesy Caltrans
175 © Steve Jurvetson
176 © Jack Kurtz, ZUMAPress
178 U.S. Forest Service
179 © Katrina Kenny, University of Adelaide (image also used on cover of Old Standard and Brown/White Aristocrat bindings)

180 Mongolian Paleontological Center
182 PLoS ONE
185 Museum of London Archaeology
187 NASA-GISS, Nicole Rager-Fuller/Lightroom/National Science Foundation
189 © USGS; C. M. Bailey, College of William & Mary
190 © Jeremy Hogan, AP Images
192 Molycorp
193 © Shutterstock
194 © Dan Stober, Standford News Service
196 © Serge Mostowy and Pascale Cossart, Pasteur Institute
198 © iStockphoto
199 MGH-UCLA Human Connectome Project, Massachusetts General Hospital
201 Damian Scarf; William Van Der Vliet
203 © Adam Block/Mount Lemon Sky Center/University of Arizona; NASA; WORLD BOOK illustration
204 © AP Images, Luca Bindi, Museum of Natural History, Florence
206 © Boston Globe/Getty Images
207 © Dave Bowden, NIWA
208 © Wildlife Conservation Society
209 © Rick Bowmer, AP Images
211 © Jim Maragos
212 © Craig Barritt, Getty Images; © Imagechina/AP Images
213 Hulton Archive/Getty Images; Woods Hole Oceanographic Institution
214 NASA/JHU Center for Coastal & Ocean Mapping; NOAA
215 WORLD BOOK illustration by Lucy Lesiak
217 WORLD BOOK illustration by Precision Graphics
219 © Shutterstock
222 Stephanie Kalaberer, Murdoch University
223 © Manuel Leal, Duke University
225 © UPI/Landov
227 © Claudio Lattanzio/EPA/Landov
229 © Lui Siu Wai/Xinhua/Landov
231 NASA
232 SpaceX; © John Raoux, AP Images
233 NASA/JPL/University of Arizona
234 NASA/JPL-Caltech/MPS/DLR/IDA
235 NASA/JPL-Caltech; Max Plank Society/DRL/NASA/JPL
236 NASA/JPL-Caltech/University of Arizona
237 NASA/JHUAPL/CIW-DTM/GSFC/James Dickson & Jim Head
238 NASA/JHU/APL/CIW
239 Case Western Reserve University; NASA/JHU/APL/CIW
240 NASA/JHU/APL/CIW